Houston Methodist: The Hospital with a Soul
Celebrating 100 Years of Leading Medicine

by Bryant Boutwell, Dr.P.H.

FOREWORD

The entire Bush family salutes Houston Methodist on the occasion of the hospital system's centennial celebrations in 2019. As proud Houstonians, we offer you a chorus of "job well done." We're equally pleased to be included in the book you hold, which contains excellent stories highlighting the hospital's impressive history.

To me, the history of Houston Methodist parallels in many important ways the progress and growth of our wonderful city. Back in 1919 when a local physician named Dr. Oscar Norsworthy offered his 30-bed hospital at Rosalie and San Jacinto to the Texas Conference of the Methodist Episcopal Church, little could he have envisioned what his hospital would become. Houston has always been the beneficiary of a special Texas-sized, can-do spirit. From the earliest days when two brothers named Allen arrived in 1836, Houstonians have demonstrated what hard work and vision can accomplish. Houston Methodist, from the beginning, has in many ways been a significant contributor to the international city Houston has become.

The hospital's early board, comprising church and community business leaders, struggled in the formative years to grow the hospital and meet the needs of the growing community. On more than one occasion they dug deep into their own pockets to keep the hospital going without compromising care. Through the 1920s to present day, the hospital's board and executive leadership have exemplified the steady and thoughtful leadership that separates the good institutions from the great. That Houston Methodist is now ranked year after year the number-one hospital in Texas and among the very best in the nation is something every Houstonian can be proud of.

As proud Houstonians ourselves, Barbara always said the Texas Medical Center was Houston's great gift to the world. Since 1951, when the hospital joined what was then a small collection of medical institutions emerging from a small forest next to Hermann Park,

Houston Methodist has added its own sparkle to our city's jewel and projected an international spotlight on both the Texas Medical Center and the city. Today Houston Methodist is a system of care with a global reach—an academic medical center training the next generation of health care professionals while leading in the fields of research and discovery. Add to that in recent years new affiliations and collaborative programs with Weill Cornell Medicine, New York-Presbyterian Hospital, Texas A&M University (where they happen to have a library I like very much), the University of Houston, Rice University, and more. Well, you get the idea. This is no longer a 30-bed hospital with screened porches.

As a former patient at Houston Methodist, I can speak from experience about the quality of patient care as could Barbara. I've come to know that the hospital's employees share a special set of values known as I CARE and that stands for Integrity, Compassion, Accountability, Respect, and Excellence. As a patient I can tell you these values are much more than words on paper. They represent a hospital-wide culture every patient and family member can expect. Every Houston Methodist employee is to be commended during this centennial anniversary for the culture of care they live and the hours of community service they provide the city as members of the Houston Methodist family.

On behalf of the entire Bush family, congratulations to Houston Methodist as you celebrate this milestone moment in your history and our sincere best wishes for the next hundred years. Needless to say, if Dr. Norsworthy could drop by for a visit today, he would be more than impressed.

George H.W. Bush
June 2018

CONTENTS

APPENDICES:

INTRODUCTION

On a hot summer day in 1949 Dr. Dan Jackson arrived in Houston from St. Louis with his family. He was new to town and needed advice. He had heard Methodist Hospital was an aging hospital near downtown at the corner of San Jacinto and Rosalie streets. "Hitch your wagon to Methodist. It doesn't look like much now, but it's going someplace," one veteran physician advised.[1] Dr. Jackson did just that.

"I set up a practice across the street from where the old hospital was. There was a large house and it had been divided into space for five doctors: a pediatrician, a general practitioner, an ear, nose and throat doctor, an eye doctor, and then I moved in. There was nothing around me in terms of people available for my practice but it was close to Methodist. … They were going to go places and I wanted to be with them."[2]

Dr. Jackson died on November 16, 2017, just two weeks shy of his one hundredth birthday. He was the last living physician to have cared for patients in the old hospital. While his firsthand recollections and gentle smile may be gone, he left behind three sons—two being physicians like their father who call Houston Methodist their professional home. The Jackson family legacy is but one of many family pedigrees in the hospital's long history.

Ruth Abeles, a veteran nurse who retired in 2018, served the hospital nearly fifty years and has her own story to tell. "This is a place people don't leave," she tells me on the run outside a busy intensive care unit in Dunn Tower. "I left once, thinking the grass was greener but returned like so many others."[3] Abeles was there the historic day in 1969 when Dr. Michael DeBakey and his team performed the world's first multiple organ transplant of a heart, lung, and two kidneys from one donor patient to four recipient patients. She recalls Dr. Christiaan Barnard, among other famous faces, flying by during that hectic day.

Dr. Barnard conducted the world's first heart transplant in South Africa barely two years earlier and was one of many well-recognized physicians, celebrities, and heads of state who made their way to Methodist Hospital to see and learn.

On the afternoon of June 15, 1976, Abeles was assisting Dr. George Noon, who in 2006 performed lifesaving heart surgery on his teacher, Dr. Michael DeBakey. On that day the city witnessed what Texans refer to as a "gully washer." The sky opened and torrents of rain fell on the Texas Medical Center, turning streets into rivers. Recalls Abeles, "Dr. Noon always ate a bowl of cereal as he drove to work early in the morning in his recently purchased MG sports car. As the water came up, employees started worrying about their cars. Dr. Noon was in the middle of a cardiopulmonary bypass, so Dr. Charles H. McCollum, a surgical colleague, grabbed Dr. Noon's keys and ran downstairs. Wading through the lower level of the parking garage, he found the car and pulled hard on the door. A cereal bowl floated across the front seat."

Back in the operating room, lights flickered and the entire hospital went dark. In surgery they grabbed flashlights and carried on. Abeles recalls, "I remember telling Dr. Noon as he sutured by the beam of a flashlight that it reminded me of some volunteer work we had done in third-world countries, only without the bugs. Without missing a beat, he replied, 'Maybe we just can't see the bugs.'"

. . .

Stories are the heartbeat of Houston Methodist, and hospital employees love their stories. Like glue, stories bind the whole. In Dr. Dan Jackson's early days, Methodist Hospital had screened porches and fans, and the prospect of a new hospital in the new medical center with air conditioning was "downright exciting." At the old hospital his nameplate by the back door had a light that lit up when the operator had a message. That was Dr. Jackson's social media.

Today what was a small, 100-bed Methodist Hospital is now a family of eight hospitals collectively known as Houston Methodist, representing an academic medical center with international reach. It ranks among the best health care institutions in the world—the number-one hospital in Texas year after year with more than twenty-four thousand employees along with several thousand physicians, each with a story to tell. Together, these stories of Houston Methodist provide a colorful mural—an impressive painting in words that chronicles a century of momentum and growth. It's a very large canvas with a past, the present, and ample blank canvas for a future that stretches into the next centennial.

For more than four decades I've collected the stories of this city and the Texas Medical Center. As a young college intern in 1974, I arrived at MD Anderson Hospital and Tumor Institute clueless to the history of this medical city. Dr. R. Lee Clark, the founding president, suggested I collect the stories, noting I would meet many interesting people in the years ahead. He was not wrong. The street signs of the Texas Medical Center provided my early road map introducing me to Anderson, Bates, Bertner, Cullen, Freeman, Hermann, Moursund, and so many others who are now like old friends.

I was elated when given the opportunity to write this book. Like you, I want to know how this hospital came to be the top-ranked hospital in Texas. More important, I want to know how the Dr. Dan Jacksons of this institution found their way here and why Ruth Abeles says it's a place that employees don't want to leave. I want to know how the senior administrators (only eight in a century) led in times of great challenge and turmoil. While no institution in this city has escaped the devastation of floods, economic challenge, and occasional winds of controversy, some, like Houston Methodist, seem to rebound and prosper better than most. The word *resilience* comes to mind.

From the very beginning in 1919 to this very day, the hospital's board members— dedicated leaders representing both church and community—continue to add their own important stories to the enterprise. What are those stories and how do they define the institution and the city itself? Hospital board, administration, and medical staff working together in good times and bad is key to Houston Methodist's success, and I want to explore those stories as well.

And don't forget the community of donors with gifts large and small who have provided Houston Methodist something money cannot buy: confidence, trust, and a faith-based sense of purpose. Behind every building, program, and patient outcome is also a story with a community dimension. Buildings with names like Alkek, Brown, Bintliff, Dunn, Fondren, Jones, Scurlock, Smith, and Walter only scratch the surface of the Texas-sized vision and selfless community-wide support that has made this centennial year possible.

Writing this book has been a privilege and a joy. As Confucius advised so many years ago, "Study the past if you would define the future." I now ask the reader to step back in time and study the past. In doing so you will see, as I have, that this is a very special institution that mirrors the city's growth and success in many ways. In good times and in bad this is a hospital that has a demonstrated commitment to service informed by the past.

This is a story that begs telling and celebrating in this, Houston Methodist's centennial year.

Bryant Boutwell, Dr.P.H.
Houston, Texas
August 2019

ONE

PREQUEL

Abbe Emmanuel Domenech was only twenty-three in 1848 when he left France for Texas to investigate for the Catholic Church potential sites for additional missions in the new state of Texas. Domenech hoped to one day become a Catholic priest, so this directive from Bishop Jean Marie Odin, the second Catholic bishop of Texas, was an opportunity not to be ignored. His travel from Galveston on July 31 up "the little Buffalo river" was memorable and duly recorded in his well-worn diary.[1]

He had heard Houston was about a day's journey up this winding, overgrown waterway. It was named "Houston" in honor of General Sam Houston, who was the hero of San Jacinto and the first president of the Republic of Texas. In 1836 the town's founders, brothers Augustus C. and John K. Allen, had paid an average cost of $1.42 per acre for 6,642 acres on the west bank of Buffalo Bayou where a smaller bayou known as the White Oak converged.[2] The Allens were businessmen intent on selling this land to make a profit. Their sales pitch was as bold as their vision. "No place in the new republic was healthier than Houston having an abundance of excellent spring water and enjoying the sea breeze in all its freshness," they wrote. "It is handsome and beautifully elevated, salubrious and well-watered."[3] The name, Houston, was the proud stamp of a genuine Texas hero and the lots began to sell.

The Allens hired a surveyor named Gail Borden to lay out the town's grid with streets twelve feet wide—streets that turned to mud at the hint of rain. Perhaps the Allen brothers' claim that the city was "well-watered" held more validity than the early settlers appreciated. Borden soon gave up surveying after successfully tinkering with a process to condense milk, thereafter establishing his own fortune in dairy products.

During the first two years this new town of Houston had grown from twelve residents to some two thousand. One log cabin became a hundred log cabins. But Mother Nature was not kind. Houstonians would soon learn that Buffalo Bayou flooded and that the humid heat of summer cultivated pesky mosquitoes accompanied by deadly outbreaks of yellow fever. In 1839 the illness killed an estimated twelve percent of the town's two thousand residents.[4] Health care was thereafter very much on the minds of Houstonians.

On June 27, 1842, six years before Emmanuel Domenech began his trek from Galveston, President Sam Houston of the short-lived Republic of Texas moved the capital from Columbia to Houston. A small capitol was constructed on the site of what is today Houston's Rice Hotel. During the next six years, Texas became the twenty-eighth state in 1845, and the United States and Mexico were at war 1846–1848. The Treaty of Guadalupe Hidalgo ended the conflict, along with Mexico's claims to Texas, and among other things recognized the Rio Grande as America's southern boundary.

Prior to the end of Mexico's rule, Anglo-Americans seeking permission to settle in Texas had to accept the Catholic faith without option as stated in the Mexican constitution of 1824. "The religion of the Mexican nation is and will be perpetually the Roman Catholic Apostolic. The nation will protect it by wise and just laws and prohibit the exercise of any other."[5] While the mandate was clearly defined, enforcement was loose. In defiance of Mexican law, Protestant missionaries furtively slipped into Texas and practiced their faith quietly. Just a year before his death at the Alamo, Colonel William Barret Travis had written to the General Conference of the Methodist Church on the East Coast to request Methodist pastors for the new Republic. The Methodist Church responded by assigning three missionaries to Texas.[6]

Near Pecan Point (Red River County) the Methodist William Stevenson preached the first Protestant sermon in Texas around 1825, followed four years later by Sumner Bacon, a Cumberland Presbyterian. In 1831 an Episcopalian named John W. Cloud was at Brazoria prior to the arrival of early Baptists, and five years later Protestant groups were found commonly in areas around Nacogdoches-San Augustine, San Felipe, Galveston, and the new town of Houston. By 1836 there were at least thirty-two ministers in the field—twelve Methodists, thirteen Baptists, three Cumberland Presbyterians, three regular Presbyterians, and one Episcopalian. With Texas independence at hand, Protestants increased rapidly across the new Republic with Methodists by far dominating their numbers until after the Civil War.[7]

Surprisingly, the oldest Methodist church in Texas is considered to be the First Methodist Church of Bastrop. In the spring of 1833, a layman named James Gilleland conducted an informal and illegal church service in a small storehouse in that early settlement south of Austin. It was not fancy. Planks were placed on boxes or kegs for seats and a barrel served as a pulpit.[8]

Emmanuel Domenech knew little of this early history on that hot July morning in 1848, but was certainly eager to see what all the talk of Houston was about. His journey up Buffalo Bayou was an eye-opener that he captured in colorful prose.

The sky was a very furnace of fire, and the bay sparkled like a polished mirror. … We entered the little Buffalo river, bordered with reeds and bulrushes, in the midst of which herons, and cranes and thousands of ducks were disputing. By-and-by the banks increasing in height, approached so near each other, and formed so many narrow and tortuous windings, that at every instant the boat was caught either by the bow or the stern. At length the high lands appeared, covered with magnolias with their large white flowers and delicious perfumes.[9]

As his boat approached the small town, Domenech continued to chronicle his impressions: "The priest at Houston, a young Frenchman, was one of my travelling companions. We left Lyons together. I proceeded at once to his house. We embraced like dear friends who had not seen each other for an age. Houston is a wretched little town composed of about twenty shops, and a hundred huts, dispersed here and there, among trunks of felled trees. It is infested with Methodists and ants."[10]

Needless to say, Domenech's words would not win him a popularity contest in Houston—past or present. His description of Austin fared no better: "Austin, the seat of the Texian Legislature, is a small dirty town, and contained only one wretched hotel." The visiting Frenchman failed to mention that the town also had a small Methodist church and an old wooden shack that stood on a hill, serving as the state's capitol. In 1853, just four years after his visit, a group of thirty-five physicians, most on horseback, convened at that small Methodist church to hold the first meeting of the Texas Medical Association.[11]

Two years after writing his less-than-glowing reviews, Domenech was ordained in San Antonio, becoming the first Catholic priest ordained in Texas, according to many historians. His distaste for the hardships of missionary life led him back to France, and by 1850 he was received by Pope Pius IX, who heard his stories firsthand and personally paid for his return to Texas. Perhaps the Pope suggested he take another look.

What Domenech overlooked on first glance was the fact that these early Houstonians—Methodists and citizens of *all* faiths—had something special in common. Like the ants Domenech detested, these early Houstonians were relentless in their industry to work together, overcome any and all obstacles nature presented, and build a city to match their pride and dreams for the future. With the organization and work ethic of an ant colony, these Houstonians were one in their collective effort that in time would turn heads on an international scale. This spirit of hard work and giving back for the common good has become the hallmark of the nation's fourth-largest city we know today—a city known worldwide for generosity, vision, and accomplishment.

Domenech was not the only visiting European to be less than impressed with the new city. George Hermann's parents, John and Fannie, had come to Houston from Davos, Switzerland, shortly after the Allens arrived. They looked around disappointed and departed for Veracruz, Mexico. Shortly before Domenech's brief visit, they returned and established a successful bakery on the banks of the Buffalo Bayou. On August 6, 1843, they had a son named George who would rewrite the story of the city's future and leave his city a park and a charity hospital in his name—Hermann. His gift to the city and example to reinvest his fortune inspired others, and a great medical center would rise in the forest behind the hospital Hermann built. This Texas-sized medical city would in time (1951) become the home of Houston Methodist.

Where Domenech saw huts, mud, and ants, George Hermann's father and other early Houstonians, including a young merchant from Massachusetts named William Marsh Rice, saw potential and opportunity. They built thriving businesses along the banks of Buffalo Bayou and prospered. While George Hermann, a lifelong bachelor, left his city a park and a hospital, Rice arrived in Houston in 1838 penniless after a shipwreck off Galveston. He left his city a first-class university named Rice.[12]

As future stories will tell, these service-oriented attributes exemplified by early Houstonians are also the very fabric of the Methodist Church—a church that in 1919 will purchase a small hospital near the city's downtown and build it into an international treasure for health care, education, and research that is today known worldwide as Houston Methodist.

TWO

BEGINNINGS
1919-1929

During the 1920s:

Houston's population is 138,276 (1920)

New products include the Band-Aid, Popsicles, Wheaties, the yo-yo, Cracker Jack

Houston oil refineries proliferate along the Houston Ship Channel

Women get the right to vote (1920)

Insulin is discovered (1921)

Mayor Oscar Holcombe orders hand-operated traffic signals to "stop all the cussin'" (1921)

Statue of Sam Houston is unveiled at the entrance to Hermann Park (1925)

A high school teacher is fined $100 for teaching Darwinism (1925)

National Democratic Convention is held in Houston and the city opens a new airport known today as Hobby Airport (1928)

First Academy Awards ceremony takes place at Hollywood Roosevelt Hotel in Los Angeles (1929)

Black Friday ushers in the Great Depression (1929)

A Hospital is Born

Oscar Laertius Norsworthy was one year old when his father died in 1872. Born in the small East Texas town of Jasper, he attended rural schools and worked on a farm until he was sixteen, when he went to work in a sawmill.[1] With good grades and a strong work ethic, he was accepted into Tulane Medical School in New Orleans. The University of Texas had established its medical school in Galveston in 1891, but Norsworthy chose a Louisiana school. In 1890 he had enrolled at the military department of The University of Texas to study civil engineering only to leave within a year for medical school and the more established Tulane University.[2] In his 1905 graduating class he was one of eighteen Texans

---

8

in the class of seventy-four.[3] Following his internship at Charity Hospital in New Orleans, like many young doctors of his day he would eventually travel to Vienna and Germany to round out his education.[4]

In Dr. Norsworthy's day, physicians had to be versatile. Specialties were a concept of the future. The first medical specialty to form a board setting standards for ongoing evaluation and certification of physicians was ophthalmology and otolaryngology in 1917.[5] In New Orleans he made extra money as a city ambulance surgeon and was recognized for his surgical skills. House calls were common, and well-trained physicians like Dr. Norsworthy joined local and state medical societies and got involved.

He soon found his way to Houston and engaged in general practice, making house calls and seeing patients primarily at the Rudisill Sanitarium (forerunner of the Baptist Hospital)—then a two-story wooden building at Smith and Lamar with seventeen beds and ten student nurses. It was there on Christmas Eve 1905 he delivered a child in what he later said was the most difficult birth he had ever been a part of. The child would survive and be given the name Howard. Howard Hughes.[6]

In the summer of 1867, thirty years before Dr. Norsworthy arrived in Houston, the city endured its worst epidemic of yellow fever. With a population of fewer than five thousand, Houston lost 492 citizens in a matter of months. Among the dead were eight doctors, including the city's health officer.[7] By 1900 a physician named Dr. Walter Reed provided proof that mosquitoes, not miasma (bad air), were the culprit.

Medical care in Houston had evolved slowly during the 1800s. There is some evidence that the first hospital to appear in Houston was a temporary facility that Sam Houston and the Congress of the Republic of Texas authorized in October 1837 to care for sick soldiers.[8] Records were poorly kept in those days and most families saw their physicians in their homes. When long-term care was needed, the family was the primary caregiver. Medicine was primitive; there were no antibiotics or knowledge that germs even existed. A hospital was to many a place to die, not a place you ever wanted to go.

The coming of the railroads brought the first formal change. In the early 1870s the city's health officer, Dr. Joshua Larendon, established the city's first railroad hospital, the Houston Infirmary.[9] In March 1887 hospital care in Houston advanced overnight when six nuns from the Sisters of Charity of the Incarnate Word arrived by train from St. Mary's Infirmary in Galveston. They were greeted by Father Tom Hennessy and shown to an abandoned, pre–Civil War frame structure and two small cottages at Franklin Avenue and Caroline Street. They asked for a prayer to bless the new mission and went to work. St. Joseph's Infirmary (renamed St. Joseph's Hospital in 1952) opened its doors three months later in June 1887.[10]

In 1904 a Baptist minister, Rev. Dennis R. Pevoto, then pastor of Clark Avenue Baptist Church, identified the need for a hospital open to all individuals regardless of race, religion, or ability to pay. With the help of Mrs. Charles Stewart, Pevoto acquired the

Rudisill Sanitarium in 1907 from Ida J. Rudisill for $18,000.[11] It was chartered the Baptist Sanitarium, the first Baptist health care institution in Texas and the second Baptist hospital in the nation. It was here Dr. Norsworthy could be found listed as a general surgeon along with a number of the city's most respected physicians of the day.[12] Fifteen years after Dr. Norsworthy delivered future tycoon Howard Hughes, Dr. Ernst Bertner, the future father of the Texas Medical Center, oversaw his own complicated delivery in the Baptist Sanitarium on August 22, 1920. On that day a future cardiovascular surgeon named Denton Arthur Cooley was born. Years later, Dr. Cooley's longtime surgical colleague at the Texas Heart Institute, Dr. O. Howard "Bud" Frazier, quipped lovingly, "Yes, Bertner said his head was too big."[13]

Ida Rudisill stayed on as the first superintendent of nursing and unofficial manager. A nursing school, the first chartered in Houston, opened there in 1907 as well. Dr. Norsworthy took note of how a well-run hospital invested in training nurses provided great value to the community. By 1920 the Baptist Sanitarium had grown to 200 beds and two years later changed its name to Baptist Hospital. In years to come it would evolve into Memorial Healthcare System and move to southwest Houston off Beechnut Boulevard. In 1997 Memorial joined forces with George Hermann's hospital in the Texas Medical Center to become Memorial Hermann Health System.

Dr. Norsworthy rose quickly in stature as a well-respected Houstonian known for his personable bedside manner and surgical skills. Many of the city's wealthiest citizens trusted him with their care as evidenced by his delivery of Howard Hughes. Additionally, he was an active member of local and state medical organizations as well as a member of the Clinical Congress of Surgeons of the American College of Surgeons.[14] In 1910 he chaired a committee for the Texas Medical Association to identify and expose medical quacks "including masseurs, magnetic healers and snake charmers." That year his committee found 421 offenders but only ten were convicted. Dr. Norsworthy's frustration was evident in his committee report: "The problem was complicated by this discovery: of the district attorneys and district judges interrogated, 3 believed in quackery, 1 believed in Christian Science, 35 upheld legitimate medicine, and 13 were unconcerned."[15]

Dr. Norsworthy, like many of Houston's leading physicians of the day, recognized that the hospitals in the area were falling short in matching the needs of the rapidly growing city. Already a centralized public hospital for indigent patients was being discussed. Dr. Norsworthy decided to open his own private 30-bed hospital in 1908 at San Jacinto and Rosalie. Having his own hospital would give him more control over his patients' needs and easy access given the proximity of his personal residence. The hospital also offered him an opportunity to start his own nursing school.

Skilled nurses were in demand, and the training program Dr. Norsworthy observed at the Baptist Sanitarium inspired him. There was value in training nurses as well as economic advantage. Many hospitals of the day developed nurse training programs, knowing that for the cost of room, board, and instruction, the hospital received a cheap source of labor since nursing students worked around the clock doing everything from scrubbing floors to tending patients. Given that many graduating nurses chose work in private homes over hospitals, the need for nurse training programs seemed perpetual as the city rapidly grew.

Three years after Norsworthy Hospital opened, Southern Railroad Hospital had its beginning on May 11, 1911, at 2015 Thomas Street overlooking White Oak Bayou. It was one of the city's first modern hospitals with 102 beds. The impressive brick building was promoted as heated by steam, cleaned by vacuum cleaners, and lighted by electricity and gas.[16] It also brought to town Dr. R. W. Knox, chief surgeon of the Southern Pacific Lines, who in turn attracted other top-notch physicians, some of whom would switch allegiance to Dr. Norsworthy's hospital. In the 1970s the old Southern Railroad Hospital became a rehabilitation facility for MD Anderson Cancer Center. It later took on an important new role as Harris County's Thomas Street Health Center, which in the late 1980s became an early national leader in HIV/AIDS care.

These, of course, were not the only Houston hospitals of the day, but they were the major centers of care in Dr. Norsworthy's sphere—hospitals that influenced his decision to build his own. The original Norsworthy Hospital was a rectangular, five-story building (including a basement) and seventy-foot front presence on the corner of San Jacinto and Rosalie streets. The address was 3020 San Jacinto as listed in the 1919 Houston City Directory. Today the area is known as Houston Midtown.

A prominent feature of the building was a four-story porch gallery on the front façade. The operating room was on the top floor with all the accessories of a modern aseptic hospital, including terrazzo floors, white enamel walls and ceiling, and excellent lighting for both day and night operations. Adjoining the operating room was a sterilizing room for instruments and dressings, a dressing and sterilizing room for surgeons, and an anesthesia room.[17]

It offered ward beds, single rooms with or without a private bath, or two connecting rooms with or without a private bath. In all, thirty patients could be accommodated. Interesting to note, private baths were a novelty at the time and established Norsworthy Hospital as a trendsetter.[18] From the time the hospital opened, the nursing staff was challenged to accommodate larger numbers of patients through creative bed configurations.

Radium and the Spanish Flu

In 1895, the very year Oscar Norsworthy graduated from medical school at Tulane, a German mechanical engineer and physicist named Wilhelm Röntgen produced and detected electromagnetic radiation in a wavelength range known as X-rays, or Röntgen rays. Three years later Marie Curie, working at the Sorbonne in Paris, announced to the world she and her husband, Pierre, discovered a mystery substance called radium. It was powerfully radioactive, and by 1903 Pierre suggested that radium's ability to induce deep flesh burns might have potential for cancer therapy.[19]

Dr. Norsworthy's interest in radium had more dimensions than therapeutic potential. Medical quacks abounded in the early 1900s and they too had taken notice of radium. Certainly, his distaste for the legal system's poor performance in convicting these charlatans only intensified his interest to learn more about radium. Consider that such products then on the market included Doramad Radioactive Toothpaste with claims that radiation "increases the defense of teeth and gums" and Vita Radium Suppositories, which claimed to make "weak and discouraged men ... bubble over with joyous vitality."[20] Clearly, radium seemed to be a double-edged sword—something of great medical value or a quack's opportunity to exploit the gullible and desperate.

In 1910 Norsworthy was considered among the city's best hospitals because of its well-trained and capable physicians. Houston's health department had one pathologist and a bacteriologist who checked the purity of milk, water, and foods and coped with transmissible diseases of the day, like smallpox, tuberculosis, diphtheria, scarlet fever, typhoid fever and scabies (mites). Just five years earlier, the first dental school in the state opened in downtown Houston. The Texas Dental College would become The University of Texas School of Dentistry in 1943.[21]

In 1910, a busy year for the city, Houstonians numbered eighty thousand and took pride in their fifteen miles of electric streetcar lines and 190 miles of paved streets. Anyone wanting to go to Bellaire by streetcar had to transfer at Eagle Street (ten blocks south of Norsworthy Hospital) and take a lone tram across the vast, unsettled stretch between Houston and the small town of Bellaire,[22] then on the east side of William Marsh Rice's 9,449-acre ranch.[23] In 1910 Union Station opened at Texas and Crawford, making it the busiest intersection in town. Today, when the Houston Astros are in town, it's still one of the busiest intersections. Nearby, at the corner of Main and Clay, First Methodist Episcopal Church, South opened its doors in 1910 as well.

It was also in 1910 that Dr. Norsworthy, age thirty-eight, fell in love with Sarah Sanford Gibbs of Huntsville, Texas. Sarah, two years younger, was from a well-to-do family. In fact, her first cousin, Mary Gibbs, would marry Jesse Jones a decade later. How Sarah met Oscar Norsworthy is not clear, but the bride's brother, Dr. James Philip Gibbs, was a well-respected Huntsville physician and likely crossed professional paths with the groom. What we do know is that the Norsworthys were married in Huntsville at the bride's home on November 10, 1910. A graduate of Waco Female College, the new Mrs. Norsworthy had graduated valedictorian of her class. Upon arriving in Houston, she transferred her membership from Methodist Church of Huntsville to St. Paul's Methodist Church—a new church at the corner of Milam and McGowen, where the Norsworthys were involved members known for their support of charities.[24]

Three years after their wedding, tragedy struck. Their son, Oscar Laertius Norsworthy, Jr., was born on October 7, 1913, and lived only one day. The loss must have weighed heavily on Dr. Norsworthy. He had lost his own father, Louistion, when he was one and his sister, Levina, when he was two.[25] With great equanimity he poured himself into his work, seeing more patients and serving his local and state medical societies with distinction. While his personal life suffered, the city around him was on a roll.

The year his son died, the Houston Symphony was established, twelve oil companies located in Houston, including Humble Oil Company, known today as ExxonMobil. The following year, 1914, George Hermann died and the city literally shut down for his funeral procession. Thousands watched as the procession made its way through downtown to Glenwood Cemetery. Hermann left his gift of land to create Hermann Park and the bulk of his estate for a charity hospital in his name.

Another gift to the city arrived on November 10, when President Woodrow Wilson left a Cabinet meeting and rushed to the Oval Office to push a button that remotely fired a cannon in Houston, signaling the opening of Houston's Ship Channel. Later that summer Anderson, Clayton & Company moved all of its cotton merchandizing operations from Oklahoma to Houston. The new ship channel played a key role in the success of companies like Anderson, Clayton & Company, whose fortune would be reinvested in Houston's medical community in ways few could imagine at the time.

In April of 1917 the United States declared war on Germany during World War I. Almost simultaneously a new, mysterious enemy emerged on the world stage that would take more lives than the war itself. It went by the common name of influenza, the Spanish flu. To Dr. Norsworthy and the international medical community, this strain would prove to be a nightmare.

At Camp Logan, an army training camp in what is now Houston's Memorial Park, 3,091 cases of influenza were reported in September and October 1918.[26] Worldwide an estimated twenty million, perhaps as many as one hundred million, perished. Especially hard-hit were military training bases in the United States, where thousands of soldiers were confined in small areas as they trained for World War I. A lone letter discovered sixty years after the flu struck at one such base, Camp Devens in Maryland, summarizes the horror. Its author, Roy, was never found, perhaps himself lost to the terror he witnessed and reported as follows:

> When the soldiers are brought to the hospital at the Army base, they rapidly develop the most vicious type of Pneumonia that has ever been seen. Two hours after admission they have the Mahogany spots over the cheek bones and a few hours later you can begin to see the Cyanosis extending from the ears and spreading all over the face, until it is hard to distinguish the colored man from the white. It is horrible. … We have been averaging about 100 deaths a day [and] it takes special trains to carry away the dead.[27]

Norsworthy Hospital, like every other hospital in Houston and across the nation, was overwhelmed by the influenza pandemic of 1918. There were simply not enough staff or beds. Patients were doubled up in beds placed in hallways, on rooftops, wherever space could be created. Most agonizing was the sense of helplessness after the illness first appeared in the spring of 1918 as regular flu only to disappear and return with a vengeance in the fall as an entirely different strain. It was called the Spanish flu only because Spain publicized its devastation while other countries said little.

Clearly, Dr. Norsworthy had a great deal on his mind in 1918 as the needs of his patients and entire community commanded his attention. Not only had he lost his son five years earlier, now his neighbors, professional colleagues, and patients were dying. Equally concerning was his wife's health, which remained fragile since the loss of their son. It was also clear that his small 30-bed hospital was inadequate for the needs at hand and he simply no longer had the resolve to expand. His interest now was to leave Houston to pursue additional training in the therapeutic benefits of radium. But first he had to find a buyer for his hospital.

The question was, whom could he trust with the high ethical standards he lived by? He found his answer in the church—Methodist Episcopal Church, South.

The Methodists of Houston

Step back in time. Methodism was born in Houston in 1837 when fourteen members of a Sunday School Society met. By 1844 the first Methodist church building in Houston was also the first brick church in Texas. The Allen brothers had reserved the north side of Texas Avenue between Travis and Milam for a church then known as Methodist Episcopal Church, South because the Methodist church had split into north and south entities over slavery. Bishop James O. Andrew of Georgia married a woman who owned slaves and the debate began. Northern Methodists were unable to organize a church in Texas until 1853. During the decade after Texas became a state in 1845, Methodists were the largest denomination with numbers across the state reaching forty thousand by 1860.[28] A century later, in 1968, the national denomination merged with Evangelical United Brethren Church to form United Methodist Church, now one of the largest in America.[29]

In 1883 the city's first telephone exchange was created, arc lights appeared, two newspapers named the *Post* and the *Chronicle* appeared, and that first brick Methodist church added a 130-foot tower and was renamed Charles Shearn Memorial Methodist Episcopal Church, South. The name was a mouthful, but this was a church where many of the town's leading families gathered. A sign of the times, African American members were given a separate building facing Milam before moving to the corner of Travis and Bell to establish Trinity Methodist Church.[30]

In 1907 the Shearn Methodists sold the property for $115,000 and moved to a new location, Main Street and Clay, where the church remains this day as First Methodist.[31] Another well-known Methodist church, St. Luke's, would hold its first service in Lamar High School in 1945 and open its first church building in 1951 a few miles west of downtown

Houston on a former farm-to-market road Houstonians named for a German flour mill entrepreneur, Mitchell Westheimer.

Many of Dr. Norsworthy's friends and patients were members of Shearn Methodist Church. After all, they pledged their church membership vows to give of their "prayers, presence, gifts, service and witness." These vows can be traced back to two brothers, Charles and John Wesley, who had in 1728 gathered like-minded friends in study and faith at Oxford University's Christ Church. Charles had not been the most disciplined student and organized the group to get himself back on track. His father, a clergyman of the Church of England, would expect no less.

The Wesley brothers' group engaged in organized Bible study, gaining the rather unflattering nickname of "Bible-moths." They were also called "The Holy Club," but because they lived by "method," the name "Methodist" was a good fit. An invitation by James Oglethorpe, the founder of the colony of Georgia, brought them to the United States in 1875. The "Methodist" movement spread quickly from Britain into the Americas and beyond.[32]

. . .

In December 1919, the Norsworthys made the Texas Conference of the Methodist Episcopal Church, South a generous offer. While his property, buildings, and medical equipment were appraised at $87,000, he was not interested in profit and suggested that $35,000[33] to be paid over time would do. He had a large lot adjacent to his hospital available as well. In time, he forgave much of the debt. More than money, he was interested in placing his hospital in the right hands, and these Methodists were people of faith with business know-how. If they were willing to meet his conditions to expand the hospital with the addition of a new building and to operate the hospital under his name until the new building would be completed, they had a deal. He would also stay on the board just to keep an eye on things.

Church and business leaders met in the boardroom of First National Bank on December 9, 1919, to accept the offer. The group had been called together by the presiding elder, Robert W. Adams. John T. Scott, Sr., Mississippi born, was an active member of the old Shearn Methodist Church and president of First National Bank. A highly respected businessman, Scott also served throughout his distinguished career the Houston Cotton Exchange, the Houston Board of Trade, Rice University, the Houston Public School Board, and The University of Texas Board of Regents.

On this day in 1919 he added chairman of the newly formed Methodist Hospital board to his résumé—a position he would hold for the next twenty-three years. Fellow officers of the board included Walter W. Fondren, vice president; Samuel F. Carter, treasurer; and Robert L. Cole, secretary. Adams, as elder, was named "General Superintendent of the Hospital Movement," and given a salary of $5,000 a year plus expenses. In addition to the officers, original board members (there were twenty) included Dr. Norsworthy as an adviser to the church on medical affairs, along with notable Houstonians James A. Elkins, James Marion West, Sr., and William Lockhart Clayton. Other founding members were representatives from neighboring Texas cities, including Galveston, Beaumont, Huntsville, Jacksonville, Longview, Marlin, Nacogdoches, Pittsburg, Richmond, and Tyler.

From day one the Methodist Hospital board was dedicated, hardworking, and generous with time and resources. At least four of them, including Scott, represented banking interests. Most of the original board members were self-made and self-educated men. Most had been born in the Old South and come to Texas as youths to make fortunes in cotton, timber, legal services, and, especially, oil. Three stories illustrate the self-made qualities and can-do spirit that defined the early board's generosity and community service.

• • •

William Lockhart Clayton, known to family and friends as Will, was from Tupelo, Mississippi. At a young age his family moved to Jackson, Tennessee. There he met the Anderson brothers, Frank and Monroe. Monroe Dunaway Anderson was perhaps the most trusted young man in Jackson as he worked behind the teller's window at People's National Bank. You may recognize his initials more than his name—M. D. Anderson. In 1904 Will, Frank, and Monroe started a cotton brokerage company in Oklahoma known as Anderson, Clayton & Company. By 1907 Monroe took up residence in the city to investigate whether Houston would be a better location. It was.

By 1914 Will Clayton was in Houston, and his now-Houston-based company was making a fortune merchandizing cotton from the fields to world markets. As an original board member for Methodist Hospital, Clayton continued to serve the hospital's board until his death in 1966. His business partner, Monroe Anderson, amassed a fortune of more than $20 million[34] before his death in 1939, a fortune that served as the corpus for his MD Anderson Foundation. The implications were important for Methodist Hospital as future stories will tell.

• • •

James A. Elkins came to Houston from Huntsville, Texas, in 1917 and started a law firm with his friend William Vinson. Vinson & Elkins, LLP opened that year with three lawyers and grew into one of the largest law firms in Texas. In addition to serving the new Methodist board, Elkins, later to be Judge Elkins, was also president of City National Bank. Back in Judge Elkins's early days in Huntsville, a distraught father came to him for help. The man's teenage son, Gus, had broken a neighbor's window with a slingshot and the old widow was mad as a hornet and suing. Judge Elkins took the case and went to the angry woman, noting little Gus was "a mindless child" and suggested a trial would only expose and shame the poor family. The lawsuit was immediately dropped.[35] Years later Judge Elkins and Gus Wortham often shared a laugh over the incident. Gus and his father went on to start a small insurance company in 1926 that would grow into American General, an international trendsetter in the insurance industry. Like Judge Elkins, Wortham moved to Houston from Huntsville and served his community generously with a special interest in the arts.

• • •

No other original board member directly influenced the course of Methodist Hospital more than Walter William Fondren. A native of Tennessee, he moved to Arkansas in a covered wagon at age six and was an orphan by age ten. From a young age he worked on farms and in sawmills. As a teenager he hopped a train for Texas and made it as far as Corsicana. He learned the oil business doing odd jobs before becoming a skilled rotary driller in 1901. There, in Corsicana, while working on an oil rig, the tired and thirsty Fondren wandered to a farm that offered a boardinghouse with a water well, and met Ella Florence Cockrum—the future Mrs. Ella Fondren. She was born in Hazel, Kentucky, and her father died when she was six. She quit school and helped her mother raise her six siblings and worked in the boardinghouse that supplemented their meager means.

While Walter Fondren soon left Corsicana for the Texas Gulf Coast after hearing of the 1901 Spindletop gusher in Beaumont, he stayed in contact with Ella. Although his first drilling rig failed, his reputation for unfailing honesty and integrity carried him over, and he soon secured a loan for his second attempt. This time he did not fail. On Valentine's Day 1904, he married Ella Cockrum. They would have three children. With savings of $25,000, his new bride recalled years later she thought they had made their fortune.

Marilyn McAdams Sibley, in her 1989 book about Methodist Hospital's early years, tells a wonderful story regarding the Fondren fortune. Ella Fondren had taken her husband's place on the hospital's board following his death in 1939 and remembered the moment their savings could have been lost. In her words: "Then one day he came in and said, 'Mother, I have taken all our savings out of the bank and bought land near Humble.' I thought we were ruined! I cried all night. But the money started coming in, and it's been coming in ever since."[36]

That's Humble, Texas, as in Humble Oil and Refining Company—ExxonMobil today. The Fondrens, as Sibley wrote, never forgot those hard times and felt a great responsibility to use their money wisely. Institutions like Southern Methodist University, Southwestern University, Rice University (where their three children attended college), and especially this new Methodist Hospital in Houston would all benefit from the Fondrens' philanthropic gifts.

• • •

James Marion West, Sr., also a founding board member, has his own impressive story. Born in Waynesboro, Mississippi, in 1871, he left school at age thirteen to work as a water boy at Trinity County Lumber Company to make ends meet. In time he bought the mill outright and built a fortune in cattle and lumber. In 1910 as Oscar Norsworthy was getting married in Huntsville, West was acquiring South Texas Lumber Company from Jesse Jones, who owned the *Houston Chronicle* and many of the buildings in downtown Houston. Jones, known as "Mr. Houston," would in the late 1920s join the Methodist Hospital board himself. West's ventures into large ranches led to the creation of The West Cattle Company, run by his sons, James, Jr. and Westly, after his death in 1941.

As James Marion West, Sr. joined the Methodist board in 1919, he was also setting his sights on venturing into the oil business. With his two young sons and friend Hugh Roy Cullen, an additional fortune was made off large oil-field holdings in Pierce Junction and a little-known salt dome in Fort Bend County called the Thompson Field. Like others on the board, West also served in governmental roles. Will Clayton had served numerous roles in Washington, D.C., including as the first U.S. assistant secretary of state for economic affairs in 1944. West served Texas as chairman of the Texas Highway Commission (now the Department of Transportation) starting in 1939. Jesse Jones served various roles in Washington under presidents Woodrow Wilson and Franklin Roosevelt, including secretary of commerce, 1940–45.

• • •

The new Methodist board, with recognizable names like Clayton, Elkins, Fondren, West, Carter, and Jones, exemplified the spirit of Houston and what bright, successful Houstonians with energy, talent, and a love for their city and country could accomplish. It is a trait that runs through the hospital's board to this day. For many, their descendants would continue to serve the hospital for decades to come in ways not always obvious through the name. For example, generations of the Fondren family (including Trammells and Underwoods) have served the hospital for nearly a century—an impressive ninety-three years of continuous Fondren family support. Also, the Dunn Tower's Crain Garden atrium owes its origin to a gift from Dr. Edward Lillo Crain, Jr. (1917–2003), a physician who served patients at Methodist for fifty years. Dr. Crain's mother, Annie Vive, was the daughter of founding board treasurer Samuel F. Carter.

Equally important, the board's faith-based roots and business savvy proved a winning combination capable of making lemonade out of lemons whenever needed. Without the decisions Dr. Norsworthy made at this pivotal point in his hospital's history, the story of Houston Methodist might easily have ended very differently.

The Challenges Ahead

For starters, before 1919 the Methodist Church had never owned and operated a hospital in Texas. Methodist Hospital of Houston was the first Texas hospital to be owned and operated by the church. In time the Methodists would charter hospitals in other Texas cities: Dallas (1928), Fort Worth (1930), Lubbock (1954), and San Antonio (1960). For the Houston board, these were new waters and the times were difficult. While Dr. Norsworthy had given the church a generous deal on his property and buildings, he also challenged them to expand the hospital with a new building. That he was staying connected to the board showed he intended to hold them to their pledge. His name would remain on the door and he had no intentions of seeing his hospital stagnate or fade into the past.

The Great War ended on November 11, 1918. The 1920s in Houston were not the easiest times to raise money. Across the country the average American struggled, earning $1,500 a year for a fifty-two-hour workweek. Houston's population was rapidly increasing and now approaching 150,000. By the end of the decade, the Roaring Twenties would sputter to a halt on Black Friday, October 29, 1929. The Gilded Age, exemplified in 1925 by F. Scott Fitzgerald's classic novel *The Great Gatsby*, lost its sparkle as the Great Depression enveloped the country.

The rapid growth of Houston coupled with powerful memories of the flu pandemic meant that the hospitals in town, like St. Joseph's, were all setting their sights on adding hospital beds to meet the city's needs. George Hermann's new hospital opened in 1925 in a forest that many Houstonians once thought was too far from downtown to ever be of value. That forest would become the Texas Medical Center in the mid-1940s.

Located in the shadow of downtown at 1101 Elder, the county's four-story Jefferson Davis Hospital, the first to accept indigent patients, opened on December 24, 1924. Many Houstonians were livid to learn the new hospital was built atop a Confederate cemetery. Mayor Oscar Holcombe moved quickly to calm the clamor by naming the building for the Confederacy's president, Jefferson Davis.[37] In time the hospital would change locations to Allen Parkway (then Buffalo Drive) to be supplemented in 1963 by a new county hospital in the Texas Medical Center named Ben Taub. In time Jeff Davis Hospital on Allen Parkway was torn down and the county's North Northeast Hospital was expanded, modernized, and renamed LBJ General Hospital in July 1990.

Despite the challenges of raising funds in the 1920s, the Methodist board enacted a bold plan to expand from 30 beds to a new building with 346 beds to be constructed in four phases. The new building would be E-shaped, each part representing one phase costing up to $200,000 per phase.[38] These were successful leaders and men of great faith, but they soon realized they were overly ambitious and scaled back. The plan was to have the local Methodist community and Houston at large help raise the funds needed with statewide help through the Texas Conference. Instead, they barely made it halfway on phase one and much of that money was from their own pockets. The minutes from the Hospital Report of the 1922 Texas Annual Conference in Marshall, Texas, on November 22–27, pick up the story:

> About $80,000 was realized ... the larger part of which was raised in the city of Houston. Only a small portion of the $100,000 for the Conference was realized, by reason of the newness of the enterprise and other pressing claims then upon the church. During the year 1921, owing to the educational campaign the hospital was allowed to rest. The trustees at their meeting early in

the summer decided to begin the new building sometime during the fall, and we have now under way a hospital building, that when completed and equipped, will cost $150,000.[39]

As Dr. Norsworthy watched with concern, the board scaled back to a more modest building with 100 beds. With $44,000 cash in hand and $40,000 in pledges, they hired the architectural firm of James Ruskin Bailey with a fixed limit of $90,000.[40] That Bailey was the son-in-law of board president John T. Scott created a minor problem. While Scott offered to resign, the board knew better. Removing him from the building committee was considered a reasonable compromise. For Bailey, the challenge of the hospital building nearly doubled when he was asked to also build on the lot next to the hospital an additional structure—the Sarah Francelia Bell home.

· · ·

Sarah Francelia Bell came to Houston in 1836 fleeing the settlement of San Felipe de Austin with her mother as Santa Anna's army marched to San Jacinto following their victory at the Alamo. The citizens of San Felipe de Austin actually burned the settlement rather than allow it to fall into the hands of the Mexican army. Leaving everything behind except her Bible, Bell grew up in one of the first houses in Houston. An active and devoted charter member of Shearn Methodist Church, she died August 12, 1914, leaving the Methodist Church to oversee her trust along with specific directives to build and operate a home for the widows of indigent Methodist ministers.

In this way, Bailey was asked to add a three-story, concrete frame building with brick veneer cladding to his plans. The Bell home would in time be connected to both the original Norsworthy Hospital and the new Methodist Hospital under construction. Today, both hospital buildings are gone, but the Bell home at 1111 Rosalie now houses law offices. Bailey's talent as an architect gained notice. His next commission after Methodist Hospital was in 1925, when he designed the highly praised John Kirby House in Houston.

Bids for construction of both facilities were issued in early summer, and on August 16, 1922, Central Construction Company was contracted for $81,000. The Bell home proved to be an integral part of the new hospital. It never housed more than twelve elderly widows, and they all lived on the ground floor for the sake of convenience. This left the two upper floors free for the hospital's use as a residence for nurses and student nurses or for additional patient rooms. The flat roof of the Bell home was a bonus in the days before air conditioning. It provided a popular spot for patients and staff alike who sought a breeze and respite from the dog days of Houston summers.

More important, the Bell Trust, with board membership that overlapped that of the Methodist Hospital board (Scott, Phelps, and Carter), took on new meaning when construction shortfalls arose. To save the day, the Bell Trust lent Methodist Hospital $60,000 at seven percent interest and took a mortgage on the assets. The interest rate was lowered a percentage point during the Great Depression. Final payment on the debt was made in late 1944, and Methodist Hospital was debt-free for the first time in its young history. One can only wonder if the hospital would even be here today if it hadn't been for a widow named Bell who came to Houston with only her Bible in hand.[41]

. . .

While this new Methodist Hospital in Houston was the church's first in Texas, it was not to be the only one in the state. In six years Dallas would add a Methodist hospital. This was very much on the mind of the General Conference of Methodist Episcopal Church, South when they met in Hot Springs, Arkansas, in May 1922. There, Charles C. Selecman, then pastor of First Methodist Church in Dallas, proposed creating a fund to help these Methodist hospitals care for the ill and the poor. After all, the church could not turn them away without care. So a special fund with annual dues ranging from $1 to $10,000 would allow various levels of church members' support. Selecman called this fund the Golden Cross.[42] The General Conference readily adopted this program to help the church support the work of these hospitals and provide care for those in need. The program would prove to be an important financial lifeline for the hospital during the early years.

Early Hospital Leadership

Sam Hay, Jr., twenty-eight years of age, was appointed superintendent of the hospital in 1923 as construction was well underway. He was the son of the First Methodist Church pastor, Rev. Sam Hay, Sr., who become Bishop Hay in 1922. Sam, Jr. had a big heart but lacked hospital administrative skills. The well-meaning Sam, Jr. was to hold the position barely two years, departing on December 31, 1925, "for business reasons." Years later he acknowledged: "Every time a patient died, I couldn't sleep at night, thinking there might have been something we didn't do right. I lost twenty pounds in one year and gained it back within six months after I left."[43]

To say the Bishop's son accomplished little would be a mistake. He gave the hospital one of its greatest gifts—Josie Mooring Roberts. Born in Grimes County, Texas, she was the daughter of a Methodist minister. While she had only a high school education and some business schooling, some would say she had a doctorate in street smarts and determination. One of ten children, she married at seventeen. After the arrival of her daughter, Bobbye Faye, she learned her husband had tuberculosis. Josie took charge of the situation and found a sanitarium in San Angelo, Texas. She made the 365-mile trek by car with her young daughter and sick husband only to be told he would not be admitted. "They thought he was too far gone," she recalled in a 1975 interview.

With little money she found a nursing home for her husband and a job with the telephone company to make ends meet. When her husband died her daughter was only four. With Josie's parents watching over Bobbye Faye in Houston, she went to work. "I traveled for the telephone company out there inspecting some offices for them. Then, when I came back to

Houston, that was in about '22, I guess, I went to work for the telephone company in the personnel department, employing and training people."[44]

Roberts's business sense, ability to read and manage people, and can-do attitude enabled her to stand up to any challenge in a working world dominated by men. Where Sam Hay, Jr. found bill collections uncomfortable, his new assistant manager, Josie Roberts, was seasoned by life to take on any challenge. Joining Hay at Methodist Hospital in December 1923, she would see him resign in 1925 and replaced by Rev. D. H. Hotchkiss. "I told him [Hotchkiss] I didn't want him to feel that he had to keep me in any way … if he had someone he wanted to bring in as his assistant." Hotchkiss not only wanted her to stay but told her, "I'm depending on you."[45]

Hotchkiss preferred community relations and turned day-to-day hospital management over to his able assistant. Running programs, managing the budget, and overseeing the small staff of the new hospital were all areas in which Roberts excelled, which was a good thing. As the Great Depression loomed, Roberts was put to the test. Despite the excellent care the medical staff provided, the hospital was going broke.

A memorandum from Superintendent Hotchkiss to the hospital board dated April 29, 1929, is typical of the quarterly audit reports of his day. Jesse Jones, former U.S. secretary of commerce, who soon became a Methodist Hospital board member (1930–1956), likely grimaced upon reading the report. An excerpt reads:

> A net loss of $5,580.20 is shown, which is practically paralleled
> by the Charity Service we have given, and for which Golden Cross
> contributions have not yet been received. … What is of more concern is
> that we are owing in accounts payable $23,960.11, and have to balance
> same accounts receivable $21,945.94. If what is owed to us were worth
> par we would be in good shape, but many of our accounts and notes are
> valueless. Signed. D.H. Hotchkiss.[46]

Recalled Roberts years later: "The hospital was in debt, deeply in debt; we owed about $4,000 or $5,000 [in] laundry bills. We were paying a high price per pound for laundry so I didn't do anything but call this laundry (company) and have them come out and talk to them. I got bids, and I could get the laundry much cheaper. Mr. Hotchkiss had been afraid to do that because these people were Methodists and he was afraid to do anything about it. We began to owe more and more and more. The old saying is I 'took the bull by the horns,' and believe me, I got them out of debt."[47]

Hotchkiss stayed five years. By 1932 Roberts officially took the helm and was a force to reckon with throughout the next three decades. In many ways, the debt made her and the hospital stronger.

Another gift the hospital received was A. Frank Smith. When Sam Hay, Sr. was named bishop in 1922, the church named Smith the new pastor of First Methodist Church in

Houston. Smith would prove a godsend, and his two sons, Frank, Jr. and Randy, would follow in his footsteps, serving on the board with distinction and assisting the growth of the hospital for decades to come.

Born in Elgin, Texas, in 1889, Angie Frank Smith completed his divinity degree at Vanderbilt University in 1914. By the time he arrived in Houston as senior pastor of First Methodist Church, he already had an impressive track record, including his founding role organizing a church on the campus of Southern Methodist University; it is known today as Highland Park Methodist Church. In less than ten years behind the pulpit, he was considered in the church at the national level as one of the best and brightest, not to mention kind, thoughtful, and collaborative.

Serving the hospital board, he first focused on the medical needs of children and organized a small group of women into a service organization he suggested be named Blue Bird Circle. The name was selected because the bluebird symbolizes happiness and because the members wished to be bound together in a circle of love and goodwill. As future stories will tell, the Blue Bird Circle became an institution unto itself. Smith's unassuming manner and sense of humor were invaluable attributes. One wonderful example illustrates the point. One of his friends in Houston also happened to be named Frank Smith (no relation), who in 2018, at age ninety-six, recalled with a grin, "He used to introduce me to his friends saying, 'I'm *a* Frank Smith, this is *the* Frank Smith.'"[48]

Smith's talents and faith-based vision coupled with the business savvy of so many self-made and dedicated board members created a powerful momentum for the new hospital in difficult times. Add to that can-do administrators like Josie Roberts and a talented, patient-centered medical staff and you have a winning combination. In airline jargon, that winning combination provided the lift for the wings of the old Norsworthy Hospital to soar as a new Methodist Hospital found its way to the Texas Medical Center in the early 1950s.

The New Hospital and Early Medical Staff

On Sunday afternoon, April 13, 1924, the new Methodist Hospital held an open house for the public with Sam Hay, Jr. and Josie Roberts busy conducting tours. The new building's 72 beds added to the old building's 30 to provide an inpatient capacity of around 100 adult beds, depending on the configuration, along with 10 bassinets.[49] The following morning a *Houston Post* headline reported to the community:

> The building is one of the most attractive in the city. The furnishings in
> the room, many of them supplied by individuals and church organizations,
> were all in place and everything looked so comfortable and cozy that one
> was tempted to believe it would be a pleasure to be sick here.
>
> The operating rooms, with their shiny surgeons' apparatus, and white
> furnishings, were a center of interest. The X-ray room and other specialty

equipped rooms were also of special interest. … Enrollments in the Golden Cross were accepted yesterday, the money to go to the new hospital here in Houston.[50]

On June 12 the first patients were admitted. While the offer was made to name the new building for Dr. Norsworthy, he declined. More important to him was that the board should always value the medical staff and make no promises they could not keep. He was concerned that hospitals around the country were "standardizing," and that was not a good word in his mind. The board took note and the hospital's name changed from Norsworthy to Methodist. While the quality of patient care excelled in the sparkling new hospital, the budget remained in intensive care.

Two of Dr. Norsworthy's handpicked medical staff members were Dr. Charles C. Green, former city health officer and now chief of surgery, and Dr. Marvin L. Graves, a pioneer in establishing internal medicine as a specialty and who had special interests in mental health and preventive medicine.[51] Both were asked to join the early board, which in those days met once a year. Both also served on a smaller executive committee that carried on the day-to-day business of the hospital.

Drs. Green and Graves proved to be strong anchors for attracting many of the best physicians to the city to bring their patients to the new Methodist Hospital. Yet, for some young doctors, the two would be considered overly domineering—even quietly referring to the hospital as the "Green-Graves Hospital."

Dr. J. Charles Dickson, who arrived in 1929, recalled years later:

> From the time the hospital opened until 1940 it had been the custom that all cases coming to the emergency room were referred to one doctor [Dr. Green] who had been on the Board of Trustees since the hospital opened. … This argument almost broke up the staff. Many said if the decision in regard to referrals from the emergency room was not changed, they would resign. The Board agreed … and directed that the emergency room referrals be to the doctor on call [with] this doctor only serving one month each year. Many of the doctors who said they would resign became the leaders in the Staff organization in subsequent years.[52]

Just three months after opening, the hospital was earning recognition as among the best when the American College of Surgeons named thirty-six statewide hospitals out of sixty-three with more than 100 beds to its list of approved hospitals. Houston had four: Methodist, Baptist, St. Joseph's, and Southern Pacific.[53]

Patients voiced their approval as well. Lela Ruth Newton of Willis, Texas, was so impressed with her care in 1925 that she wrote the *Houston Post*. "Here you will find the most wonderful doctors and nurses, even maids, in fact everyone there. I can tell you [that] you won't find any dirt there. ... If you ever need to go to a hospital, may I suggest you go there. You will be well-cared for both physically and spiritually. I was."[54]

Early on Methodist Hospital was already known for innovations. Dr. Green performed some of Houston's first blood transfusions when blood typing was new and Rh factors unknown. Transferring blood by syringe from donor to recipient was both bold and risky and conducted only as a last resort. Physicians statewide soon learned to keep a constant eye on the innovative new hospital the Methodists were running. The hospital also installed the first oxygen tent in Houston as a makeshift affair involving sheets and tape. Physicians throughout the city came calling to take a look.

Dr. Green was once described by Sam Hay, Jr. as "a bulldog of a man" and no one seemed to disagree. In the operating room Dr. Green's exceptional surgical skills were matched by his exceptional temper. He often clashed with nurse Amelia Eagleton, who ran the operating room with an iron fist. One day he insisted she be fired or he'd never refer another patient. As the story goes, when Dr. Green's wife became ill, it was Eagleton and her assistant, Grace Swinford, who selflessly stepped in to care for her. In time Eagleton became Dr. Green's office nurse and, later, his second wife.[55] It may have been one of the new hospital's first cases of workplace romance.

Dr. Marvin L. Graves, chief of medicine, was a Waco native. Born in 1860, he was the son of a Methodist minister and completed his premedical studies at Southwestern University, where a Dr. H. C. Ghent was one of his favorite instructors. After completing his medical degree in New York, he became physician-in-chief at John Sealy Hospital in Galveston before coming to Houston in 1925. He would start one of the city's first group practices with his son, Dr. Ghent Graves, a Harvard graduate. Both father and son served as presidents of the Texas Medical Association. Dr. Marvin Graves's grandson, Ghent Graves, Jr., was born at Hermann Hospital in 1928 and received his medical degree at Baylor University College of Medicine, as it was then known. The grandson enjoyed a long and distinguished career as well, representing a single family of doctors practicing medicine at Methodist for more than seven decades.

Dr. Hatch Cummings, Jr., another distinguished Methodist physician, married into the Graves family. It was Dr. Cummings whom Dr. Dan Jackson remembered for his kindness in 1949 when he first arrived. The Graves–Cummings family service along with the Jackson family legacy provides bookend examples that say much about Methodist Hospital as a professional home rather than a place to work.

Not to be overlooked in the hospital's early years are the many dedicated wives of the medical staff. Dr. Marvin Graves's wife, Laura, organized the Women's Auxiliary, hosted meetings in her parlor, and served as its first president in 1928. Within a year there were nearly six hundred members dedicated to support "the growth and greater efficiency of the hospital." Given that 1,620 patients were admitted in 1928, the new Auxiliary proved an invaluable support for the hospital that continues to this day.

During its first year the Auxiliary raised $527.65, and the Children's Committee (one of seven committees) redecorated the children's ward and provided six beds and mattresses, bed linens, books, and more. More important than dollars raised, they began a century-long tradition of volunteer service. In 2017, Auxiliary volunteers raised $442,211 through gift shops and other programs to assist patient care needs, provided Hurricane Harvey relief for employees, and awarded scholarships to teen hospital volunteers. As of February 2018, the Auxiliary had donated more than $6 million to Houston Methodist.[56]

Nursing students were also key to the hospital's success in these early days. The devastating smallpox epidemics that took the city by storm throughout the 1800s and the influenza pandemic of 1918 underscored the need for Houston to add hospitals, physicians, and nurses. As noted, there was an advantage for hospitals to train nurses since they represented free labor in return for room, board, and what was then loosely defined instruction. That began to change in 1890, when the first formal school of nursing in Texas was established at John Sealy Hospital in Galveston. The graduate nurses were much in demand to improve the quality of education at hospital training schools statewide. While the male-dominated medical profession did not always welcome women into the hospital workplace, Dr. Norsworthy set an early standard by establishing his nursing school.

Sam Hay, Jr. opened Methodist Hospital's School of Nursing on September 15, 1924, with eight nurses. Most had high school diplomas and enrolled in the three-year program. Records show five completed the program and graduated in 1927 with Rev. A. Frank Smith delivering the commencement sermon at First Methodist Church.

The Nursing Practice Act of 1909 greatly enhanced the requirements for hospitals with nurse training programs. Prior to 1922 the programs offered a "systematic course of instruction" without any standards for what that meant. On April 4, 1922, the State Nurses' Registration Bill provided new rigor to the process, including inspections and accreditation of nursing schools throughout the state.

The Methodist Hospital nursing program of the mid-1920s now required coursework in anatomy, chemistry, nutrition, bacteriology, obstetrics, pediatrics, and other specialty topics. Students received uniforms, room, board, laundry, and fifty-plus-hour workweeks. An ad in the *Houston Post* on November 14, 1924, promoted the new program: "A School of Nursing Instruction conducted where young ladies can prepare for a life work of service, taught by competent instructors and surrounded by Christian influences. This Hospital Owned and Controlled by the Methodist Church—and Rendering Service to All Classes of People. Sam R. Hay, Jr., Bus. Mgr., Mrs. V.L. Reeve, R.N., Supt. Nurses."[57]

Registered nurses like Reeve were in demand. Paid $150 a week, she resigned after a year. Jessie T. Bain, R.N., took her place on September 15, 1925. Bain, like Josie Roberts, proved a force to reckon with. That Bain had recommendations directly from the accreditation board meant she held considerable power, and she knew it. Dr. Ray Collins, the first intern at Methodist, noted the Northern-born Bain loved to remind the Texas doctors how things were done in New York. "Everything had to be absolutely a certain way—her way." Within three years, she resigned and returned to New York.[58]

. . .

With a new hospital building, a dedicated community board, a talented medical staff consisting of many of the most respected physicians in town, an experienced assistant administrator named Josie Roberts, a nursing school with a no-nonsense director, and a growing city flush with new wealth and can-do citizens—the coming decade held great promise. Yet there was the Great Depression to deal with along with as-yet-unseen challenges and opportunities. The hospital's new building providing 100 beds was just one phase of the planned four. Was that enough?

THREE

GROWING PAINS
1930-1940

During the 1930s:
>*Census ranks Harris County as the state's most populous at 292,352 (1930)*
>
>*Franklin Delano Roosevelt is elected to the first of four terms as president (1932)*
>
>*First Houston Fat Stock Show and Rodeo (now Houston Livestock Show & Rodeo) (1932)*
>
>*The University of Houston becomes a four-year university and plans move to a new 110-acre*
>* tract donated by Ben Taub and the J. J. Settegast estate (1934)*
>
>*Elvis Presley is born in Tupelo, Mississippi (1935)*
>
>*Buses replace Houston streetcars (1936)*
>
>*Amelia Earhart disappears (1937)*
>
>*Orson Welles broadcasts "The War of the Worlds" (1938)*
>
>*Rudolph the Red-Nosed Reindeer is created as part of a department store coloring book*
>* promotion (1939)*

On September 3, 1928, a British professor of bacteriology named Alexander Fleming made a life-changing discovery in his laboratory at St. Mary's Hospital in London. Fleming's discovery of penicillin was published in June 1929, earning him a Nobel Prize in 1945. Oxford University, the same university where John Wesley started his Methodist movement, built a penicillin factory in 1938 and began manufacturing the new drug that would save thousands of lives during World War II and millions worldwide. At the young Methodist Hospital in Houston, physicians armed with vaccines developed in the 1920s and new antibiotics on the way were empowered as the age of modern medicine yielded new treatments and preventive measures undreamed of at the turn of the century.

Also new on the scene was a physician whose contributions and leadership proved key to the hospital's growth during the next five decades. In 1935, the year Dr. Oscar Norsworthy died, Dr. James Greenwood, Jr. arrived as head of neurosurgery. Tall and soft spoken, he was known as "Dr. Jimmie" to distinguish him from his physician father, Dr. James Greenwood, Sr.

In 1912 the father opened a sanitarium on six acres out on Old South Main Street at Oak Hill "for nervous diseases, alcohol and drug addiction [and] selected cases of mental disease and pellagra."[1] He was a brilliant man who pioneered early blood transfusions while developing a perpetual calendar in his spare time. Dr. Jimmie grew up in the family home on the sanitarium's grounds. He was living a life in medicine long before his formal medical training even began.

His arrival at Methodist in 1935 was like a shot in the arm for a hospital struggling in uncertain financial times and questioning its destiny. Moreover, his oldest son, Jim, in 2019 recalled his father's deeply held Christian values. "I was moved by his 'testimony' about the importance of prayer to him, particularly in difficult surgical situations [as] brain surgery had all sorts of perils and uncertainties, and he never hesitated to ask for divine guidance and help in serving his patients. He was a great surgeon but had humility in understanding that often God was more in control of outcomes than he was."[2]

As president of the medical staff in 1942 and 1957, Dr. Greenwood was a constant voice of common sense. Josie Roberts not only liked him, but she also listened to his advice. "If we had anyone that we thought was a good doctor, who specialized in a certain field, we tried to make it easy for them as far as getting what he needed. The right equipment, the same tables, the same lights, and the instruments they used. If he was going to work at our hospital, we wanted him to have whatever he needed,"[3] Roberts recalled.

"Dr. Jimmie" was also an important catalyst for attracting other talented neurosurgeons to join Methodist. There were not that many neurosurgeons to begin with in those days, but those like Dr. Marshall Henry found their way to Houston to join Dr. Greenwood's team and made their own mark. Dr. Henry arrived in 1952 just after the hospital moved to the Texas Medical Center and is remembered by many for his talent and camaraderie. Dr. William K. Brown, a member of the internal medicine department for more than fifty-three years before retiring in 1993, recalls riding in an elevator with Dr. Henry and his three sons, who he estimates were all 6'4" tall. Like their father, he recalls, the rest of the Henry family emanated kindness and the best qualities of Houston. "He was a great guy. And there were so many people on the staff … so many good ones and so many good surgeons,"[4] Dr. Brown says.

That camaraderie and family feel were key to the hospital's formula for attracting and keeping the best even in the worst financial times. Dr. Greenwood was just one of many early physicians who were enabled by the administration and board to be the best they could be. The strategy has never changed and has paid dividends for patients and hospital alike over the years.

He also brought important firsts to the hospital. Dr. John Overstreet, who arrived in 1953 and headed surgery at Methodist from 1965 until his retirement in 1993, considered Dr. Greenwood a talented surgeon and innovator known to make many of his own surgical tools and instruments, including the two-point electrocoagulation forceps that are to this day a staple in neurosurgery. The forceps made possible electric cauterization to stop bleeding by sending an electric current between the tips of the forceps without sending the electric current into the patient's body. Jim Greenwood recalls that his father sought no patent for the invention in the interest of allowing its immediate universal manufacture and widespread use. Dr. Greenwood used the forceps in 1941 to successfully remove an intramedullary spinal cord tumor from a patient—a first in medical history.

Six years earlier he established another important first, recalled Dr. Overstreet. "He did the first craniotomy [opening the skull] for a brain tumor at The Methodist Hospital."[5] That procedure in November 1935 turned heads in professional circles throughout the country. Dr. Harold L. D. Kirkham, a plastic surgeon and colleague of Dr. Jimmie's father, assisted. Another early Methodist surgeon, Dr. L. L. D. Tuttle, Sr. (known as "Alphabet" in medical school), shared an office with Dr. Jimmie and assisted, noting he "would be worrying all afternoon anyway."[6] Dr. Tuttle, whose initials stand for Lee Lyman Dewey, was head of surgery prior to Dr. Overstreet's arrival in the 1950s. Dr. Tuttle's son, Dr. Lee Tuttle, Jr., was only four at the time and would follow in his father's footsteps, serving Methodist Hospital for four decades himself before retiring in 2001, establishing yet another family legacy.

Minutes from the board's October 29, 1929, meeting list thirty-eight physicians on staff, including fourteen consulting staff. Early names on that list, like Graves, Green, Dickson, Griswold, Landcaster, Pritchett, Davis, Kirkham, York, McHenry, Mitchell, and Boyd, attracted a second generation with names like Ernst, Cummings, Greenwood, Jackson, Overstreet, King, and many others who will write the next chapter of the hospital's history.

Step back in time to walk the halls of the hospital on Rosalie. Dr. R. K. McHenry was in charge of the X-ray department and Dr. Martha Wood (perhaps the first woman physician to join the hospital staff) was a highly respected pathologist. Her laboratory was one of the hospital's largest departments, consisting of just two rooms with limited chemistry tests. Blood banking was done under a small hood in the corner of one room.

Frances Low joined the hospital in 1926 as dietitian and stayed fifty years. She made do with wooden dining tables seating up to fifteen for staff meals and a single Frigidaire refrigerator for the entire hospital. Her luxury item was a mechanical dishwasher. Just as the church's Golden Cross came to the rescue of administration assisting with budget deficits, the newly organized Women's Auxiliary came to the kitchen's rescue with a new refrigerator. The hospital cooks had an important role for board meetings as well. The meetings always seemed to go better when Josie Roberts requested bountiful, home-cooked proportions of the board's favorite foods, including fried chicken and mashed potatoes smothered in cream gravy.

Downstairs, Frank Doleza could be found working in the hot, humid basement. He was the hospital engineer, overseeing everything from lightbulbs and clogged drains to the grim task of disposing of amputated limbs.[7]

Nurse Stella Horton provided a snapshot in time. In 1982 at age seventy-one, she recalled her first day at the hospital when she responded to an invitation for National Nurses' Day in 1929 and went for a quick look. Until that day she had never set foot in a hospital. Somehow, she got mixed into a class of new nurses and found herself in a room with eleven other women getting instructions on how to greet patients. When the nurse in charge was called away, Horton was told to "take care of things." At that moment she knew this was no ordinary tour.

Nearby a patient suffered a violent seizure and Horton blurted, "What do I do?" Another patient yelled, "Get the book! Get the book!" A nearby textbook recommended applying electricity to control seizures, so she "ran to the patient's bed, unscrewed the lightbulb from the socket overhead, pulled down the wire, and shoved the patient's finger into the live socket." The patient's arm jolted and the patient returned to a restful comfortable state. It was a day that proved so exciting, recalled Horton, that she enrolled in the hospital's nursing program and graduated in 1932.[8]

In those days before antibiotics, some treatments that seem primitive today worked well. Maggots raised from sterile flies at the new Rice Institute were delivered daily for treating wounds by the hospital's nurses. Before the maggot turned into a fly it had to be replaced with another.

Horton's first assignment after graduation was in Dr. Norsworthy's "radium ward." The science was crude and dangerous but paved the way for modern-day radiotherapy. Horton recalled just how primitive it was. "One day a doctor who had just returned from a convention in Washington, D.C. showed me a small, strange container. When I asked him what it was, he told me 'radium.' We were to put the container on the area of the patient's body and then remove it after a certain period of time. We were told to put it back in a lead box, but we never put a lid on it. Nobody told us to." Her hair turned prematurely white within the year, Horton said.[9]

When Dr. J. Charles Dickson completed his residency in Philadelphia, staff meetings consisted of several hundred doctors. His first staff meeting in Methodist Hospital in 1929 was in the old Norsworthy Hospital basement. It was a good turnout he was told, as he looked around the room and counted nine doctors. As a medical student in Nebraska in 1924 Dr. Dickson had ninety-nine drugs to memorize. By the time he retired from Methodist Hospital in 1981 his binder of approved prescription drugs was three inches thick.[10] If he were practicing today he'd need more binders.

Each year on National Hospital Day the staff welcomed all those born at the hospital. Local newspapers carried the invitation to "reunite and practice the old alma mater yell,

'Wow-wow-wow!' To be followed by gurgles of satisfaction as refreshments are passed around and the newest books are discussed." With cake, cookies, and great pride, the hospital opened its doors to the community and celebrated the moment with timeless pictures of happy children and proud staff.[11]

While Jessie Bain supervised the early nursing staff, Georgia Foster operated the central supply room. Education was a priority then as it is today. Weekly conferences with guest speakers and readings were held Fridays at noon. Dr. Fleming's first publication on penicillin likely filled one of those Friday sessions.

The operating rooms and X-ray and laboratory departments were all on the fourth floor. Using the hospital's elevator was no easy task. It was enclosed in a steel cage with hand-operated gates and a pull rope that groaned and jerked. Staff remember the infamous elevator had a habit of stopping between floors and blowing fuses and circuit breakers at all hours. It was said that more women delivered their babies as a result of riding the elevator than the more accepted obstetrical delivery techniques.[12]

Frank Ernst arrived as high school student for a part-time job. He started at the switchboard and progressed to admissions. He ran errands, learned how to tame the elevator, composed letters for the administration, and even helped out in the operating room. He was hooked and in time married a nursing student, went to medical school, and returned to the hospital as Dr. Frank Ernst. After a successful medical career at Methodist, he left his entire estate to the hospital.[13]

Increasing demand for medical services reflected both the hospital's growing reputation and the city's rapid growth. In the 1930s the complete package price for delivery of a newborn was $18. A tonsillectomy cost $16. During the expanded hospital's first six years (1924–1930), 15,765 patients were admitted with operating expenses of $787,653. Medical staff conducted 8,613 surgical operations and handled 1,319 maternity cases.[14]

Given this was a church-owned enterprise, charity care took on a life of its own and constantly challenged the administration to make ends meet. D. H. Hotchkiss informed the board on October 27, 1930, that "the Hospital has become in reality a Conference institution" and that debts were "far exceeding the entire value of the Hospital property and plant."[15] Three months later he said, "We are already owing many current obligations, and our tradesmen are urgently asking payments due them. We need to preserve the good name of the Methodist Church and its Hospital, and some relief must be provided."[16] Board members were known to quietly reach into their own pockets to cover the deficits.

Also, in 1930 the hospital's Houston-based auditors, St. John, Smith & Co., issued their own recommendation to the board, "We also recommend that more authority be extended Mrs. Roberts as Chief Clerk and Assistant Superintendent, for in her we believe the Institution to possess a highly valuable employee and of invaluable assistance to the chief executive."[17]

Something had to give and it did. For starters, Jesse Jones as a trustee was appointed to the board, recognizing they needed all the help they could get. By 1931 Hotchkiss resigned and the board would soon enact the auditor's suggestion to put Josie Roberts in charge. In a medical world dominated by men, they placed their faith in a strong woman to right the ship and were not disappointed. Her appointment and a set of fortuitous events behind the scenes were to change the fortune of Methodist Hospital in ways no one could predict. Each event was essential for the hospital's growth and success and is well worth a brief detour to examine.

. . .

On September 12, 1930, as Hotchkiss was writing his frank financial report for the board, William Clifford Hogg died at the young age of fifty-five—not in Houston but while vacationing in Europe with his sister, Ima. Hogg's father, James Steven Hogg, was the first native-born governor of Texas (1891–1895) and made a fortune in oil and real estate at the turn of the century. Will Hogg had taken the family's fortune to new heights. As the Methodist board was busy building a hospital, Hogg was busy building as well. His eleven brief years in Houston during the 1920s represent one of the most overlooked legacies in the city's history.

If you like the oak trees that line Main Street near the Texas Medical Center, River Oaks, Memorial Park, and the Museum of Fine Arts, you should know Hogg had a major hand in all. Not one for publicity, he once told a reporter, "If you put my name in your column of tripe, I'll kick you so hard you'll taste the shoe leather for the rest of your life."[18]

As a member of The University of Texas Board of Regents (1913–1917), Hogg supported moving The University of Texas Medical Branch from Galveston to Houston in 1923—even sending a formal resolution to Governor William Hobby in hopes of forcing the issue. Hogg was so enthused that he purchased 134 acres behind George Hermann's hospital with hopes the state's only medical school at the time would relocate across the street from the new Rice Institute. The effort failed and a disappointed Hogg sold the land back to the city at cost. Interesting to note, coyotes howled into Hermann Hospital's open windows in those days before air conditioning, alarming patients and prompting hospital administrators to requisition fencing. Meanwhile, the city held the land (coyotes included) and debated adding it to George Hermann's adjacent park. Any other use would require a citywide vote.[19]

. . .

Nine years after Will Hogg died, Monroe Dunaway Anderson suffered a stroke. Since his arrival in Houston in 1907, Anderson, Clayton & Company had done exceptionally well merchandizing cotton worldwide. Monroe had $20 million in his personal savings. With more than seven hundred employees, most of whom he knew by first name, the frugal bachelor lived in downtown hotels throughout his adult life and each morning carried a sack lunch in hand as he walked to his office in the nearby Cotton Exchange Building. The Bender Hotel's bell captain, Oscar Collins, said years later that he had no idea he was holding the door for one of Houston's richest men. "I thought he was a mild-mannered shoe salesman or floorwalker in some of the nearby stores."[20]

In 1924, just four months after Methodist Hospital expanded on Rosalie, Monroe's brother Frank died from a burst appendix. Unfortunately, penicillin was not yet available. The Anderson brothers' business partner and brother-in-law, Will Clayton, had just celebrated with the Methodist Hospital board the opening of the new hospital and now prepared for the funeral of his sister's husband. For Monroe, his only brother's sudden loss had a profound effect. Monroe immediately started thinking about his own mortality and sought the advice of his trusted attorneys at the firm of Fulbright and Crooker (later Fulbright and Jaworski). Colonel William Bates and John Freeman were more than Monroe's attorneys; they were among his small circle of closest friends, which included a local banker named Horace Wilkens, who later succeeded Anderson as trustee of his foundation.

For starters, Anderson created a generous pension program for his employees to ensure financial security for those who helped build the successful international business it had become. Those with seniority received stock that made them millionaires in the years ahead. Then Anderson asked an important question. Should he die, how would his partners buy out his portion of the company as had been planned? The answer, advised Bates and Freeman, was complicated due to the tax laws. Instead, they suggested, create a foundation.

The MD Anderson Foundation was established on July 9, 1936, with an initial contribution of $10,000 to support "the promotion of health, science, education, and advancement and diffusion of knowledge and understanding among people."[21] Anderson's concerns for his mortality were well timed.

On a warm summer day in 1938 as he sat at the counter of the Majestic Grill at the corner of Travis and Rusk, Anderson's arm went numb. He was taken back to his hotel, where his physician, Dr. Joe Henry Graves (the younger brother of Methodist Hospital's Dr. Marvin Graves), diagnosed a stroke. Anderson was hospitalized at the Baptist Hospital, which was close to his residence and office, and Dr. James Greenwood, Jr. was called in to care for him during his last year.[22] Suffering from pre-existing kidney problems, he died on August 6, 1939, at age sixty-six. Trustees Bates, Freeman, and Horace Wilkins, newly appointed, now had to figure out how to fulfill their friend's humanitarian directives. They placed an ad in the local papers for community ideas, but the suggestions received were disappointing, including an offer to sell them a circus.

Freeman recalled years later, "We had nothing specific in mind at the start." Then one day Bates spotted a newspaper article about the Texas legislature passing a bill to create a state cancer hospital to be run by The University of Texas. Bates and Freeman contacted Dr. John Spies in Galveston and Dr. Homer Rainey, president of The University of Texas, to discuss the possibility of putting that state cancer hospital in Houston.[23]

Since a vote was required by the citizens of Houston to sell the city's land behind Hermann Hospital, the trustees did their homework. The idea for a state cancer hospital was first proposed by a druggist named Arthur Cato, who was a state legislator from Weatherford, Texas, and whose parents had died of cancer. His House Bill 268 proposed a state cancer hospital "to treat all Texans regardless of ability to pay." Cato's bill passed on May 28, 1941. By 1942 Bates and Freeman had inked an agreement with The University of Texas to move the cancer hospital to Houston and name it in honor of their departed friend, M. D. Anderson. They next decided to line up a medical school and knew better than to look south to Galveston. Instead, they looked north to Dallas and Baylor University Medical School.

This was a pivotal moment in Methodist Hospital's history. Both the forest that would become the Texas Medical Center and the medical school that would become Methodist Hospital's academic partner for half a century hung in the balance. As Josie Roberts and the hospital's board struggled with finances through the post-Depression years, they were not alone. The young Baylor University Medical School in Dallas was going through a similar struggle. Their story adds an important dimension to Methodist Hospital's destiny.

• • •

On September 15, 1900, a new medical school filed for a state charter with the Texas secretary of state to be called the University of Dallas Medical Department. Actually, there was no University of Dallas but no one asked. The new medical school opened in November in an abandoned synagogue across the street from what is today Dallas's Adolphus Hotel.[24] The school had no teaching hospital, but the city agreed to let the students attend patients at a hospital the city had built on land originally designated for a park. Appropriately, the hospital was named Parkland. The twenty students (some "doctors" practicing without formal diplomas) traveled between classroom and hospital by wagon.

The first dean, Dr. Charles Rosser, stayed less than a year. A new professor of ophthalmology and otolaryngology named Dr. Edward H. Cary had so impressed the school that he was named dean after serving as volunteer faculty only six months. Dr. Cary, like Dr. Norsworthy, was energetic and a builder of programs. Dr. Cary went on to become president of the Texas Medical Association in 1917.

During his first year as dean he awarded fifteen diplomas. The second year, 1903, only four were awarded under his high standards. In 1910 a schoolteacher from Louisville, Kentucky, named Abraham Flexner surveyed 155 medical schools in the United States and Canada for the Carnegie Foundation and issued a report card known as the Flexner Report.[25] Flexner was looking for schools like the new Johns Hopkins School of Medicine in Baltimore, which he considered the gold standard. Those lacking university affiliations and excellence in patient care, education, and research were called out in the report to reorganize or close. Many took the second option.

Anticipating these winds of change and in need of financial support, Dr. Cary established an alliance with Baylor University in Waco and the school's name changed to Baylor University College of Medicine in 1909. Like Methodist Hospital in Houston, the young medical school's budget was on life support in the early years. While Baylor University pledged additional funds in the 1920s, that support was not forthcoming and the Great Depression only made things worse. Dr. Cary resigned to become dean emeritus and chairman of the advisory board. He was succeeded by Dr. Walter H. Moursund, a trusted faculty member at the school since 1911 who specialized in pathology and bacteriology.

The Baylor medical school continued to train excellent physicians, but by the mid-1930s serious discussion included the option to close the school. It desperately needed funds, so in 1939 Dr. Cary started the Southwestern Medical Foundation. By the early 1940s movie theater mogul Karl Hoblitzelle donated sixty-two acres adjacent to the proposed site for a new Parkland Hospital to provide a campus for the new medical school off Harry Hines Boulevard.[26]

As dean, Dr. Moursund faced a major dilemma as Dr. Cary and his foundation offered land and money to join the new organization. While the medical school agreed to a contract on June 23, 1942, the short-lived agreement was canceled on April 27, 1943.[27] In Dr. Moursund's words, "As the academic year progressed [1943], it became evident that the Southwestern Medical Foundation construed the agreement made with Baylor University to give the foundation absolute and complete control of the administration of the medical college. In accepting the agreement, the Baylor trustees, rightly so, had no intention of divesting themselves of the ultimate control of the medical college."[28]

In this way Colonel Bates and John Freeman found themselves conferring with Baylor University president Pat Neff to make an offer of land and money to bring Baylor's medical school to Houston. Bates, in a 1974 interview one year before his death, noted, "It just so happened that our law firm had two clients who were trustees of Baylor University in Waco. … Mr. Carr Collins of Dallas and Mr. D. K. Martin of San Antonio. I was representing Mr. Martin at the time, and I had known Mr. Collins's father quite well."[29] The MD Anderson Foundation trustees assured Baylor they had no interest in controlling the school in any way and Baylor University's board approved the move to Houston in May 1943.

Five months earlier, on December 13, 1943, a full-page ad in the *Houston Post* carried the headline, "Cure Through Research. Vote for the Texas Medical Center Tuesday."[30] Houstonians went to the polls and said yes. The MD Anderson Foundation now owned a forest that would become the largest medical center in the world.

• • •

These stories of Will Hogg, Monroe Anderson, a medical school from Dallas, and a forest that would become a Texas-sized medical center have transformational implications for the small community hospital at San Jacinto and Rosalie. Had it not been for these events the story of Methodist Hospital might have ended right here. However, the stars were aligning in important ways. Unaware of the significance of these events, Methodist

Hospital board members in the 1930s were asking hard questions. Some were ready to throw in the towel and sell.

Fortunately, another star aligned they could not miss. As the hospital's auditors had suggested, Josie Roberts was the right person at the right time. The board put her in charge of the hospital in 1931, the same year Al Capone went to prison and "The Star-Spangled Banner" became the national anthem. Under her guidance with the trust and support of the medical staff and the board, things only got better. Despite the Great Depression and a second challenge from Dr. Norsworthy to come, she had no intention of failing.

Depression Years

"From the top of prosperity in 1929 to the bottom of depression in 1933, the country's GNP dropped by a total of 29 percent, consumption expenditures by 18 percent, construction by 78 percent, and investment by an incredible 98 percent. … By almost any standard, the United States was in its worst crisis since the Civil War," summarized historian Robert S. McElvaine.[31] In Houston, the mayor dismissed a number of city employees and six hundred demonstrators marched in protest. The *Post-Dispatch* announced that "Houston is comparatively free of discontent due to economic conditions." After all, Houston had a busy port and proliferating oil refineries. Methodist Hospital's new board member, Jesse Jones, famously brought all of the city's bank presidents into one room late one night and hammered out an agreement that Houston banks would circle the wagons and watch each other's backs. None failed.

Looking back, Roberts recalled the challenge of those Depression years when she took the bull by the horns. "So, we had a lot of things to cut corners. We did. I had a wonderful staff of people. I had a good medical staff. Just because we had good service and we had good food, we never lacked for patients. We got to making expenses and so forth."[32]

Dr. J. Charles Dickson recalled the board had serious discussions "about selling the hospital to a group of private doctors and going out of the hospital business."[33] Roberts's effort to break even and make a little money during these dire times started with collections. She drafted a progressive series of letters directed to patients with long-standing unpaid bills. The first was a gentle reminder from the hospital's registrar. If the first four failed to motivate payment, in time the fifth was signed by the superintendent and delivered. Inspired by these rumbles from the board to close down if things didn't improve, the wording was tough and pure Josie Roberts.

> Dear Sir (or Madam): There is a limit to all things! Even to the patience of the most lenient and considerate. We have tried to be all of these things, but apparently to no avail. I am however giving you one last opportunity to do something in regard to your unpaid balance before placing it with our Legal Department which will involve additional expense and trouble. … Trusting you will be governed accordingly, we are Yours very truly, (signed) Superintendent.[34]

With the board and medical staff's support, she kept an eye on every detail. Closets, reception areas, and cubbyholes were searched out and converted for additional space. In time she physically connected the old hospital with the new, creating more space options. Early medical staff recalled she never asked the board for help until every possibility had been exhausted. When absolutely necessary, she requested loans (typically $10,000) but always with a payment plan she delivered on.

One particular challenge in the early 1930s was the constant shortage of space for children when infantile paralysis was on the rise in the city. With the help of A. Frank Smith, now bishop of Methodist Episcopal Church, South and who would become resident bishop of Houston in 1934, and the Blue Bird Circle, Roberts's idea for a 30-bed children's building became a reality. The crippled children's program, as such programs were known then, was organized by the Arabia Temple Shrine and originated at Hermann Hospital in 1927; it came to Methodist in 1932. It was just the kind of project the dedicated women of the church were looking for, and the new children's building opened on September 1, 1934, as the Blue Bird Hospital for Underprivileged Children. Around the hospital it was affectionately referred to as the "cottage" or the "little hospital."[35]

The one-story frame building was 64 by 34 square feet and built on the grounds of the hospital at a cost of $7,200—paid in full upon completion. With separate wards for boys and girls, the most popular feature by far was the sun porch that also served as a recreation room. Smith summarized the genesis of the little hospital for local reporters: "For some time the organization [Blue Bird Circle] has been increasingly interested in the magnificent and constructive work being done by the local Temple of the Shriners for crippled children. Out of that interest has issued the biggest single enterprise yet undertaken by the Blue Birds."[36]

A fire during the Christmas holidays of 1938 shocked the community. The cottage burned to the ground. Fortunately, all escaped. The Blue Birds rallied with help from the church and community to rebuild. Their fundraiser was a memorable hit aided by silent movie star Colleen Moore's must-see dollhouse (on loan) that drew Governor W. Lee O'Daniel and other notables.[37] While in years to come the Blue Bird Circle and the Shriners would part ways, this joint venture should be remembered as the genesis for the hospital's top-ranked orthopedic programs to this day. Dr. Joe W. King arrived at Methodist Hospital after completing his residency training at Hermann in 1948. Over the next four decades he would build the hospital's orthopedics department into one of the best in the nation.

The Norsworthy Challenge

While Dr. Oscar Norsworthy remained a medical adviser to the hospital's board and kept a close watch on progress, he moved to San Antonio in 1928, where he continued his clinical work with radium. His wife, Sarah, died in November 1933 at age sixty and two years later he remarried in San Antonio. Only a week after his wedding, the news reached Houston that he had died suddenly of heart failure in the Biltmore Hotel in Los Angeles on his honeymoon.

The reading of Dr. Norsworthy's will presented a new challenge for the hospital's board as reported in the *Houston Chronicle* under the headline, "Dr. Norsworthy Leaves Fund for Aid of Hospital."

> Either Methodist or Hermann Hospital will receive $7,200 per year under terms of a bequest in Dr. O. L. Norsworthy's will, filed with County Clerk Henry Dudley Monday. ... Charles F. Carter, executor of the will, said he left an estate valued in excess of $50,000. ... Dr. Norsworthy specified that Methodist is to receive the money providing it attains the highest rating of the American Hospital Association and has 200 beds within five years after his death, or 300 beds 10 years after his death. The hospital now has 75 beds.[38]

The new Norsworthy challenge fell flat with the board. The board had jumped through hoops in the early 1920s to reach 100 beds and was in no mood to jump through more in these post-Depression years. Board member Robert Cole even suggested the Norsworthy estate was "rather unimposing for the portentous program" and "the ambitious scheme" outlined in his will.[39] After all, when Dr. Norsworthy's first wife died, the good doctor canceled the $10,000 mortgage they owed. With that gift they were not looking for new debt.

After James Marion West, Sr. (whose son was known as "Silver Dollar Jim West" for his penchant for tipping with silver dollars) replaced Walter Fondren as the board's vice president in 1923, Fondren remained one of the board's strongest voices for growth while quietly covering many hospital deficits out of his pocket. The Fondrens, Walter and Ella, pushed aside all talk of closing down or keeping status quo and came up with their own secret plan.

The plan authorized Josie Roberts to purchase an entire block of land on San Jacinto across the street from the hospital. At the upcoming October 1938 board meeting Roberts was to announce an anonymous donor was willing to donate the land and build a 75-bed children's hospital with the condition that the trustees erect on the property adjoining the current hospital a building that met the terms of the Norsworthy challenge. To meet that condition the anonymous donor would underwrite fifteen percent of the cost not to exceed $500,000.[40]

Recalled Roberts years later: "He wanted me to tell the board about his proposal, but not to tell them who it was. Well, you can imagine telling a bunch of men something and them not knowing who it was. But anyway, I did. ... Well, there was an awful lot of discussion. [Walter Fondren] finally got up and told them that he and his wife were the ones that were making that proposal."[41]

One can only imagine the nervous excitement of the moment as Fondren further elaborated that his wife was giving the new property and children's building across the street and he was giving the fifteen percent of the cost for the other new building. The board called a meeting for the next day with Bishops Smith and Hay to discuss further. They would take the upcoming holidays to mull over the matter. Little did anyone know that Walter Fondren did not have that much time.

On January 5, 1939, Fondren was in San Antonio with his wife attending a Methodist Church meeting as a lay representative. Roberts remembered he was not feeling well. Fondren told his wife he was going across the street to the St. Anthony Hotel. His heart failed before his wife could get to him. With great sadness his family and Houston mourned a lost community treasure. Fondren was laid to rest in Glenwood Cemetery not far from George Hermann and close to where so many other Houston icons, like Capt. James Baker, Howard Hughes, Will Clayton, Roy Hofheinz, and Dr. Denton Cooley, would be interred.

Walter J. Fondren was one of the great oilmen of his time; honest to a fault and charitable to the Methodist Church and hospital in so many ways. In his early days as he helped Ross Sterling build what is today ExxonMobil, he would bring home drilling samples of sand and mud for Ella to examine. He placed full trust in her judgment to sniff out oil in the samples and she was rarely wrong. "She's got the best nose for oil I've ever seen," he loved to say.

After his death, Ella Fondren was determined to use the family's wealth wisely and vowed not to forget that her husband had been an orphan and she had grown up poor. "That money was a trust," she would explain. "I want it to go where it can do the *greatest good* for the most people."[42]

· · ·

Two months after her husband's death a committee of the board, including Dr. Marvin Graves, met at Ella Fondren's home and encouraged her to go ahead and build the children's hospital across the street on the land already purchased. However, the board decided the hospital could not raise the money to meet neither the conditions Dr. Norsworthy had placed before them nor the conditions of her husband's fifteen percent pledge for a new hospital. Dr. Graves reported to the full board Ella's displeasure, noting "she could not see her way clear to do so [build a children's hospital across the street] although she was willing to carry out the terms of her husband's offer."[43]

The greatest good in her mind was much bigger than going it alone. The greatest good was growing the hospital together as a board, medical staff, and church family. She had great faith that opportunities would avail themselves to do just that. She would not give up on the idea that Methodist Hospital could be much more than the small, community-based hospital it was on the corner of San Jacinto and Rosalie.

The first opportunity came a few months later in 1939, when the board asked her to take her husband's seat on the board, a position she would hold until her death in 1982. The second came three years later in 1942, when the MD Anderson Foundation trustees made an offer to the hospital's board that would change everything.

HOUSTON METHODIST
HISTORICAL IMAGES

Houston's earliest plan. Courtesy of Houston Metropolitan Research Center – Houston Public Library.

First Methodist Episcopal Church, South at Main Street and Clay Street, 1922. In its early days it was known as Shearn Methodist Church.

Downtown Houston, 1905.

Interior of First Methodist Episcopal Church, South, 1922.

Nurses during the influenza pandemic, 1918.

Dr. Oscar L. Norsworthy, a prominent Houston physician and churchman, sold his 30-bed hospital to the Texas Conference of the Methodist Episcopal Church in 1919. It was the beginning of today's Houston Methodist.

Norsworthy Hospital, early 1900s.

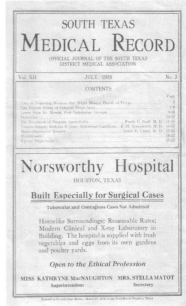

Dr. Oscar L. Norsworthy's reputable hospital advertises assets on the front page of the South Texas Medical Record, 1918.

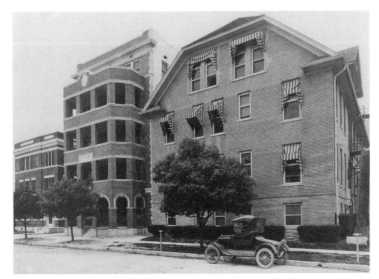

In 1924, the newly expanded hospital (center) brought the total bed count to 100. The Sarah Francelia Bell Home is far left, and the original Norsworthy Hospital is at right.

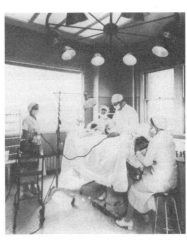

Methodist Hospital operating room, 1920s.

Laura Graves, the wife of Dr. Marvin L. Graves, organized the hospital's Women's Auxiliary in 1928 and hosted meetings in the parlor of her home. Today the organization is called the Houston Methodist Auxiliary.

In an annual celebration on National Hospital Day, Methodist Hospital in the mid-1920s welcomed back babies born at the hospital.

Graduating nurses, 1929.

Walter W. Fondren, one of the founders of the Humble Oil & Refining Company (known today as ExxonMobil), was vice president of Methodist Hospital's original board of directors.

Samuel F. Carter, the founding board treasurer for Methodist Hospital.

John T. Scott, Sr., president of the First National Bank of Houston, led the Methodist Hospital board for its first 19 years.

William Lockhart Clayton, an original board member.

Walter Fondren overseeing drilling operations, early 1900s.

James Marion West, Sr., an original board member.

ST. JOHN, SMITH & CO.
"FACTS TO OUR CLIENTS"
601 KIRBY BLDG.

HOUSTON, TEXAS

April 15, 1930

Rev. D. H. Hotchkiss,
Methodist Hospital,
Houston, Texas

Dear Sir:

While we believe the Institution is in competent hands under the management of Reverend D. H. Hotchkiss, at the same time, we feel that some assistance should be afforded him to the extent of sharing in some degree a part of the great responsibilities placed upon him. We also recommend that more authority be extended Mrs. Roberts as Chief Clerk and Assistant Superintendent, for in her we believe the Institution to possess a highly valuable employee and of invaluable assistance to the chief executive.

Auditor's report recommends Josie M. Roberts be granted more authority. She was named hospital administrator in 1932.

The Smith family, June 1939. (From left) Betty, Randy, Bishop A. Frank Smith, Bess Smith, and Frank, Jr.

Josie M. Roberts as a young woman.

The "little hospital," also known as the "cottage," 1934. Formally, it was the Blue Bird Hospital for Underprivileged Children.

Ella F. Fondren, 1940s.

"Houston Post" full-page ad, December 13, 1943. Citizens voted to sell the forest behind Hermann Hospital to the trustees of the MD Anderson Foundation, providing a future home for the Texas Medical Center.

Dr. L. L. D. Tuttle, Sr. joined the hospital in 1927, serving as the head of surgery and, in 1941, as president of the medical staff. In medical school his nickname was "Alphabet."

U.S. Cadet Nurse Corps, 1944.

The Texas Medical Center began as a field and forest along with a Texas-sized vision.

Dr. Hatch W. Cummings, Jr. replaced Dr. Marvin L. Graves as chief of the hospital's medical service in 1946 and also served as president of the medical staff twice.

Oilman and philanthropist Hugh Roy Cullen and his wife, Lillie, 1945.

Team Roberts–Fondren, 1944. Ella F. Fondren (seated) sought the "greatest good" for her fortune and never forgot her humble roots. She would settle for no less than a 300-bed Methodist Hospital in the new Texas Medical Center.

The Methodist Hospital board in the late 1940s determining the future of the hospital. The board was divided over how much debt to take on and how big the new hospital should be: 300 or 220 beds? Ella F. Fondren (left) and Josie M. Roberts (right) won the day for the bigger hospital to be built in the Texas Medical Center.

Ted C. Bowen (shown in 1953) served as Methodist Hospital administrator for 29 years, 1953–1982.

Kathleen G. Ellis developed the Methodist Hospital Service Corps in 1947 based on her Red Cross experience with the Gray Ladies during World War II.

Dr. Joe W. King (shown in 1948) was chief of orthopedics and served as president of the medical staff 1959–1960.

Dr. Dan Jackson as an intern. He brought his young family to Houston in 1949 and "hitched his wagon" to Methodist Hospital. When he died at age 99 in 2017 (two weeks short of his own centennial birthday), he was the hospital's last living physician to have worked in the original hospital on Rosalie Street.

Bishop A. Frank Smith

Laying of the Cornerstone
THE METHODIST HOSPITAL
Four Thirty o'Clock P.M.
May Thirty-First, Nineteen Hundred Fifty
TEXAS MEDICAL CENTER
Houston, Texas

Flyer for the laying of the cornerstone in the Texas Medical Center, May 31, 1950.

Laying the cornerstone of the new Methodist Hospital in the Texas Medical Center, May 31, 1950. Because of illness, Dr. Ernst Bertner is parked close to the podium. He was determined not to miss this historic event.

Methodist Hospital nearing completion in the Texas Medical Center, February 1951.

A Service Corps volunteer staffing the new hospital's Bertner Street information desk, 1951.

Methodist Hospital's new 300-bed building in the Texas Medical Center, 1951.

(From left) Drs. John W. Overstreet, J. Charles Dickson and Joseph W. Robertson in the doctors' coffee bar and lounge, 1950s.

Wiess Memorial Chapel, 1951. In 1989 this chapel, including its original stained glass windows and furnishings, was relocated to the new John S. Dunn Tower.

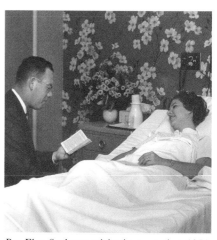

Rev. Elton Stephenson ministering to a patient, 1951.

(From left) Drs. James A. Greenwood, Jr. and Robert C. L. Robertson in the doctors' coffee bar and lounge, 1950s.

(From left) Drs. Joseph W. Robertson, Joe W. King, Curtis H. Burge and J. Charles Dickson and administrator Ted C. Bowen, 1950s.

The fledgling Texas Medical Center, 1953. Methodist Hospital is seen in the center of this photo. Baylor College of Medicine is the elongated building behind Methodist. St. Luke's Episcopal Hospital is to the right of Methodist, and MD Anderson Hospital and Tumor Institute (as it was then known) is in the upper right corner of the new complex. Hermann Hospital and the new Professional Building (tall tower) are at top.

Dr. John W. Overstreet arrived at the hospital in 1953 and led the department of surgery 1965–1993.

Dr. Michael E. DeBakey sewing a Dacron graft, 1955. Photo courtesy of Baylor College of Medicine.

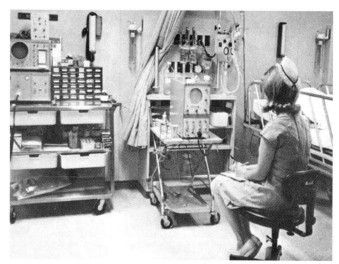

A new and innovative intensive care unit, 1958.

Charles Henderson, Jr. (left) was known as "Uncle Charley." Throughout the 1950s he was a beloved hospital volunteer for the chaplain's office who gave of his time and personal finances to help patients.

The Women's Auxiliary holiday bazaar, 1960.

West Wing extension under construction, October 1960.

Dr. Michael E. DeBakey (left) and Mary Lasker at the Lasker Awards, 1963.

The West Wing extension (Fannin Street entrance) opened in 1963 featuring the tile mosaic mural Extending Arms of Christ. The mural was refurbished and moved (all 1.5 million tiles) to the new Paula and Joseph C. "Rusty" Walter III Tower in 2018, where it overlooks the Barbara and President George H.W. Bush Atrium.

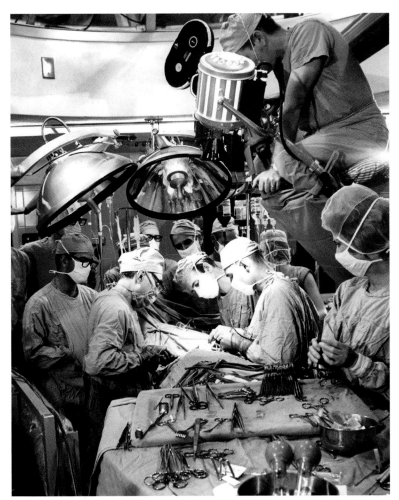

Dr. Michael E. DeBakey makes history with the first simultaneous broadcast from the U.S. to Europe by using the "Early Bird" satellite, the world's first commercial communications satellite. The 1965 broadcast from Houston aired on all three national networks, and simultaneously around the world, as Dr. DeBakey implanted an artificial aortic valve.

The Duchess and Duke of Windsor (far left) are escorted by (from left) Dr. Michael E. DeBakey, Ted C. Bowen, Pat A. Temple, RN, and Gloria Hahneman, administrative assistant to Dr. Joe W. King, 1964.

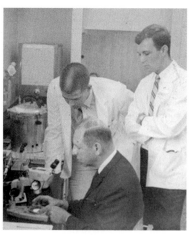

Dr. Edwin M. Ory (seated in this 1960s photo) was chairman of the infectious diseases department.

Groundbreaking for the Fondren and Brown Cardiovascular and Orthopedic Research Center, October 27, 1964. (From left) Princess Lilian, Dr. Joe W. King and Ella F. Fondren.

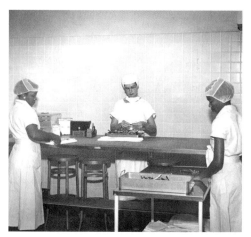

Operating room nurses prepare for surgery, 1960s.

The Methodist Hospital Annex, 1965.

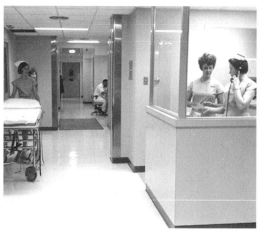

A nurses' station, 1960s.

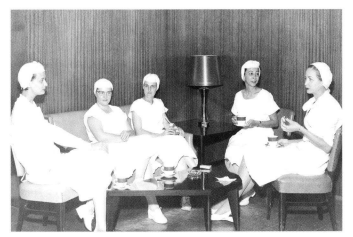

The lounge for the operating room nurses, 1960s.

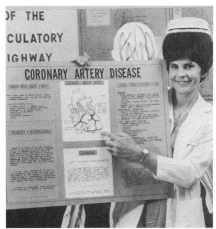

The 1970s was known as the Golden Age of Hearts for innovations in cardiovascular diagnosis and treatment as well as for public education.

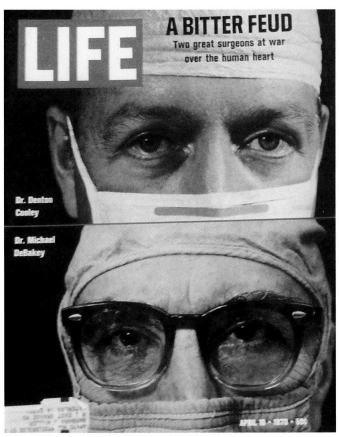

Cover of Life magazine, April 1970.

Dr. Antonio M. Gotto, Jr. (shown in 1971) served as chief of the internal medicine service at Methodist Hospital and dean and provost of Weill Cornell Medical College.

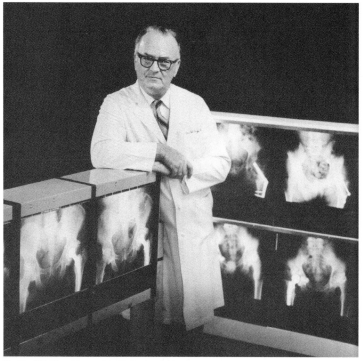

Dr. Bobby R. Alford led the otolaryngology departments at both Methodist Hospital and Baylor College of Medicine 1967–2010. He worked with six other experts to create a national institute for biomedical research with the National Aeronautics and Space Administration.

Dr. Joe W. King (shown in 1972), head of orthopedic medicine. His love of baseball established the hospital's reputation as a leader in sports medicine to this day.

The great flood of 1976.

The Neurosensory Center housed in the Alice and David C. Bintliff Blue Bird Building, 1977.

The 1978 unveiling of the bronze bust (shown in photo at right) of Dr. Michael E. DeBakey, commissioned by Princess Lilian and her husband, the former King Leopold III of Belgium. It can be seen today in the Betty Adams Crain Garden of the John S. Dunn Tower.

Three decades of board leadership. A. Frank Smith, Jr. (left) led the board 1977–1991, followed by John F. Bookout's leadership 1991–2007.

Eddy Scurlock, who served on the board 1953–1988, imparted vision and leadership in many ways, including purchasing the Bill Williams Chicken House, which provided Methodist Hospital with the land where Scurlock Tower stands today.

Scurlock Tower, 1980, named in honor of Elizabeth and Eddy C. Scurlock. The land owned by a fried chicken restaurateur, Bill Williams, ironically became the epicenter for preventive medicine and cardiovascular research.

Larry L. Mathis, president and CEO, 1983–1997.

What is known today as Houston Methodist Baytown Hospital first opened as San Jacinto Memorial Hospital in 1948 and joined The Methodist Hospital System in 1983.

Larry L. Mathis (far left) and his team (from left), M. James Henderson, Michael V. Williamson, John King, and Ronald G. Girotto, donating blood.

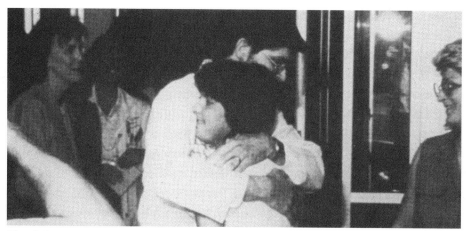

Tracy Baird, recipient of a new heart and lungs, departs the hospital, April 1986. It was the first successful heart-lung transplant in Texas and one of the few worldwide even attempted at the time.

Dr. Stanley H. Appel (from left), entertainer Jerry Lewis and Dr. Michael E. DeBakey at an ALS Conference.

The John S. Dunn Tower, completed in 1989, increased the hospital's total bed capacity to 1,527, making The Methodist Hospital the largest private teaching hospital in the country.

John F. Bookout, former president and CEO of Shell Oil Company and chairman of the hospital's board 1991–2007, now chairman emeritus. His leadership was instrumental in transforming The Methodist Hospital in the mid-2000s into an independent academic medical center.

Peter W. Butler, president and CEO, 1997–2001.

Houston Methodist Sugar Land Hospital opened in 1998 with 22 beds. The first open heart surgery, minimally invasive surgery, and brain surgery in Fort Bend County were performed here.

METHODIST
Values

Rev. Tom Daugherty, vice president of Spiritual Care, spearheaded a systemwide collaboration to revitalize The Methodist Health Care System's spiritual mission that resulted in the I CARE values.

I CARE

INTEGRITY.

COMPASSION.

ACCOUNTABILITY.

RESPECT.

EXCELLENCE.

The Methodist Health Care System announces the I CARE values, 2000.

Ronald G. Girotto, president and CEO, 2001–2011.

Houston Methodist Willowbrook Hospital opened in 2000 with 68 beds. In 2019, the hospital has 312 beds with plans for expansion to serve the growing community.

Tropical Storm Allison devastated hospitals throughout the Texas Medical Center in 2001, including The Methodist Hospital. Lessons learned benefited the hospital in many ways. When Hurricane Harvey struck in 2017, every Methodist hospital in the system stayed open.

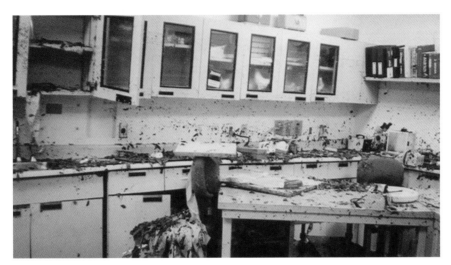

Tropical Storm Allison hospital damage, 2001.

Gretchen Mills, R.N, director of nursing for Dunn 10 East, receives a pin from hospital vice presidents Debra F. Sukin (center) and Vicki Brownewell during the Magnet status designation ceremony, September 2002.

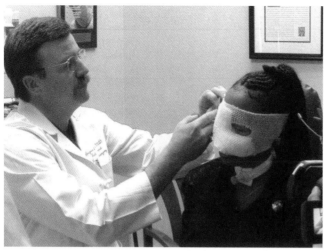

Dr. Eugene L. Alford and other physicians at The Methodist Hospital donated their services to a woman who was shot by her boyfriend in 2003. The story gained national attention and was featured on "The Oprah Winfrey Show."

Dr. Stephen T. Wong (Ph.D.) leads Houston Methodist's department of systems medicine and bioengineering and exemplifies the caliber of faculty the hospital has recruited since the formal affiliation with Baylor College of Medicine ended in 2004.

The Methodist Hospital's affiliation agreement with Weill Cornell Medical College and NewYork-Presbyterian Hospital was signed in Houston on June 24, 2004. (From left) Ronald G. Girotto, The Methodist Hospital president and CEO; Judge Ewing Werlein, Jr., former chair of The Methodist Hospital board; Sandy Weill, namesake of the college and chair of the Weill Cornell Medical College board; John F. Bookout, chair of The Methodist Hospital board; Herbert Pardes, M.D., president and CEO, NewYork-Presbyterian Hospital; and Dr. Antonio M. Gotto, Jr., dean and provost of Weill Cornell Medical College.

The Methodist Hospital holds the first graduation ceremony for its residency and fellowship programs in the Betty Adams Crain Garden, 2006.

The Hospital Administation and
the Board of Directors of
The Methodist Hospital

Request the Honor of your Presence at

THE FIRST GRADUATION CEREMONY

CELEBRATING

THE GRADUATES OF
THE METHODIST HOSPITAL
RESIDENCY AND FELLOWSHIP PROGRAMS IN

Anatomic and Clinical Pathology
Blood Banking and Transfusion Medicine
Cytopathology
Family Medicine
General Surgery
Minimally Invasive Surgery
Obstetrics and Gynecology
Plastic Surgery
Surgical Pathology
Transitional Year

Friday, June 9, 2006
7:00 pm
The Methodist Hospital
The Crain Garden

RSVP by May 24, 2006   713-441-1833

Methodist   The Methodist   LEADING MEDICINE™
Hospital

Dr. Robert G. Grossman (shown in 2006) is the co-founder and a former director of the Houston Methodist Neurological Institute, and former chair of the neurosurgical service at Houston Methodist.

Invitation to the first graduation ceremony for The Methodist Hospital's residency and fellowship programs, 2006.

The Methodist Hospital Research Institute opens, 2010.

The Methodist Hospital Outpatient Center (glass façade) opened in 2010 on Fannin Street adjacent to Scurlock Tower, Smith Tower, and the Houston Marriott/Texas Medical Center. Rice University is in the immediate background, and the distinctive Williams Tower is in the distance adjacent to Houston's Galleria shopping district.

Dr. George P. Noon and members of his team, 2010. In 2006 Dr. Noon performed lifesaving surgery on his mentor, Dr. Michael E. DeBakey.

Houston Methodist West Hospital opened as the largest hospital in the Katy-West Houston area in 2010.

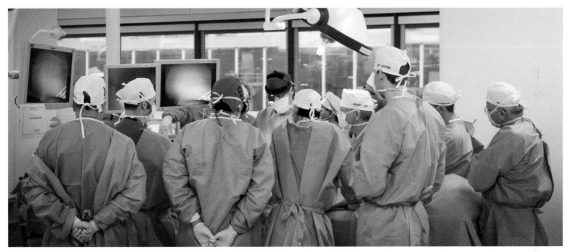

MITIE^{SM}, Methodist Institute for Technology, Innovation, and Education, opened in 2011 and is the most advanced facility in the nation for training surgeons to master new technologies.

Dr. Marc L. Boom was named president and CEO of The Methodist Hospital in 2012, becoming the first physician–CEO in the history of the hospital.

The Methodist Hospital System changed its name to Houston Methodist in 2013 to differentiate itself from the dozens of Methodist hospitals nationwide and to honor the city of Houston.

Houston Methodist Clear Lake Hospital joined Houston Methodist in 2014, serving the Bay Area.

Houston Methodist Continuing Care Hospital opened as CHRISTUS St. Catherine Hospital in April 2000 and became part of Houston Methodist in February 2014.

Houston Methodist announces a partnership with the Texas A&M Health Science Center, 2014. They joined forces to expand physician education, clinical training, and research innovation.

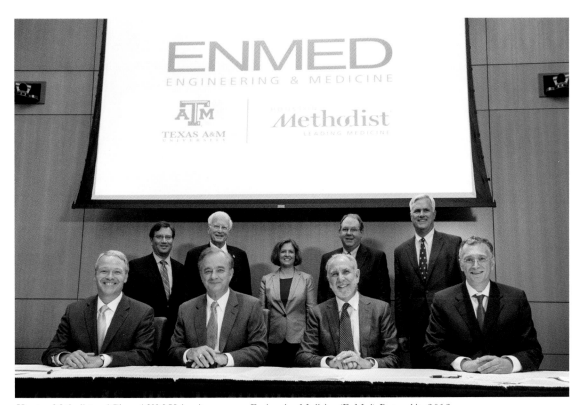

Houston Methodist and Texas A&M University announce Engineering Medicine (EnMed) Partnership, 2016.

As part of the I CARE in Action program, Houston Methodist employees volunteer at Rebuilding Together Houston, 2016. The action program was started in 2012 to give employees an opportunity to contribute to the Greater Houston community.

The Jerold B. Katz Foundation's commitment of $21 million in 2017 remains the largest single philanthropic commitment to the Houston Methodist Research Institute. It established the Jerold B. Katz Academy of Translational Research, including eight endowed Katz Investigator awards.

Houston Methodist The Woodlands Hospital opened in 2017.

Houston Methodist employees finding ways to get to the hospital during Hurricane Harvey, 2017. Despite a U.S. record for rainfall from a single storm, Houston Methodist remained open during the disaster.

2018 I CARE luncheon. (Standing from left) Evangeline Bernardino, Laurie Sturdevant, Spencer Allen, Maria Fuentes, Maizeba Watson, and Angela Vargas. (Seated) Mike Sturdevant and Dianne Palmer.

Rev. Charles R. Millikan, D.Min. (shown in 2018), vice president, Spiritual Care and Values Integration, Houston Methodist, and Dr. Ronny W. and Ruth Ann Barner Centennial Chair in Spiritual Care.

Paula and Joseph C. "Rusty" Walter III made a historic $101 million commitment in 2017—the largest in the hospital's history.

Barbara and President George H.W. Bush Atrium dedication in Walter Tower, May 2, 2018.

The new 22-story Paula and Joseph C. "Rusty" Walter III Tower (Walter Tower) is dedicated, May 2, 2018.

Centennial Physicians Dinner, April 25, 2019, recognizing Marquee Honoree Micahel E. DeBakey, M.D. and the one hundred notable physicians from Houston Methodist's first century.

First Row: Jennifer Arnold | Antonio M. Gotto Jr., M.D., D.Phil. | Antoinette C. Ripepi, M.D. | William L.
              Winters, Jr., M.D.** | George P. Noon, M.D. | Charles H. McCollum III, M.D. | Marc L. Boom, M.D.
              Kelty R. Baker, M.D. | C. Eugene Carlton, Jr., M.D. | John O. Roehm, Jr., M.D. | Gene Crain
              Nancy Chapman Colb | Milton M. Boniuk, M.D. | Richard L. Harper, M.D. | Eugene L. Alford, M.D.
Second Row: Dina R. Mody, M.D. | Michael J. Reardon, M.D.** | Stuart M. Dobbs, M.D.** | Robert G. Grossman, M.D.
              Lawrence Rice, M.D. | James E. Muntz, M.D. | Stanley H. Appel, M.D. | Miguel Quiñones, M.D.
              C. Richard Stasney, M.D.** | Gerald M. Lawrie, M.D. | Michael Raizner, M.D. | Joan Harrell
              James E. Harrell, Jr., M.D. | Marty Harrell
Third Row: James M. Musser, M.D., Ph.D. | Susan Lummis | Sue Price | Jaime Gateno, M.D., DDS | Timothy B.
              Boone, M.D., Ph.D. | Susan M. Miller, M.D. | Patrick R. Reardon, M.D. | Eugene C. Lai, M.D., Ph.D.
              Wade R. Rosenberg, M.D. | Victor Fainstein, M.D.** | Ranjit C. Chacko, M.D. | Neil S. Kleiman, M.D.
              | Juan J. Olivero, Sr., M.D. | William A. Zoghbi, M.D. | David S. Baskin, M.D.

Centennial Leadership Lecture, September 17, 2019, recognizing marquee honoree John F. Bookout along with current and former board members and their descendants and loved ones.

First Row: William L. Winters Jr., M.D. | John F. Bookout III | Joseph C. "Rusty" Walter III | Marc L. Boom, M.D.
              Judge Ewing Werlein, Jr. | John F. Bookout | Gregory V. Nelson | Lynda K. Underwood
              David M. Underwood, Jr. | Marcy E. Taub | Robert K. Moses, Jr.
Second Row: Olive Jenney | Melissa McCollum Moss | Ginger Renfroe Blanton | Eddy S. Blanton
              Elizabeth Blanton Wareing | Emily A. Crosswell | Louis Delhomme, Jr. | Doris Delhomme Hervey
Third Row: John S. "Steve" Dunn, Jr. | Marvy A. Finger | Larry L. Mathis | Ronald G. Girotto | Martha S. Walton
              Emily Walton Calver | Rev. Kenneth R. Levingston | Mary A. Daffin | Vidal G. Martinez
              Lindsay Cohn Holstead | Alice Arnold Helms | Steven D. Arnold | Antonio M. Gotto, Jr., M.D., D.Phil.
              Suehing W. Y. Chiang
Fourth Row: Ramon M. Cantu | Mark A. Houser | James M. Musser, M.D., Ph.D. | Stuart M. Dobbs, M.D.
Fifth Row: Susan H. Coulter | Elizabeth P. Butler | Martha Smith DeBusk | Evan H. Katz | Faisal N. Masud, M.D.
              Edwin "Ed" H. Knight Jr. | David C. Baggett, Jr. | Dan O. Dinges | Juliet S. Ellis, CFA
              Marcus "Marc" A. Watts | Duane N. Andrews, M.D.
Sixth Row: John P. Cooke, M.D., Ph.D. | H. Dirk Sostman, M.D., FACS | Kelty R. Baker, M.D. | Mary Ann Carroll

FOUR

THE GREATEST GOOD
1940-1950

During the 1940s:

Houston's population approaches 400,000 (1941)

New master plan for Houston emphasizes a loop highway system (1941)

Attack on Pearl Harbor (1941)

D-Day landings in Normandy (1944)

President Roosevelt dies suddenly and is succeeded by Harry Truman (1945)

World War II ends (1945)

"Baby and Child Care" by Dr. Benjamin Spock is named most popular book of 1946

Engineering begins on Gulf Freeway, first freeway in Texas (1947)

*Jackie Robinson breaks Major League Baseball's color barrier and debuts at first base
for the Brooklyn Dodgers (1947)*

*Ella Florence Fondren establishes the Fondren Foundation in honor of her husband,
Walter W. Fondren (1948)*

Harry Truman is elected president (1948)

A devastating epidemic of poliomyelitis flares in Houston (1949)

In 1911, six years after Dr. Oscar Norsworthy graduated from medical school at Tulane, Ernst Bertner received his medical degree from The University of Texas Medical Branch in Galveston. It had not come easy. According to family, Ernst William Bertner, or Billy as friends and family called him, was a rather precocious child growing up in Colorado City, Texas, a hundred miles southeast of Lubbock. His father, a German immigrant, ran a barbershop and sent his only son to high school at the New Mexico Military Academy in Roswell hoping extra discipline might get the boy on track. The father then bought a drugstore hoping his son would find a calling. It worked. Ernst Bertner took to the challenge and asked to enroll in The University of Texas Medical Branch's pharmacy school in Galveston. The gregarious Bertner found the pharmacy was a social gathering place and a community service, and both aspects appealed. In Galveston his interest in pharmacy studies soon changed to medicine and all seemed well.

Then came the holiday break and the young medical student returned home to find his father holding a telegram from Dean William Carter reporting young Bertner had failed four of his six subjects and should "resign" to find another line of work. Things were not off to a good start as the future father of the Texas Medical Center returned to Galveston by train to convince the dean he would buckle down and work hard.[1] In 1911 he graduated as one of the best in his class. What happened next was pure serendipity. For his postgraduate training he went to New York City and while interning at St. Vincent's Hospital he was assigned by Dr. George D. Steward to serve as the anesthetist for a minor procedure[2] on a Houston patient in town on business. That patient, Jesse Jones, was known as "Mr. Houston" because he built and owned many of the city's largest buildings as well as the *Houston Chronicle*. In hindsight, the chance meeting changed the very trajectory of young Dr. Bertner's medical career.

Jones took a liking to the young Texan and made him an offer to return to Houston and become the house physician for a new hotel he was building called the Rice Hotel. Dr. Bertner did just that, married, and lived in the Rice Hotel the rest of his life. The Rice, built on the site of the old Capitol Hotel, where Sam Houston once ran the Republic of Texas, opened in 1913 and was now the home to many of Houston's movers and shakers with a direct hand in shaping the city's future. In fact, John Freeman and his wife lived just down the hall from the Bertners. Freeman recalled years later, "Colonel Bates, Mr. Wilkins, and I were close friends, and we often found ourselves consulting with Dr. Bertner on the top floor of the Rice Hotel."[3] Clearly, Dr. Bertner was in the right place at the right time sharing his medical expertise with the trustees of the MD Anderson Foundation as they conceptualized the new Texas Medical Center.

Throughout the 1930s and '40s members of the Methodist Hospital board debated the hospital's future, as recalled Dr. J. Charles Dixon, a member of the hospital's medical staff 1929–1981 and president in 1940 and 1953–1955. Dr. Dixon noted there were "considerable concerns to whether the hospital financially was going to be able to succeed, and several of the yearly [board] minutes over several years included discussion about selling the hospital to a group of private doctors and going out of the hospital business. Also, it was mentioned that the location was not a very satisfactory one and they should buy land near Hermann Park and build a completely new hospital. This discussion went to the extent of appointing a committee to seek out land."[4]

Meanwhile, Ella Fondren was new on the board as the 1940s arrived. She not only liked the hospital's capable superintendent, Josie Roberts, she joined forces. The two women had much in common: both were fiercely independent widows, smart, determined, and of like mind to grow the hospital.

Together they traveled the country attending hospital conferences and workshops to learn all they could about hospital best practices, including a thorough understanding of design and operational aspects of the country's top-ranked hospitals. The April 1945 *Methodist Hospital News Bulletin* on the occasion of Roberts's twenty-first anniversary proudly reminded employees, "Mrs. Roberts is recognized not only in Texas but all over the United States as an outstanding hospital executive."[5] By the time of her retirement in 1952 she had served as president of the Texas Hospital Association and president of Pilot International, a business and professional women's club. She had also served as first vice president and a trustee of the American Hospital Association.[6]

These were war years and building programs across the country ground to a halt as steel and construction materials were reserved for the war effort. These were also years of change in the hospital board as founding members died, including James Marion West, Sr. in 1941. That same year John Scott left the board after two decades of service. Raymond Elledge, a highly respected Houston attorney, was elected to succeed Scott. Meetings changed from annual to monthly as seats on the board increased to thirty-five.

After the MD Anderson Foundation trustees lined up the cancer hospital and Baylor's medical school, John Freeman recalled the decision to develop something larger. "We decided that the medical center was just too big for any one foundation—it had to have the support of Texas, that's why it was called the Texas Medical Center."[7] Down on Rosalie, the Methodist board took note and discussed at their May 1942 meeting the possibility of getting a site in the new medical center. Chairman Elledge and Judge James Elkins were designated to request a meeting with Bates about the possibility. The outcome was favorable.

By late 1944 the board had a formal offer to join the new center at an undesignated site in the center. This triggered lengthy discussions about whether it would be better to stay and expand on the Fondren property across the street or move and build new. Already Baylor's medical school had moved fifty truckloads of equipment and furniture from Dallas to a temporary home in a converted Sears, Roebuck and Co. warehouse on Buffalo Drive (now Allen Parkway).[8] The dean, Dr. Walter Moursund, managed to convince a few of the Dallas faculty to follow him along with some students who held their first classes there on July 12, 1943. By 1945 Baylor's medical school would break ground for its permanent building in new medical center.

Dr. Moursund and his medical school's arrival from Dallas had happened so fast that even the membership of the Harris County Medical Society was caught largely unaware. A number of physicians felt slighted, even downright threatened by the arrival of the new academic enterprise. The medical society met on May 8, 1943, to discuss the matter as some members called for Baylor's removal. The heated meeting ended late in the evening only after all agreed a committee would further study the situation. Within the week Dr. Moursund addressed the group and calmed the waters.[9]

Within days the Harris County Medical Society voted to cooperate with Baylor. Dr. Marvin Graves from Methodist Hospital was appointed chairman of the Medical Society's Liaison Committee, which met with Dr. Moursund the following week. Before he died in 1959 Dr. Moursund recalled in his memoirs that "the committee gave helpful advice and assistance, particularly in the organization of a clinical faculty and in the promotion of cooperative relationships between the staffs of the hospitals of the city."[10]

Dr. Moursund not only calmed the waters with the physicians, but he also enhanced the city's medical reputation in ways few could appreciate at the time. In need of a chairman of surgery for his medical school, he went to Tulane University School of Medicine in New Orleans, where Dr. Oscar Norsworthy had trained five decades earlier. He had heard about a young Lebanese surgeon from Lake Charles, Louisiana, who was a protégé of Dr. Alton Ochsner and had a reputation for excellence and tireless drive. As future stories will tell, Dr. Moursund's decision to bring Michael E. DeBakey to Houston in 1948 would benefit Baylor, Methodist Hospital, the Texas Medical Center, and medicine in general on a global scale.

Things had moved quickly during the war years. Since 1942 local newspapers informed citizens that "the hospitals of Texas are worried about where to get enough doctors for the duration of the war."[11] By 1943 hospitals across Houston joined forces to recruit student nurses, provide first aid courses for all hospital nonprofessional employees, and establish blood and plasma banks. In May 1943, 102 nurses graduated from the city's four nursing schools: Methodist, Memorial (formerly Baptist), Hermann, and Jeff Davis. Eleven graduates represented Methodist Hospital at commencement, with Dr. Bertner delivering the main address. "Need for More Nurses to be Stressed" was that morning's headline in the *Houston Press*. A sign of the times, the story concluded with: "Usual commencement plans, such as open houses in the various hospitals, will be omitted almost entirely. Overworked staffs will not be asked to do anything which would be added effort."[12]

Fortunately, the dark days of war typically come with a silver lining because it is during wars that medical advancements often accelerate and some individuals develop extraordinary leadership skills from living on the edge where decisions can mean life or death. While an entire book could be written about the wartime experiences of Methodist Hospital employees, a few brief examples are provided.

Future board member and chairman emeritus John F. Bookout, Jr. was the lead bomber pilot for the 413th squadron of the 96th Bomb Group, honing leadership skills he would use throughout his twelve years as president and chief executive officer for Shell Oil and more than forty years on the Methodist Hospital board. His leadership in the early 2000s facilitated Houston Methodist's status today as a leading academic medical center with global reach.

Kathleen G. Ellis volunteered for the Red Cross Gray Ladies, a wartime volunteer program allowing thousands of Americans to contribute nonmedical care. After the war she suggested to Josie Roberts that the Gray Ladies model offered a good template to build a hospital volunteer program. The Methodist Hospital Service Corps program began in 1947. Just as the Auxiliary had represented women since 1928 from area Methodist churches in support of the hospital in the gift shops and through numerous initiatives, the Service Corps evolved in the postwar years as an indispensable volunteer organization within the institution. The corps made a human difference by staffing information desks, providing updates to families in busy waiting rooms, and providing coffee and snacks to family members and visitors who needed a friendly smile and kind touch.

Board members like Jesse Jones and Will Clayton were in Washington, D.C. during the war. Jones oversaw the Reconstruction Finance Corporation 1932–1945 and served as U.S. secretary of commerce 1940–1945. Throughout the war, he was considered one of the most powerful men in Washington. Clayton was appointed U.S. undersecretary of state for economic affairs in 1946 with an important role shaping the Marshall Plan in 1947. Oveta Culp Hobby, a founding trustee of the Texas Medical Center board who supported the hospital's invitation to join the new medical center, was the first director of the Women's Army Corps and first secretary of the U.S. Department of Health, Education, and Welfare before returning to Houston to run the family-owned *Houston Post*.

Following the war years, the Texas Medical Center transformed rapidly from a forest of trees to a forest of medical buildings. Interviewed shortly before his death in 1980, John Freeman summarized the progress: "Up until late 1945, we had made commitments to The University of Texas, Baylor, the Methodist Hospital, St. Luke's Hospital, the Shriners Hospital for Children, the library, and Hermann Hospital—for expanding their facilities."[13]

In February 1944, Dr. Bertner, the newly appointed acting director of the new MD Anderson Hospital for Cancer Research (as it was then called), dedicated the cancer hospital at its temporary home known as "the Oaks." The six-acre property had been the estate of Captain James A. Baker, Sr., grandfather of future U.S. Secretary of State James A. Baker III, and was purchased by The University of Texas as a temporary home for the new cancer hospital that would open in the medical center in 1954.[14]

The Methodist board, with invitation in hand to join the new medical complex, weighed their options. Given that construction in the city was essentially frozen, they had time and proceeded carefully. After all, the board consisted of many of the city's business leaders who had just come through the uncertain years of the Great Depression. Their aversion to assuming debt was real. What they needed was some good news. To the surprise of all, it came in March 1945. It was more than good news—it was a game changer.

• • •

John Freeman's statement that the new medical center would be bigger than any one foundation could support did not fall on deaf ears. In March 1945 oilman and philanthropist Hugh Roy Cullen electrified the community when he announced $1 million gifts each for Baptist Memorial, Hermann, Methodist, and St. Luke's hospitals. His first announcement, on March 2, designated unrestricted gifts for Baptist Memorial and Hermann. Baylor's medical school received $800,000 the following year to enable the completion of its first building, appropriately named the Cullen Building, which opened in 1948.

Upon hearing the news of the first two $1 million gifts, William N. Blanton, a Methodist Hospital board member (1946–1967), executive vice president of the Houston Chamber of Commerce, and an active member of St. Luke's Methodist Church, set a meeting with Cullen to talk about Methodist Hospital. Cullen and his wife, Lillie, added a $1 million gift on the spot and asked for Bishop Smith to drop by the next day to receive formal word.

The Cullens later revealed that the hospital's work with children with disabilities was a key factor in their decision. Also impressive was the fact that the hospital now treated more non-Methodists than Methodists and that the hospital's nursing program was working overtime to bridge the citywide nursing shortage.[15] Episcopal Bishop Clinton S. Quin also set a meeting with Cullen and received a similar $1 million commitment to build St. Luke's Episcopal Hospital. In just one week the Cullens had written $4 million in checks and were only getting started. Within two years they would establish the Cullen Foundation, endowed with more than $80 million in oil properties to benefit their community for decades to come.[16]

Josie Roberts would never forget the news of the million-dollar Cullen gift, recalling that Smith did not wait until his meeting with Cullen to call her. "I nearly died I was so thrilled. … The most important turning point was when Mr. Cullen gave us a million dollars and the MD Anderson Foundation gave us land [seven acres pledged soon after]. That turned the whole program. We immediately decided that we would come to the Medical Center."[17]

Ella Fondren and Roberts were like-minded in wanting the greatest good for their hospital. The seven acres the hospital was given in the new medical center was originally designated as ten acres, then downsized to five before compromising at seven. Most board members were satisfied but not the Fondren–Roberts team.

One board member got an earful when Roberts challenged him that seven acres in the new medical center was nowhere near enough. "This man was a very high businessman and he looked me in the eyes and said, 'Ms. Roberts, I don't think you know how much seven acres is.' I said, 'Mr. So-and-So, I'm afraid I do and that's the reason I know that seven acres isn't going to be enough for that Methodist Hospital.'"[18] Of course, time proved her right.

There was also the issue of exactly where that seven acres would be situated in the 134-acre forest. The cancer center and Baylor's medical school land had already been designated. Methodist Hospital's footprint was originally offered on the north side of the new complex close to the zoo. Again, Roberts protested with Fondren's support, noting they would be hemmed in next to a "smelly zoo" in an inconvenient location. Together they challenged the board to go back and move the location to the west side off South Main where they could share a laundry and power plant with the proposed Texas Children's and St. Luke's hospitals.

The MD Anderson Foundation trustees had also offered the hospital a challenge grant to their invitation to join the new medical center. For every dollar Methodist Hospital raised, the foundation promised to give fifty cents, up to a total of $500,000. Chairman Raymond Elledge and Bishop A. Frank Smith officially launched the new hospital building campaign in the closing months of 1945. Already they had $50,000 bequeathed in the will of Laura Ghent Graves and $25,000 on a pledge of $100,000 from Mr. and Mrs. Walter Goldston. Goldston would succeed Elledge as chairman in 1948 and expand the board to thirty-six members to further broaden the base of the campaign moving forward.[19]

Throughout 1946 as fundraising progressed, the trustees of the MD Anderson Foundation realized they needed to create an organization to run what was quickly growing into a big enterprise. The new Texas Medical Center, Inc. (TMC, Inc.) was chartered in October 1945 with a banquet the following February in the Rice Hotel. Dr. Bertner was appointed founding director, a position somewhat akin to mayor of a small city. The new entity developed its own board, including several members of the Methodist board, to oversee the new medical center's infrastructure, such as processes for deeding land, planning streets, negotiating utilities, addressing parking (not an issue in the early days), and organizing community governance.

TMC, Inc. also hired consultants James A. Hamilton and Associates from Minneapolis to develop a report, *Hospital and Health Survey of Harris Co. for the Texas Medical Center, Inc.*[20] Their report, issued in 1947, presented a planning document with baseline data on the city's health care capacity and projected needs. While most of the 125 recommendations were well accepted by the institutions in the new medical center, several suggestions caused a stir.

"Recommendation 95. That the Out-Patient Department be owned and operated by The Texas Medical Center. … Recommendation 98. That the Out-Patient Department encompass the central medical record and medical statistics tabulating rooms, through which would pass all records of out-patients and in-patients alike."

Was TMC, Inc., suggesting they would have a direct hand in patient care, taking autonomy away from the hospitals and physicians? In response to a loud outcry, those recommendations were quickly dropped. There would be no central outpatient building. Each institution would be nonprofit and independently operated by its own board and administrative structure. The new thirty-three-member Texas Medical Center board would include members of the institutions' boards to provide their voices in all matters governing the medical center going forward. The Texas Medical Center board would also invite membership from the community at large. Over the years, some of the city's best and brightest business and civic leaders, including President George H.W. Bush, have guided the growth and international reputation of the Texas Medical Center—that forest early Houstonians considered too far from downtown to be of value.

. . .

With gifts coming in for the new hospital, along with the Texas Medical Center's pledge of land, financial support, and operational autonomy—there was no turning back.[21] Now a new debate emerged. How many beds, how big a hospital? Having done their homework, both Ella Fondren and Josie Roberts understood the opportunity was now at hand to build a modern, well-planned, 300-bed hospital. Nothing less would do.

Fondren's agreement to give up on expansion at San Jacinto and Rosalie was contingent on her vision for a 300-bed hospital. Hines Baker, a hospital board member who was president and CEO of Humble Oil and Refining Company (1948–1957), disagreed along with a contingency of other board members. With grants, gifts, and the future sale of the Rosalie property, the board was hoping the final cost for a 300-bed hospital would be no more than $2.5 million—a price tag they could handle while minimizing debt. However, with the end of the war, building costs were skyrocketing and debt avoidance fading fast.[22]

That Roberts was busy and on the move is an understatement. In 1948 she made one trip with Fondren that had nothing to do with surveying hospitals. It had to do with finding an assistant administrator to support her growing responsibilities. That trip took them to St. Louis to meet a young man who grew up and worked in the local bank in Alto, Texas, deep in the piney woods of East Texas. Ted Bowen had just finished his medical hospital administration degree at Barnes Hospital at George Washington University in St. Louis when news of Pearl Harbor came. The U.S. Army said they didn't want Bowen, who was deaf in one ear.[23] So he returned home to the bank in his hometown.

As the war effort accelerated, the Army had a change of heart. They sent Bowen to Muskogee, Oklahoma, to run a 2,100-bed army hospital. After the war he returned to Barnes Hospital in St. Louis but not for long. Recalled his widow, June, in a 2004 interview: "One of the men on the board of the Methodist Hospital knew about Ted. ... So, Miss Roberts and Mrs. Fondren made a deal to go to St. Louis and have Ted come down and meet them at the train station."[24] The Fondren–Roberts team soon had Ted Bowen Houston-bound to meet the entire board.

In July 1948 Bowen arrived as Roberts's assistant administrator. He brought his bride-to-be, June, who found a job as secretary for Dr. DeBakey. Together, the Bowens would make their own indelible mark on Methodist Hospital for the next fifty years.

That same summer the board's new chairman, Walter Goldston, created a building committee chaired by O'Banion Williams. Williams would later chair the board 1954–1963. Fondren and Roberts joined the building committee. With Bowen overseeing the hospital on Rosalie, Roberts now had the time to focus on the new hospital. The Houston firm of Watkins, Nunn, McGinty, and Phenix, selected as the architects, presented some bad news that summer: the cost of a 300-bed hospital might run as high as $5 million.

Hermann Hospital was preparing to open their new Robertson Pavilion in 1949 (air conditioned, no less), and this added more discomfort given that Hermann's budget by all accounts at the time was running in deficit with unfilled beds. Additionally, numerous hospitals were on the drawing board in satellite communities around Houston that might absorb future patients for decades to come. For good reason, board members, like Hines Baker, remained firmly opposed to assuming the debt a 300-bed hospital presented. His suggestion to leave several floors unfinished as empty shells to save money drew strong pushback, as did the suggestion that church leaders on the board go back to their congregations and ask them to dig deeper in their pockets.

A motion was on the table for a 300-bed hospital to be built for $3.77 million or a 220-bed hospital for $3.27 million. Both options included an agreement to share a power plant and laundry facility with Texas Children's and St. Luke's.[25]

The board's meeting on February 22, 1949, had all the makings for a dramatic standoff and did not disappoint. When Fondren sensed a rally to go small, she used the ace up her sleeve and stunned the room to silence. Some had underestimated this woman whose husband once said had the best nose for oil he had ever seen. Fearless and determined, she stood slowly and delivered her now-famous retort: "Gentlemen, I have only one vote, but let's have one thing clear. I for one refuse to support a building of less than 300 beds. Not one penny of my money will go into a hospital of less than 300 beds."[26] She spoke from the heart for the greater good of the hospital she loved. The board decided 300 beds was a good number, a decision they would not regret in the years ahead.

As the 1940s came to close a typical day at the 100-bed Methodist Hospital on Rosalie was recorded precisely as follows: "care for 118 patients, 8 operations, 32 X-rays, examinations and treatments, 195 laboratory examinations, 150 pharmacy orders, four blood transfusions, two births, 820 meals, 16 new patients. There were 131 active physicians on staff, 35 consulting physicians, 14 resident physicians, 3 interns, 3 externs, 45 graduate nurses, 3 X-ray technicians, 8 medical technologists, 3 pharmacists, 4 record librarians, 8 volunteer workers, 5 dietitians and 2,973 pounds of dirty laundry that needed washing."[27]

This was Methodist Hospital of November 1949. A month later the board proudly stood together—both church and medical family as one—to break ground for a 300-bed Methodist Hospital in the Texas Medical Center. The hospital was about to get much, much bigger.

FIVE

NEW HOSPITAL, NEW PARTNERS
1950-1960

During the 1950s:

The Korean War begins (1950)

"I Love Lucy" makes its television debut (1951)

The first commercial jet flies from London to Johannesburg (1952)

John F. Kennedy marries Jacqueline Bouvier in Newport, Rhode Island (1953)

Disneyland opens in Anaheim, California (1954)

Jonas Salk's polio vaccine is distributed (1955)

Houston metro area population reaches one million (1955)

Jesse H. Jones dies (1956)

Hugh Roy Cullen dies (1957)

The Soviet Union launches Sputnik I (1957)

The Hula Hoop is introduced (1958)

President Dwight D. Eisenhower creates the National Aeronautics and
    Space Administration (1958)

Fidel Castro seizes power in Cuba (1959)

Alaska and Hawaii become states (1959)

Jack Kirby of Houston-based Texas Instruments introduces the first microchip (1959)

Growing up in Lake Charles, Louisiana, Dr. Michael Ellis DeBakey recalled, his mother would gather her five children every Sunday to deliver clothing she had mended and food she had cooked to a local orphanage. Late in life Dr. DeBakey remembered the lesson he learned from this routine. "One Sunday I objected when she packed a cap I liked.

She said, 'You have a new cap. These children don't have parents to give them a cap.' In that moment I learned a lesson, and it never left me. Throughout my lifetime, I've been very grateful to be able to do things for others."[1] From his arrival in Houston in the late 1940s until his death in 2008, Dr. Michael DeBakey and his quest for patient-centered excellence would shape the future of both Baylor's medical school and Methodist Hospital in important ways.

Born on September 7, 1908, Michael DeBakey was the oldest of the five children born to Lebanese immigrants Shaker and Raheehja Dabaghi (later anglicized to DeBakey). School proved little challenge for his bright mind, and before finishing high school he had already read the entire *Encyclopedia Britannica*. At Tulane University in New Orleans he completed in two years enough credits to get into Tulane's medical school, where he developed a strong interest in blood circulation and transfusions.

Before graduation in 1932, DeBakey developed key innovations for an existing roller pump design that would one day be used in the heart-lung machine, allowing surgeons to bypass blood flow through the human heart and enter the organ. It was the sixteenth-century surgeon Ambroise Paré who called the heart "the chief mansion of the soul."[2] For surgeons like Paré the human body's pump was forbidden territory that only the brave or foolish dared to enter.

Three years before DeBakey graduated from Tulane a young German surgeon, Dr. Werner Forssmann, dared to enter. Some considered him more foolish than brave, yet in 1956 he was awarded a Nobel Prize for his effort. Opening a large vein in his arm near the elbow, he inserted a long cannula (a wirelike tube or catheter) and pushed it up his arm toward his heart. With the aid of nurse Gerda Ditzen he then walked down two flights of stairs to the basement to get an X-ray proving he had actually entered his heart. He had not, so he pushed farther and captured another image proving his self-experimentation had worked.

Criticized, and even fired from his job, he soon changed his focus in medicine to urology for good. Yet he had developed a technique for catheterization of the heart and opened the door for a new generation of cardiologists and surgeons to go where no others had gone. Thanks to Dr. Forssmann's daring experiment, the specialty of cardiology accelerated with the ability to measure blood flow, pressure gradients, and repair valvular defects inside the inner sanctum of the heart. Dr. DeBakey's innovative roller pump providing continuous flow of oxygenated blood would contribute in important ways to a new era of open-heart surgery, allowing the heart to be stopped and entered for repair.

It was only the beginning of Dr. DeBakey's lifetime of innovation and leadership in the field of cardiovascular medicine. He was simply brilliant with an unstoppable drive for excellence and a relentless passion for hard work. During World War II he played a key role in setting up the first mobile army surgical hospitals, better known as MASH units, earning him the U.S. Army Legion of Merit. With his surgical mentor at Tulane, Dr. Alton

Ochsner, he was also among the first to suggest a strong link between cigarettes and lung cancer. Dr. DeBakey is credited with pioneering innovations in vascular surgery, especially a treatment for aortic aneurysm, a bulge in an artery wall that can burst and cause death. Using sewing skills his mother taught him, he created synthetic flexible material grafts to replace or bypass obstructed large blood vessels. Additionally, he was a driving force in the early development of the artificial heart and the left ventricular assist device (LVAD).

Add to that his now famous roller pump—along with administrative skills and political know-how—and he was able to influence all corners of the globe to benefit cardiovascular medicine and medicine in general. In his lifetime spanning ninety-nine years, he became one of the most famous and decorated cardiovascular surgeons of modern medicine, receiving more than fifty honorary degrees.[3] Much of his sixty years in Houston would be spent at Methodist Hospital, his hospital home.

Of course, the dean, Dr. Walter Moursund, could not know all of this in 1947 when he went to New Orleans. Dr. Moursund had plans to retire in 1953 and needed a surgery chairman sooner rather than later after his first chairman of surgery, Dr. Judson L. Taylor, died unexpectedly. Dr. Moursund sensed in thirty-nine-year-old Dr. DeBakey someone who could help him build hospital relationships and expand much-needed training for Baylor students.

It took three attempts before Dr. DeBakey was appointed on July 14, 1948, the Judson L. Taylor Professor of Surgery and chairman of the department of surgery at Baylor University College of Medicine.[4] During his life in medicine Baylor's new surgical chair and future president and chancellor emeritus performed an estimated sixty thousand operations and authored or co-authored some fifteen hundred scientific publications.

His outlook on life was straightforward if not blunt: "You know that you have a certain time span, whatever God gives you. … When you are sleeping, you are just dead as far as conscious living is concerned; that's part of your death. … I try to use my time as efficiently as I can."[5]

Dr. George Noon worked close to Dr. DeBakey more than four decades and summed up his surgical mentor as a stern taskmaster who strove for perfection and expected the same. "He was able to stimulate his help to peak performance and if he didn't get the peak performance, he would re-stimulate you until you did."[6] Late in life Dr. DeBakey reminded one interviewer that he always leveled with new faculty recruits, telling them he would be demanding while giving them whatever they needed. Then, with the candor they came to know, he'd assure them that if they failed to meet his demands it would be their fault not his.

Dr. DeBakey found the new medical school less than impressive when he arrived. "They didn't have any clinical service. They had no hospital. They had no residents, no training program in surgery. They couldn't provide me with anything to work with to develop an academic department."[7] What changed was his recognition of the great potential at hand along with the personal guarantee from Dr. Ochsner at Tulane that if Houston did not work out, New Orleans would be happy to take him back.

Dr. Denton Cooley, whom Dr. DeBakey recruited in 1951, recalled Dr. Ernst Bertner was a strong voice supporting Dr. DeBakey's recruitment as well as his own. At the time, Dr. William Longmire was also under consideration for the surgical chairmanship at Baylor's medical school. "I think Dr. Bertner was pretty instrumental in getting Dr. DeBakey to come rather than Bill Longmire."[8] Dr. Longmire, a Johns Hopkins surgical resident like Dr. Cooley, established himself as the founding surgical chair at the University of California, Los Angeles's new medical school in 1951.

What was needed were strong hospital affiliations for the newly arrived medical school. How Baylor came to affiliate with Methodist Hospital requires a brief overview of how Baylor affiliations evolved. In simple terms, community hospitals offer clinical services and patients. Medical school faculty have primary roles to teach students (M.D. and Ph.D.) through the clinical experiences offered by the hospital and conduct research. While Houston Methodist as an independent academic medical center today does all three (patient care, teaching, and research), the functions for years were primarily separated by medical school and hospital. If the medical school did not own its own hospital, it needed to affiliate with one. Upon arrival in Houston, Dr. DeBakey and his dean were soon at work lining up hospital affiliations that would last for decades—including a fifty-year partnership with Methodist Hospital.

On April 15, 1949, the 1,000-bed U.S. Navy hospital just two miles from the new medical center was transferred to the Veterans Administration with the help of Dr. DeBakey's connections and persuasive skills in Washington, D.C. The VA hospital became the medical school's first hospital affiliation.

During the late 1940s Baylor also affiliated with Jefferson Davis Hospital thanks to a strong working relationship Dr. DeBakey cultivated with Ben Taub, the hospital's chairman of the board 1935–1964. That affiliation agreement began on August 1, 1949.[9]

Another early affiliation Dr. Moursund established for Baylor was Hermann Hospital. There Dr. DeBakey found only 20 beds available to the Baylor clinical faculty. Dr. Hatch Cummings, Jr., who had replaced Dr. Marvin Graves as chief of the Methodist Hospital medical service in 1946, recalled that the staff at Hermann Hospital had the idea that they would take care of all patients and that the Baylor faculty "could make rounds on them and talk about them and teach off of them but wouldn't have control of their care."[10]

Dr. DeBakey found that unsatisfactory. When he went down to the old Methodist Hospital on Rosalie, the outlook of Josie Roberts and the medical staff was welcoming and responsive. Roberts recognized that this young Dr. DeBakey was an up-and-comer and she instructed the hospital staff to give him anything he needed. When he cited the fans in the operating room as inadequate, they added air conditioning to the surgical suite and X-ray room, and reminded him they would soon have a fully air-conditioned hospital in the new Texas Medical Center close to the medical school.

Dr. DeBakey, the relentless perfectionist with high expectations, found in that old, worn-down hospital on Rosalie an administration and a medical staff he liked. Moreover, he found something there his mother had taught him to live by—compassion, concern, and kindness. When he was well into his nineties, he said: "Of all the patients which I have … they always comment about the fact that they find that this hospital has a soul and that the nurses and the doctors in the medical scene, everyone who touches them, comes in contact with them, feels kindness and concern for them and their families."[11]

Dr. J. Charles Dickson, the chief of the otolaryngology service who led the Methodist Hospital medical staff in the late 1940s and early 1950s, recalled that Dr. DeBakey and the medical staff got along very well. Dr. Dickson, along with so many of the Methodist medical staff, championed an affiliation with the new medical school in town and recalled the board's willingness to listen to the medical staff and make changes when needed. For example, in the 1930s, when young physicians nicknamed the "Young Turks" by senior staff members threatened to leave over their concern that Drs. Green and Graves had too much control over patient care, the board listened and made changes. And good thing. Those young physicians would become innovative departmental leaders guiding patient care in the decades ahead. It was a hospital they had hitched their wagon to, a hospital where their voice mattered. By the early 1950s their collective voice agreed that a strong academic partner like Baylor's medical school would propel them from good to great.

· · ·

Methodist Hospital had been among the first hospitals in the city approved by the American Medical Association to train resident physicians (new graduates needing accredited postgraduate training), and on July 1, 1947, the first two residency positions were approved.[12] Education had always been a priority at the hospital, even in the early years, recalled Josie Roberts in 1975. Student interns had been circulating through the hospital since the late 1920s. Roberts recalled, "We had doctors that were interested in education as well as an administrator that tried to push it for them. … I shouldn't call names, but anyway, they [two other Houston hospitals] were twice as large as we were but you see, they were not interested because an educational program costs you money."[13] Clearly, the prospect of a medical school affiliation in conjunction with a gleaming, new 300-bed hospital was an exciting prospect for the hospital's medical staff already invested in teaching both nurses and young graduate physicians.

The importance of an affiliation between a hospital and a medical school is perhaps best explained by Dr. Antonio Gotto, Jr. Dr. Gotto, known as Tony to his colleagues, served as Baylor College of Medicine's chairman of medicine 1977–1997 and as dean and provost of Weill Cornell Medical College in New York City (affiliated with Houston Methodist in

June 2004) from 1997 until his retirement in 2012. While some medical schools across the country own their own hospital, most do not and require a formal affiliation agreement outlining the obligations and expectations of each partner. Consider it a medical marriage, Dr. Gotto notes, while adding:

> The medical school does not have patients, it does not have hospital beds, it does not in itself directly provide medical service, but it provides the doctors who can provide the service, and it provides the teaching and research. The hospital provides patient beds, it provides the medical care, and so in a clinical department in a medical school without a hospital would be a department in theoretical medicine. A hospital without a medical school would be a department of practical or applied medicine. And the two working together can give the theoretical as well as the practical aspect.[14]

Recalling the years leading up to the Methodist–Baylor affiliation in 1951, Dr. J. Charles Dickson credited the pathology departments of the two institutions for paving the way. "Dr. Martha Wood, the Methodist pathologist, became ill and asked that she be relieved for a time as pathologist. Dr. A. N. Boyd, a member of the [hospital's] executive committee, suggested that he talk to a friend of his in the pathology service at Baylor, Dr. Paul Wheeler. In this way Dr. Wheeler and the pathology department at Baylor covered the pathology service at Methodist during Dr. Wood's illness with Dr. [Stewart] Wallace named acting pathologist at Methodist on April 10, 1945."[15]

It turns out Dr. Wood was not able to return to work and the relationship with Baylor's department of pathology became permanent. Dr. Wallace was a "first-class gentleman" and a "dynamic personality" in the opinion of the Methodist medical staff.[16] As Dr. Dickson recalled: "The experience with the pathology department at Baylor was so successful, it very definitely influenced the staff and the executive committee to recommend to the hospital administration and board of trustees that a more serious formal affiliation be made. The Methodist board at the time was discussing the possibility of moving into the medical center and the pieces all seemed to fit together."[17]

. . .

Two major transformational events in Methodist Hospital history occurred almost simultaneously in the early 1950s: the hospital's affiliation agreement with Baylor University's medical school and the opening of the new 300-bed hospital in the Texas Medical Center. Both deserve additional attention.

Formal Affiliation with Baylor University Medical School

In June 1950, a formal affiliation agreement was signed between Baylor and Methodist—a marriage of sorts that would help each achieve greatness together while propelling the reputation of the Texas Medical Center on an international scale. The thirty-year agreement could be terminated at any time by mutual consent or by either party with eighteen-month written notice. As Marilyn Sibley summarized in her 1989 book about Methodist Hospital: "Each institution retained all jurisdictional powers incident to separate ownership, including all responsibility for expenses incurred in its operation. The hospital retained control of admission of patients, and the two institutions agreed to reopen the agreement if other teaching institutions entered the medical center and needed clinical facilities and patients for teaching."[18]

Key to every affiliation agreement is an understanding of how the medical staff are selected and appointed. Regular medical staff of the hospital were to be selected from members of the faculty of Baylor, but a grandfather clause gave all current members of the regular staff the option of joining the Baylor faculty. Some, not all, took that option.

Sibley's summary of provisions establishing a medical board to recommend to the hospital board the professional policies to be followed in the hospital and the process for appointing regular hospital staff is especially pertinent. "The medical board consisted of eight members and was chaired by the dean of Baylor University College of Medicine. The president of the regular medical staff served as vice-chairman; the administrator of the hospital, as secretary. The other members included the president-elect of the medical staff, one member elected annually by the regular medical staff to serve one year, and three members appointed annually from the regular medical staff by the chairman of the medical board."[19] For the next fifty-three years it would be a rewarding relationship despite bumps in the road along the way.

The New Hospital

Groundbreaking ceremonies for the new Methodist Hospital took place on December 12, 1949, only weeks after the board voted seventeen to five to award the contract to Thomas Bate and Sons for a 300-bed hospital. The cornerstone was laid May 31, 1950, with Bishop A. Frank Smith leading a formal worship service coinciding with the meeting of the Methodist Conference in Houston that week. It was a proud moment for all, including Dr. Ernst Bertner, who insisted on attending despite being in the final stages of his battle with cancer. Sadly, it would be the last ceremony he would attend.[20] He died July 28, 1950.

The chief architect of the new hospital, Milton Bowles McGinty, trained at Rice University down the street from the new medical center and traveled on scholarship throughout Italy to gain creative inspiration.[21] McGinty recalled seeing Dr. Bertner often at the construction site with Methodist board members admiring the progress as steel, concrete, and bricks took shape. A stone's throw to the south, St. Luke's Episcopal Hospital and Texas Children's Hospital broke ground. Robert A. Shepherd, Sr., formerly a member of the Methodist Hospital building committee, now served as chairman of the board (1951–1954). Despite his busy law practice, he was also a constant fixture at the building site, conferring with Josie Roberts over every detail.

On September 10, 1951, laden with rolled blueprints and itemized lists, Roberts and Shepherd conducted their final inspection. Step back in time and walk with them as they start in Wiess Memorial Chapel, a separate building to the right of the hospital's main entrance. Inside the chapel the seating for 125 seemed in order, although some of the furnishings were not yet in place. The red carpet is plush and stained glass impressive. Stepping into the hospital itself, they proceed from the basement up.[22]

In the basement Roberts and Shepherd review the main kitchens, central supply areas, the personnel office, staff and employee locker rooms, and general storage. Up to the main entrance on the first floor they check the lobby and business suites, where records and administrative offices are located. The floors shine like a mirror as they walk past the pharmacy, assembly room, cafeteria, gift shop, flower shop, and barber and beauty shops. By noon they have finished checks on eleven operating rooms and the two observation galleries on the second floor as well as radiologic facilities, laboratories, and the medical staff lounge.

The third-floor obstetric department requires a careful check as there are seven nurseries, four delivery rooms, labor and recovery adjuncts, nurses' stations, the Stork Club waiting room, and patient rooms. The fourth floor is the children's floor and a source of great pride for the Blue Bird Circle, which raised $400,000 for its cost, including equipment, furnished classrooms, playrooms, and a long outdoor deck.

By afternoon the two have split up to inspect floors four through eight—the patient floors. Divided into two main nursing divisions, 30 beds each, here they find work is needed to add more furnishings. Each floor had private, semiprivate, and ward rooms. A bed in one of the 4-bed wards would cost $8 a day, a private room up to $20 a day. One of the few 2-bed suites would be $30 a day.[23]

The hospital's ninth floor, allocated for research, takes little time to review as it is unfinished space yet to be assigned.

The tour takes a full day, and Shepherd and Roberts summarize they are "happily intoxicated by the clean, fresh aroma of newness, that wonderful combination of wood, paint, plaster, wax, polish, carpet, and fabric." What was missing, Roberts recalled years later, was the hustle and bustle of people helping people. After all, this was a hospital. But the silence of the floors serviced by five elevators would take some getting used to. In contrast to the old hospital's hand-operated, steel-cage elevator that groaned, jerked, and blew fuses, the new elevators operated efficiently.

Like the entire Methodist family (church and medical) the new assistant administrator, Ted Bowen, was caught up in the excitement of the moment. Bowen had been warned by one senior member of the medical staff that the hospital was run by "a bunch of ladies" and he might find that problematic.[24] He didn't. In fact, Bowen thrived in his new role. When the price of a sign to promote construction of the new hospital seemed too high, he and his wife, June, got paint and plywood and made their own. When the board decided to put the old hospital up for sale and couldn't find the blueprints, team Bowen got a tape measure and graph paper. The sale of the old went to support the new.[25]

Formal dedication of the new building was the afternoon of November 10, 1951. Headliners on the podium included Hugh Roy Cullen, John Freeman, and Bishop A. Frank Smith. Two smiles in the crowd especially stood out—those of Josie Roberts and Ella Fondren. They worked for years to create the new hospital around two themes: "one, that it should be built for efficient and economical operation; and two, that the entire hospital should give forth a warm pleasing atmosphere to patients, public, and personnel."[26] Missing that day was Walter L. Goldston, too ill to attend. He led the board (1948–1951) through difficult years and was missed.

Tours conducted that afternoon and the rest of the week brought streams of local and out-of-state visitors. Houston newspapers headlined the grand event and five days later local ambulance companies transferred sixty-three patients from the old hospital at no charge. Four elderly residents from the Bell Home moved to the new hospital but stayed only until a new Methodist retirement home nearby on Holly Hall was ready.[27]

Elmer Bertelsen, writing for the *Houston Chronicle*, noted, "Innovations are so numerous … that being a patient in the new 315-bed hospital will be a virtual pleasure."[28] Even *The New York Times* ran a special story highlighting the planning incorporated into the hospital, including an innovative intercommunications system connecting the nursing stations with patient rooms "so sensitive that the breathing of the patient is audible." Mail chutes, laundry chutes, décor designed to provide a family-friendly ambience, operating rooms wired for television to facilitate educational programs, and a diagnostic and treatment center for neurological and brain-disease patients were all cited.[29] National acclaim included *Modern Hospital* featuring the building as hospital of the month.[30]

Preceding the hospital dedication, Wiess Memorial Chapel was dedicated. Harry C. Wiess, former president of Humble Oil and Refining Company, envisioned a chapel honoring his mother shortly before he died in 1948. Smith knew the Wiess family well and presided. Rev. Clyde J. Verheyden, the hospital's first director of religious affairs, and Rev. Elton Stephenson stood in the back during the ceremony admiring the overflow crowd of three hundred—impressive given the chapel only seated 125. In 1987 the chapel was dismantled and reassembled in the new Dunn Tower "to be kept open at all times that all who labor and are heavy laden may come here and find rest and peace."[31] Those who knew the chapel's namesake, Louisa Wiess, remember a woman who came to Houston from Beaumont in 1923 to be close to her son and his family. Virtually an invalid prior to her death in 1938, family recalled her religious faith kept her life useful, happy, and filled with peace to the end.

As previously noted, the "little hospital" on the grounds of the original Methodist Hospital on Rosalie and operated by the Blue Bird Circle had served the orthopedic needs of children with disabilities 1934–1949, when it moved to Hermann Hospital until 1952. At that time the Arabia Temple Crippled Children's Clinic and Hospital opened in the new medical center— later renamed the Shriners Hospital for Crippled Children in 1966. Houston Methodist's outstanding orthopedic services originally led by Dr. Joe W. King proudly trace their legacy as one of the best orthopedic programs in the country to that little cottage.

With the opening of the new hospital in 1951, the Blue Bird Circle sought a new project. Dr. Bill Fields, one of the first neurologists in Houston when he joined Baylor's medical school in 1949, noted in his memoirs that the Blue Birds contacted Baylor's chairman of pediatrics, Dr. Russell Blattner, who suggested they address the problem of childhood epilepsy.[32] That idea grew into the Blue Bird Circle Clinic for Neurological Disorders with Dr. Fields serving as medical director and Dr. Peter Kellaway (Ph.D.) in charge of the electroencephalography laboratory. Dr. Kellaway would serve with distinction as director of the program in years to come.

With the opening of the new hospital, the clinic found itself in elaborate quarters on the hospital's fourth floor with sixty-five available beds. "It was the first of its kind in the South and Southwest," recalled Dr. Moursund.[33] While children with many different kinds of neurological problems were seen there, the majority suffered from seizure disorders. In his personal recollections published in 1995 Dr. Fields remembered the Blue Bird Circle as enormously successful in everything they did. "They dyed Easter eggs, sold dishcloths which they hemmed by hand, and carried on all kinds of activities in order to raise money to support their project. These funds were the nucleus from which we could expand the work ... to include not only teaching and clinical care but research."[34]

The clinic served as the springboard for what would become the hospital's internationally recognized center of excellence for neurological disease, and forerunner to the hospital's Neurosensory Center housed in the Bintliff Blue Bird Building honoring both the Blue Bird Circle and longtime supporters of the children's clinic, Alice and David C. Bintliff. Jointly owned with Baylor College of Medicine, the building opened in 1977 with Hugh Roy Cullen's grandson Corbin "Corby" J. Robertson, Jr. chairing the fundraising effort.

What many forget is that in 1951 the new children's clinic helped break the color barrier that separated black and white patients in an era of segregation enforced by infamous Jim Crow laws. As a cottage on the grounds of the old hospital, the children's clinic welcomed both black and white patients. Now with the clinic relocated on the fourth floor of the new hospital in the medical center, the question was raised—should black children be admitted? Dr. Fields picked up the story:

> So a meeting of the women's group was held at a lovely home in
> River Oaks. ... One of the women asked, 'Dr. Blattner, what would you
> do if somebody put a black child in the same room with one of your
> children?' He replied that he would say, 'Suffer the little children to
> come unto me and forbid them not for such is the kingdom of heaven.'
> [Matthew 19:14] Well, that touched a sympathetic chord and there
> wasn't a dry eye in the house. They voted unanimously to let the black
> children come to the clinic.[35]

In this way a single clinic on one floor of the new hospital paved the way to desegregate services, board membership, and staffing at Methodist Hospital ahead of many of Houston's other hospitals.

Despite the smiles and excitement behind the opening of the new hospital, there remained in the boardroom a general sense of concern that the 300-bed hospital would never fill. The board had taken out an $80,000 loan to ready 193 beds for patient use and a planned nursing residence was canceled.[36] They figured there was ample room on the hospital's eighth floor to house nurses and residents.

It didn't take long to resolve their concerns as within a week the hospital had 143 inpatients and Josie Roberts had to start readying more rooms. By July 1952 the hospital averaged 220 inpatients daily and by year's end was eighty-five percent filled.[37] The power plant and laundry, owned jointly by the hospital with St. Luke's and Texas Children's, proved a cost saver. Methodist had a fifty percent share of the capital investment providing heating, air conditioning, engineering, and maintenance services. Roberts documented that the initial construction of the shared facility with a connecting tunnel saved nearly $50,000. Savings from the shared laundry equipment and operations and the power plant saved an additional estimated $45,000 a year combined.[38]

With the hospital up and running, Roberts announced her retirement effective February 1, 1953—twenty-nine years to the day she began. Ted Bowen, age thirty-two, was named acting administrator. He proved to have an "amazing ability to get along with doctors," recalled one member of the medical staff. By June 1953 he was promoted to administrator and given a modest raise. Ten years later his title, administrator, was elevated to president. "I liked him and pressed pretty hard for them to put him in charge," recalled Dr. DeBakey.[39] The hard-to-please surgeon was more than pleased with Roberts's administrative team and especially Bowen, who would work closely with him in the years ahead.

Shortly after her retirement, Roberts moved to Albuquerque, New Mexico, to live near her daughter, Bobbye Faye. Roberts returned to Houston seventeen years later. Before her death on October 6, 1984, at age ninety-three, Dr. Bill Fields invited "Miss Josie," as the medical staff had affectionately called her, to his home for a visit. "She was still very bright and articulate until a few months before she passed away," he recalled.[40]

Roberts was not the only one to depart the hospital in 1953. At Baylor Dr. Moursund retired, replaced as dean by Dr. Stanley Olson, formerly dean of the University of Illinois College of Medicine in Chicago. Robert Shepherd, satisfied his work as hospital chairman was done, was replaced in 1954 by O'Banion Williams, who would lead the board until 1963. A native Houstonian and graduate of Southern Methodist University, Williams served the board nearly four decades (1945–1983). He, along with his new hospital administrator, would have their hands full.

Consider some of the issues on the table in 1953 for Bowen and the hospital board: large operating deficits to tame, planning and financing a heart catheterization clinic, a radioisotope laboratory, a cardiac clinical research laboratory to fill that designated space on the ninth floor, a need for more free beds for interns and residents instruction, Social Security and pension matters for employees, and more. Bowen estimated opening the laboratories alone would cost $200,000 with an additional $50,000 per year in operational costs.[41]

During the first half of 1953 it was clear the 300-bed hospital was a good call. Bowen now had 284 of his 300 beds operating with full medical and surgical services and would soon be turning away up to twenty-five patients a day. In the immediate years to come, talk of a bigger hospital increasingly dominated conversation.

For Methodist doctors, staff, and patients alike, the 1950s were a time of innovation. The Bintliff Blue Bird Clinic for epilepsy on the fourth floor made history when Dr. James Greenwood performed the first surgery for epilepsy in the Southwest. The program itself was groundbreaking, innovative, and a first of its kind.

Dr. Presley H. Chalmers had considered surgery his career path only to find a calling in anesthesiology. With the opening of the new Methodist Hospital in 1951, he chaired the department (a position he held thirty-five years) and developed innovative anesthesia programs essential for the incredible productivity of the surgeons who increasingly needed more operating rooms and beds. In 1952 Dr. Chalmers opened a 10-bed postoperative anesthesia recovery room, the first in Houston. Four years later the hospital would establish a six-bed intensive care area, yet another first.

Innovative facilities and medical procedures abounded in the 1950s. As the hospital settled into the Texas Medical Center, Dr. Paul Harrington, a Kansas native and talented orthopedic surgeon who joined Baylor in 1946, was on a quest to find a surgical cure for scoliosis (abnormal curvature of the spine). At the time it was said many patients preferred to live with the ailment as opposed to the cures at hand involving spinal fusions without additional back support and months of physical manipulation and living in plaster casts in hopes of correcting the curvature. Dr. Harrington had a better idea and developed in 1953 a stainless-steel surgical device now known as the Harrington Rod that could be implanted to reduce curvature and provide more stability to a spinal fusion. The product of years of persistent trial and error with assistance from the engineering department of Rice University, the work was presented by Dr. Harrington in 1958 at the annual meeting of the American Academy of Orthopaedic Surgeons in Chicago, where it was met with astonishment and deep skepticism. Some called for the academy to reconsider his membership. But as with many innovations, time proved him right. It is said that up to a million people had Harrington Rods implanted for scoliosis from the early 1960s to the late 1990s.[42]

In cardiovascular surgery, Dr. DeBakey's outstanding team of faculty recruits and trainees, many of whom would join the faculty, included highly respected names in cardiovascular surgery such as Drs. Beall, Cooley, Creech, Crawford, Diethrich, Frazier, Garrett, Henly, Howell, McCollum, Morris, Noon, and Scott, to highlight some. In November 1958, the hospital opened a 24-bed cardiovascular intensive care unit, another first—a sign of the busy times.

Dr. E. Stanley Crawford (1922–1992) is but one example from this list of talented heart surgeons who joined Dr. DeBakey and made their own lasting contributions to medicine. Dr. Crawford, an Alabama native, received his medical degree from Harvard in 1946 and established a preeminent reputation as a leading expert addressing the complex diseases of the aorta. He joined Dr. DeBakey's team in 1955 and advanced the reputation of both Baylor and Methodist for the next thirty-eight years, teaching a new generation of surgeons while generating more than three hundred peer-reviewed publications and books. His textbook, *Diseases of the Aorta*, co-authored with his surgeon son, Dr. John Lloyd Crawford II, has become a standard reference text on aortic surgery.[43]

Dr. DeBakey's many firsts (too numerous to list) included the famous Dacron grafts for vascular repairs that he originally sewed on his wife's sewing machine in the mid-1950s. The synthetic, tube-shaped fabric grafts replaced sections of blood vessels, including the aorta, damaged by aneurysms or weakened areas along the vessel prone to fail. Dr. Cooley's deft surgical hands pioneered pediatric heart surgery procedures that were breathtaking, and the two surgeons working together performed demonstrations at hospitals worldwide that mesmerized veteran surgeons while intensifying the international spotlight on the Texas Medical Center, Baylor's medical school, and Methodist Hospital, where much of this work was done. By decade's end the American Medical Association awarded Dr. DeBakey the Distinguished Service Award for his pioneering work in vascular surgery.

The numbers are impressive. Between late 1953 and mid-1955 Drs. DeBakey and Cooley presented 123 separate professional presentations worldwide. By the early 1960s nearly fifty surgeons were actively conducting surgery at Methodist Hospital, logging some 8,800 general and cardiovascular operations in the years 1961–1963 alone.[44]

Dr. Paul Jordan, Jr. should not be lost in the discussion. He moved to Houston in 1964 and is remembered for numerous advances in general surgery. He was well respected and beloved by many. An innovator, he is credited as the first surgeon to perform direct surgery for atherosclerosis in the U.S. by performing a femoro-popliteal bypass using a vein graft in the early 1950s. He was also one of the first to perform the famous Whipple procedure for chronic pancreatitis other than Whipple himself while also making great advances in the treatment of peptic ulcer disease. In 1989 the Houston Surgical Society honored him with the Distinguished Houston Surgical Award, noting he was a true pioneer in surgery with a lasting legacy. In 2001 he was named to honorary/emeritus faculty status at Houston Methodist.

Methodist's numerous cardiovascular surgeons increasingly depended on equally talented cardiologists. Dr. Don W. Chapman was recruited in 1944 as Baylor's second full-time department of medicine faculty member and in time started his own private practice, assembling a talented group of cardiologists known as the Chapman Group. They further propelled the reputation of the hospital and gained the nickname "Dawn Patrol" because their access to the hospital's X-ray department in the early years was limited to before 7:30 a.m. Working side by side with leading surgeons addressing an endless stream of patients' needs, these Methodist-based cardiologists had a leading role advancing their field from a diagnostic specialty to an interventional art—pioneering pacemakers, stents, and a whole host of new technological innovations that are commonplace today. Simply stated, Houston Methodist was *leading medicine* then, as it is now.

It is important to remember that not all surgery at Methodist was cardiovascular. As mentioned, Dr. Greenwood pioneered firsts in neurosurgery. Dr. John W. Overstreet spent his fifty-one-year surgical career at Methodist Hospital as chief of general surgery for the hospital, while Dr. DeBakey was chairman of the surgical department at Baylor and leading the cardiovascular surgery team at Methodist. Both Drs. Overstreet and DeBakey trained at Tulane with Dr. Ochsner. Both built outstanding, exemplary programs of surgery and served long distinguished careers at the hospital spanning more than five decades each as active surgeons.

Ted Bowen and the hospital's board were continually challenged by this hectic pace as a small hospital grew from good to great. By mid-decade, planning was underway for a West Wing expansion of the hospital. Likewise, Bowen, who now had two assistants, Tom Fourqurean and Catarino Gonzalez, was challenged by concerns of the Methodist medical staff, especially private physicians who referred many of the hospital's patients. "We were a small group going into a big arena and nobody had been there before," Bowen recalled years later.[45]

Many of the private doctors on the hospital's medical staff felt the medical school was too controlling in their approach, perhaps a threat to their future access to the hospital. Josie Roberts had predicted such tension, telling James Speer in a 1975 interview, "I had warned our board was never to let Baylor take over Methodist Hospital, because medical schools had done that in some parts of the country."[46] It was a classic "town and gown" dispute that the leadership of both institutions sought to balance quickly and constructively. In 1954 the Methodist staff rewrote staff bylaws combining the medical board and coordinating committee into a new executive committee. With a revised affiliation (tightening the loose ends of the 1950 initial agreement) and a new committee structure, the two partners moved forward knowing that maintaining equilibrium between hospital and medical school would require continual vigilance and effort.

Not to be lost in this discussion is the rapid growth of the Texas Medical Center during this busy decade. By the late 1950s the forest behind George Hermann's hospital now had Baylor College of Medicine's Cullen Building, Methodist Hospital, MD Anderson Hospital for Cancer Research, St. Luke's Episcopal Hospital, Texas Children's Hospital, The University of Texas Dental Branch (also affiliated with Methodist Hospital), and a new Jesse H. Jones Library building owned by the Houston Academy of Medicine, the nonprofit arm of the Harris County Medical Society. If only Monroe Anderson could see what the trustees of his foundation accomplished. It had been a busy decade, and the next would be even busier.

SIX

HOSPITAL WITH A SOUL
1960-1970

During the 1960s:
>*Population of Houston approaches one million at 938,219, making the city the seventh largest*
>>*in the country (1960)*
>*Hurricane Carla strikes the Texas Gulf Coast (1961)*
>*NASA's Manned Spacecraft Center moves to Houston (1961)*
>*The University of Houston becomes a state university (1963)*
>*John F. Kennedy is assassinated in Dallas (1963)*
>*Lyndon B. Johnson is elected president (1964)*
>*Astrodome opens—originally named Harris County Domed Stadium (1965)*
>*Medicare and Medicaid go into effect (1966)*
>*First Super Bowl is played, in Los Angeles Memorial Coliseum (1967)*
>*Dr. Christiaan N. Barnard performs first human heart transplant in Cape Town,*
>>*South Africa (1967)*
>*Richard Nixon is elected president (1968)*
>*Houston Intercontinental Airport begins operations (1969)*

Medical advances were in high gear in Houston's Texas Medical Center in the 1960s. From the perspective of heart surgery, these years are often referred to as the "golden age." Hospitals like Methodist were at the forefront—not just in cardiovascular care but across the spectrum of medical specialties. Advancements in orthopedics, general surgery, psychiatry, first-of-a-kind kidney and lung transplants, innovative postoperative care facilities emulated by others nationwide—all were leading medicine. Following behind was an emerging field of biomedical ethics attempting to catch up and address the humanistic complexities that predictably accompany rapid advances in science and technology.

In writing the centennial history of Houston Methodist, one is tempted to focus on the medical prowess and breathtaking advances in medicine that defined the decade and hospital itself. After all, this was a time when Drs. DeBakey and Cooley graced the covers of magazines like *Time* (1965) and *Life* (1968, 1970) and received international awards too numerous to list, while bringing royalty (European and Hollywood) to Methodist Hospital. Well-known figures like Jerry Lewis, Frank Sinatra, Joe Louis, Guy Lombardo, Vikki Carr, Al Hirt, Marlene Dietrich, Leo Durocher, and Clifton Webb all came to Methodist for their care.

Perhaps Dr. Atul Gawande summarized it best in his 2014 bestseller *Being Mortal: Medicine and What Matters in the End*. "We think our job is to ensure health and survival. But really it is larger than that. It is to enable well-being. And well-being is about the reasons one wishes to be alive. Those reasons matter not just at the end of life, or when debility comes, but all along the way."[1]

Ella Fondren understood that excellent patient care involves much more than great facilities and talented health care providers—it involves the patient and their families. It provides a listening ear and a helping hand to coordinate care *all along the way* as Dr. Gawande so eloquently wrote. When asked in the mid-1950s to join a Texas Medical Center special committee on religious activities, Fondren and her good friend Julia Bertner said "yes." They joined a group of like-minded representatives from neighboring hospitals who understood that no matter how far or how fast the medical sciences advance, excellence in health care is about treating the *whole* patient, not just the disease.

Chaired by Dr. Dawson C. Bryan, president of the Council of Churches of Greater Houston, the group's report was a recommendation for an Institute of Religion to "develop an interfaith center of education, pastoral care, and research that would attend to the whole human being in his spiritual and physical dimensions."[2]

The new Institute of Religion was chartered in 1955 with partial financial support from the Fondren Foundation and housed in a new building adjacent to both Methodist and St. Luke's hospitals. Methodist board member Eddy Scurlock chaired the institute's board of trustees throughout the 1960s.

This is the very core of what Dr. DeBakey meant when he said this was a hospital with a soul. Throughout the life of Houston Methodist, as the small hospital became the largest in the South, it is important to remember this is a place where board meetings begin with a prayer and every patient and family member are considered the most important people in the room. This was not just a good idea on paper—it was and is ingrained into every patient encounter and every employee to this day. It is that common thread binding the canvas upon which this centennial mural is painted in words.

In 1951, as Methodist opened Wiess Chapel, Rev. Clyde J. Verheyden joined the hospital as director of religious affairs and public relations. A former associate pastor of

First Methodist Church in Houston, Verheyden had World War II experience as a chaplain and a battlefield appreciation of nurses and their invaluable contributions to the physical, mental, and social well-being of each patient—the very definition of health as defined by the World Health Organization.[3]

Given the perpetual shortage of nurses, especially acute in Houston's post-World War II years, Verheyden soon turned his attention to increasing collections to support nurses through the Golden Cross program. Recognizing more was needed, in 1951 he organized the Good Samaritan Club, whose membership went from five to five hundred in the first year and continues to fund an ever-increasing number of scholarships for nursing students. His film, *Take Care of Him*, portrayed the rewards of nursing in a faith-based hospital like Methodist and enjoyed wide distribution in churches, seminaries, hospitals, and care centers throughout Houston and beyond—reinforcing the hospital's growing reputation as a place where care in the holistic sense of the word is modeled.

As the Texas Medical Center grew, Methodist played a role in developing a community-wide solution for training nurses, just as the Institute of Religion represented a community-wide program for training chaplains. The University of Houston discontinued its nursing school in 1955 and turned to Methodist Hospital to reinstate the three-year diploma program for nurses. This was considered too big a task for any one hospital, so Methodist leadership joined forces with other Texas Medical Center hospitals and the Texas Medical Center board to support a centralized school of nursing.

In this way Texas Woman's University (TWU) in Denton established a nursing school in Houston. TWU's nursing program started in 1954 at Parkland Hospital in Dallas and by 1972 was accepting both men and women into their graduate and undergraduate programs in Denton, Dallas, and Houston. Their home in the Texas Medical Center occupied what is today Houston Methodist's north campus where Walter Tower is newly located. In 2001 Tropical Storm Allison severely damaged TWU's buildings, and they were in need of repair or rebuilding. Thanks to win-win board negotiations involving a property swap, TWU now has the new TWU Institute for Health Sciences nearby at 6700 Fannin while Houston Methodist has TWU's former location north of the hospital and across from the Texas Medical Center Jesse Jones Library—an adjacent footprint to Houston Methodist where Walter Tower stands and a master plan involving the Mary Gibbs Jones Building (TWU's former offices and classrooms) is now being formulated.

The 1960 arrival of TWU's nursing program in the Texas Medical Center allowed Methodist Hospital to phase out its nursing school with the last class of twenty-one nurses graduating on July 21, 1961. In nearly four decades the hospital graduated 438 nurses.[4] Thanks to a gift from Houston businessman March Culmore, a centralized residence for nurses was built in the Texas Medical Center and named in his honor with $750,000 presented from his estate to both Methodist and St. Luke's Episcopal hospitals. While Methodist no longer operated its own nursing school, the Good Samaritan Club did not stop there. They expanded scholarship programs to include licensed vocational nurses and nurses' aides. Sixty-eight years later, at the time of Methodist's centennial, the Good Samaritan Foundation continues the work Verheyden began and is recognized as the largest private grantor of nurse scholarships in Texas.[5] Since its founding in 1951 the foundation has given more than $18.5 million in grants and scholarships for nursing education.[6]

The work that Verheyden began is today overseen by Rev. Charles R. Millikan, the vice president for spiritual care at Houston Methodist and the first such leader to hold a coveted endowed chair—the Dr. Ronny W. and Ruth Ann Barner Centennial Chair in Spiritual Care. Millikan, a fourth-generation Methodist minister, serves on committees throughout the hospital system and is supported by a staff of nearly three hundred serving Houston Methodist's eight hospitals. The hospital chaplains and their volunteers alone made more than a quarter of a million visits in 2016 to patients of all faiths. In the 1990s a grateful patient provided a Muslim Prayer Room that "is used hourly, not daily. Every day," said Millikan with pride.

Step into his office and he will waste no time showing you one of his prized possessions. It is his framed birth certificate hanging proudly behind his desk, showing his tiny footprints from seven decades earlier when he was born in the original Methodist Hospital on Rosalie. There at the bottom is Josie Roberts's signature and right across the hall from his door in the administrative suites of Dunn Tower her portrait stares directly at his desk. "And she watches me all day. So, I've been returned."[7] From research committees to educational programs to ethics consultations to the executive board suite, you will find church representatives at work.

· · ·

Now step back into the 1960s. While hospital and church leadership worked to support the spiritual dimension of the hospital, Chairman O'Banion Williams and the hospital's board worked to increase the physical dimension. Ted Bowen remembered that Methodist "ran 110 percent census for years and years and years. … We turned down thirty, forty, fifty people a day. It was very difficult."[8] In 1955 records show 13,919 patients were discharged. By 1965 that number had nearly doubled to 25,850 and by 1970 approached 31,000 patients.[9]

Williams's letter dated August 3, 1956, began the process for doubling the size of the hospital. The letter was directed to Dr. Fred Elliott, who had taken over the executive directorship of the Texas Medical Center upon the death of Dr. Bertner in 1950.

A native of Pittsburg, Kansas, Dr. Elliott came to Houston in 1932 to lead Texas Dental College out of debt and into a 1943 affiliation that changed its name to The University of Texas Dental Branch. He also affiliated his dental school with Methodist Hospital for teaching opportunities and then laid plans for the school's new building that opened in 1955 next to MD Anderson Hospital for Cancer Research. He accomplished everything a dental school dean could, then stepped into Dr. Bertner's job building the Texas Medical Center into a modern medical city.

Dr. Elliott's dental school faculty in the 1930s included a dentist named Dr. Walter Cronkite, Sr., who helped the new dean and his wife find a home upon arrival in Houston. The Cronkites' son, Walter, threw the morning paper into the dean's yard before television news made Walter Cronkite a household name. Dr. Elliott also crossed paths with a young fellow in Kansas City with a big imagination. He started his dental practice in a Kansas City office building and picked up the story: "While there, I became acquainted with a gentleman on the second floor of the building. Although it was not more than a speaking acquaintance, it was one that came back to my mind each time I saw one of his productions on screen and on television in later years. I am talking about Walt Disney."[10]

When Texas Children's Hospital opened in 1953, the now executive director of the Texas Medical Center wrote his old acquaintance and asked for some artwork for the new children's hospital. Drawings of Mickey Mouse and Donald Duck soon arrived. It should also not escape the reader that, like Dr. Elliott, two of Methodist Hospital's future presidents, Larry L. Mathis and Ronald G. Girotto, are from Pittsburg, Kansas.

The 1956 letter Dr. Elliott received from the Methodist board included a request for more land to expand the hospital (no doubt a source of amusement for Ella Fondren) stating, "The demand for services has increased each year and is now critical. Our tentative construction aim is to build a unit between our present building and Fannin Street to the west. We have strong recommendations that our expansion should provide, in the main, facilities for heart and brain surgery, diagnosis and research."[11]

Also mentioned was the need for more parking. "Our architect has designed a multistoried parking garage in connection with our proposed new building for 300 cars to take the place of our present public parking area." Williams reminded Dr. Elliott that room for a parking garage would be facilitated by the Texas Medical Center providing a building to house nurses. "As you know, the bulk of the March Culmore estate was left for this purpose."[12]

The documentation included reports from the Doctor's Planning Committee of the Medical Staff signed by Drs. Ernst, Dickson, Cummings, Tuttle, Sr., Olson, and Greenwood, Jr. (Dr. Stanley Olson was Baylor's new medical school dean, serving 1953–1967). The medical committee provided strong support for the expansion, stating in their minutes, "The doctors felt the present Staff could maintain its high degree of cooperation in a 600-bed hospital with relatively few medical staff additions." Additionally, they recommended "the assignment of beds in the new unit to specialties, such as neurosurgery, psychiatry, speech and hearing, etc., as well as possible development of patient rooms on the basis of acute, convalescent, and diagnostic care were important factors to be considered in expansion."[13]

Just as Josie Roberts and Ella Fondren had traveled the country to plan the hospital's move from Rosalie, board members, administrators, and members of the medical staff along with the architect, Milton McGinty, visited nineteen leading hospitals and medical centers in the country. One of those visits was to NewYork-Presbyterian Hospital and Medical Center in New York City, an institution that will have an important role in Houston Methodist's future.

It must have been clear to Dr. Elliott and the TMC board that the Methodist board had its ducks in a row. Like Dr. Bertner before him, Dr. Elliott was impressed with the hospital's planning and documentation—a hallmark trait the institution would ably repeat many times over in the years ahead.

Groundbreaking for the West Wing was June 1, 1960 (Ella Fondren's eightieth birthday) with Bishop A. Frank Smith on the podium. This would be his last official ceremony before retirement. Earlier that year Fondren broke her hip in a fall while visiting Dallas to dedicate the Fondren Health Center at Southern Methodist University. She was immediately flown back to Methodist, where chief of orthopedics Dr. Joe W. King operated and watched over her the next six months as she recuperated in Room 807. The room was quickly dubbed "Miss Ella's room." The woman who had invested so much in the hospital had no intention of slowing down. As she turned the first spade of dirt to launch the expansion, she already had in mind plans for another building.

Ted Bowen stood proudly by at the groundbreaking with a *Houston Chronicle* news clip tucked in his suit pocket that reported:

> What will become the largest private hospital in Houston, and
> one of the largest such institutions in the entire South, will start going
> up tomorrow. … The cost is being shared by several trust funds,
> individual donations, and $1 million from the state-controlled Hill-
> Burton Foundation. One third of the entire cost was shouldered by
> the Houston Endowment Fund, the Fondren Foundation, the MD
> Anderson Foundation, the Ford Foundation and the medical staff of
> Methodist Hospital.[14]

The $9 million West Wing expansion increased the hospital's number of beds by 376, added new surgical facilities and support laboratories, and enlarged the power plant and laundry.[15] An eight hundred-car parking garage in cooperation with St. Luke's and Texas Children's hospitals also emerged adjacent to the site. When the garage was completed and dedicated in 1963, Houston, with a population approaching one million, was getting used to impressive additions to the skyline. The new Sharpstown Mall had opened just two years earlier as the first air-conditioned mall in the world. And 2.6 miles south of the hospital the shell of a domed stadium, the Astrodome, was turning heads nationwide. Dubbed the "eighth wonder of the world," the stadium opened April 9, 1965, as Mickey Mantle and the New York Yankees came to town. Dr. King, president of the medical staff in 1960, was a big baseball fan and soon brought his staff's orthopedics expertise to the new Houston Astros, establishing the hospital's long-term reputation as a leader in sports medicine.

With increased research facilities, state-of-the-art surgical suites, new imaging and clinical laboratories, expanded pathology, and model surgical waiting areas and post-op facilities, word was out across the country that something special was happening in Houston. The golden age of hearts now grabbed international headlines and Methodist Hospital was often ground zero.

As medical know-how accelerated with new state-of-the art facilities and outstanding research and medical staff (both private and school-based physicians), one aspect of the hospital defied all change—the faith-based foundation that is the very soul of the hospital. It would be very hard to miss, given the Fannin Street entrance to the hospital featured a 98-foot-long (16 feet high) mosaic mural known as *Extending Arms of Christ*. The massive retro mural with 1.5 million tiles celebrates the wisdom and skills of the medical profession from ancient to modern times—a story of medicine and faith portrayed in rich blues, oranges, greens, and yellows. Designed by Bruce Hayes and created in 1963 in the studio of Giuseppe Rampini in Florence, Italy, the focal point of the mural is a figure of Christ superimposed upon the hospital's Wiess Memorial Chapel with arms reaching out through the past and into the future "to embrace, support, and strengthen those who dedicate their lives to helping others."[16]

Fully visible for all to see, in time the mural was partially obstructed from view by the hospital's skybridge across Fannin. In 2018 it was moved to the new Paula and Joseph C. "Rusty" Walter III Tower patient care complex. Rampini's works can be found in the Ashmolean Museum of Art and Archaeology, the Victoria and Albert Museum, the Getty, the Metropolitan Museum of Art—and now Methodist's Walter Tower in the heart of the Texas Medical Center.[17]

. . .

The decade of the 1960s was a whirlwind of excitement as celebrities and royal visitors found their way to the hospital. In 1964, when his British physicians diagnosed an aneurysm in his abdomen, the Duke of Windsor was immediately referred to Methodist Hospital. The duke and his wife, the American-born duchess Wallis Simpson, arrived in Houston late in the year. Dr. DeBakey and his team handily removed the diseased section of the artery and replaced it with a length of Dacron tubing. His team wrote the book on repairing aneurysms at Methodist, and a grateful Duke of Windsor referred to Dr. DeBakey thereafter as "the maestro." *Time* magazine preferred a more colloquial moniker, "the Texas Tornado."[18]

Throughout the Christmas holidays Ted Bowen and his assistants, including Pat Temple, a nurse by training who spent twenty-six years as the hospital's first patient advocate, tended to the Duke and Duchess of Windsor's every need as the world looked on. Interviewed in 2000, Temple recalled the royal couple left their titles outside the door. "They treated us with kindness and caring. … We just said 'yes ma'am' to her and 'yes sir' to him."[19] A floral arrangement that arrived from the duke's niece Queen Elizabeth took center stage in his room filled with flowers. Marilyn Sibley's book about Methodist Hospital includes a bit of humor the duke unknowingly provided following his recovery when he was invited to Ella Fondren's elegant River Oaks mansion for an honorary luncheon. During the meal the duke casually remarked how nice it was to see "an average American home."[20]

For foreign leaders who could not come to Houston, Dr. DeBakey and his teams went to them. In this way the Shah of Iran (1988) and Russian President Boris Yeltsin (1996) received care by the DeBakey medical team. Whether working from Houston or traveling to the far corners of the world, the care given was the same high standard no matter who the patient was. It was then, and is now.

The hospital's 1963 expansion helped, but not for long, as patients seeking care at Methodist continued to arrive thanks to the hospital's growing reputation across all specialties. Dr. Manus J. O'Donnell, a cardiologist born in a small town near Belfast, Ireland, worked in the hospital nearly three decades, arriving in the mid-'60s when up to thirty new patients were admitted every weekend for heart repairs alone. In response to the demand, in 1965 the hospital opened the Annex several miles away at 1130 Earle Street, adding 200 more beds. "Yes, the patients would check in there. ... If they were DeBakey patients, they would be brought over to see him in his office. Then they were set up for surgery [and] admitted into the hospital."[21]

Dr. Juan Jose Olivero, a nephrologist (kidney specialist) trained in his native Guatemala and who served the hospital for more than three decades, recalled the Annex was the site of Houston's first outpatient hemodialysis as well as a training facility. "The nurses would come to train at the Annex before opening other facilities [throughout the community]."[22]

Dr. DeBakey recalled he had as many as one hundred patients in his care on any given day. "We had the Annex because we didn't have enough space here [in the hospital]. ... Yes, we used to finish our rounds here, jump in the car and go over to the Annex." While he was a brilliant surgeon, Dr. DeBakey was less than a good driver, according to more than a few white-knuckled passengers. "I had one resident," recalled Dr. DeBakey, "he flat out said to me, 'I'll never ride with you again.'"[23]

While Dr. DeBakey's driving skills were questionable, his talent driving the medical team to levels of excellence was legendary. Even before the hospital doubled in size in 1963, Baylor received a large ten-year grant from the National Heart Institute for the establishment of the country's first Cardiovascular Research Center at Methodist Hospital. Bowen, working with Dr. DeBakey, revised the ongoing hospital expansion program to reconfigure space on the hospital's ninth floor as construction for the new hospital West Wing progressed.

Also taking place in 1963 was the groundbreaking for a building that Ella Fondren conceived while recovering from hip surgery. Staring out of her window from Methodist's eighth floor she spotted a vacant piece of property. "We have to build something on that property," she repeated to all who listened. Bowen, along with Drs. King and DeBakey, listened. That marked the conceptual beginning of the Fondren and Brown Cardiovascular and Orthopedic Research Center. The groundbreaking ceremony on October 27, 1964,[24] was attended by Princess Lilian, wife of the former King Leopold III of Belgium. Her Foundation for Cardiological Research became closely aligned with Dr. DeBakey, who operated at no cost on the children her foundation sent to Houston. The friendship lasted years and it was Princess Lilian and her husband who in 1978 commissioned a bronze bust of Dr. DeBakey (seen today in the Dunn Tower's Crain Garden) sculpted by Georges Muguet. The former king, like the Duke of Windsor, received lifesaving surgery at Houston Methodist.

· · ·

The six-story, $9 million Fondren-Brown Building brought together Ella Fondren's foundation with the foundation of George and Herman Brown, whose names can be found on buildings throughout Houston, including the George R. Brown Convention Center. The National Institutes of Health (NIH) provided a $1.73 million grant in support of the building's research mission along with gifts from Dr. DeBakey and members of the medical staff. The new building opened in stages, joined together to make economic use of the available land and with design consideration allowing more floors to be added in the years ahead.

While the story of Walter and Ella Fondren's many contributions is now familiar to the reader, a few words about George and Herman Brown seem in order. The very year Dr. Oscar Norsworthy sold his hospital to the Methodists in 1919, Herman Brown's employer, a contractor, declared bankruptcy. In lieu of wages Herman Brown accepted eighteen mules. With the financial support of his brother-in-law, Dan Root, and his younger brother, George, they started a construction company named Brown & Root, Inc. They started out paving roads with what they had—mules and wagons. In time they grew Brown & Root into one of the largest construction companies in the world, and like so many Houstonians, they gave back to their city and Methodist Hospital in important ways. Herman Brown died in 1962, and George passed away in 1983.

The complex opened in phases starting in April 1968 with the Herman Brown Building officially opened on December 4, 1968, and the Ella F. Fondren Building a week later on December 11. The Fondren Building (165,000 square feet) consisted of a ground floor plus six floors with the structure designed to permit an additional six floors. The Brown Building (108,000 square feet), with ground floor plus five floors, was designed for an additional four floors. The Fondren Building housed both orthopedic and cardiovascular research with 50 beds for teaching and research. The Brown Building was principally devoted to cardiovascular needs with clinical and laboratory space as well as eight specialty operating rooms connected to a central monitoring and computer system and laboratory support.[25]

Planning for all these facilities included a task force of ninety-three physicians and scientists who worked with architects and administrative personnel. Birth deformities, crippling injuries of muscles, bones, and joints, and corrective orthopedic procedures coupled with pioneering work in rehabilitation and physical therapy all represented the orthopedic expertise these new facilities would support. Cardiovascular-related conditions typically were aneurysms and occlusive lesions of the blood vessels, coronary occlusive disease, congenital and acquired cardiac disorders, biochemical and tissue studies of the atherosclerotic processes, kidney disorders, hypertension, strokes, and organ transplantation, including kidney, liver, lung, and heart.

. . .

Throughout the 1960s the link between tobacco and cancer gained increasing attention at a time when cigarette vending machines could be found in hospitals nationwide, including Methodist. At MD Anderson Cancer Center down the street, cigarettes were sold in the lobby during the 1950s and ashtrays with the hospital's logo could be purchased in the gift shop.[26] Selling cigarettes in hospitals was an accepted practice until the 1960s. Perceptive physicians like Methodist's Dr. Dan Jackson had unsuccessfully questioned the practice in the 1940s but had to patiently wait until the evidence regarding the detrimental health implications of tobacco on health forced change. By the early 1970s tobacco advertising was banned on television and radio. "They finally got rid of the cigarette machines. It was kind of a victory I had to sweat for but it was worth it," recalled Dr. Jackson years later with a smile of satisfaction.[27]

. . .

While advertising and medicine have historically been an odd couple, one interesting turn of events that benefited health care at large hospitals, including Methodist, occurred when a genius advertising executive from Galveston switched from selling cigarettes to financing medical research. Albert Lasker, working in Chicago, had changed the advertising industry forever by integrating the psychology of consumers into his persuasive appeals. The success of Palmolive soap, Sunkist oranges, Pepsodent toothpaste, Kleenex, feminine napkins (a term he introduced), and yes, Lucky Strike cigarettes, made him a fortune and a revered figure in advertising. Then, in 1940, he met his third wife, Mary Woodard, a health activist who swayed his attention from selling cigarettes to selling health.

Divesting of his advertising company in 1941, he and his wife created the Lasker Foundation with $45 million to fund medical research.[28] He was brilliant. When Mary Lasker volunteered to help an organization called the Birth Control Federation, he suggested a better name would be Planned Parenthood. For the American Society for the Control of Cancer, he thought American Cancer Society sounded better. After his death in 1952, Mary Lasker continued her good work and soon met Dr. DeBakey, who was in Washington testifying in support of medical research.

The two forged a friendship that lasted their lifetimes. Their work together supporting applied research at the national level benefited Methodist Hospital both directly and indirectly in ways that should not be lost in the hospital's story. Just one example of many is the establishment of the Commission on Heart Disease, Cancer, and Stroke. Mary Lasker prevailed upon President Lyndon Johnson in the early 1960s to establish the commission, and her friend and medical ally, Dr. DeBakey, was asked to serve as chair. The DeBakey commission through meticulous, evidence-based documentation and persuasion in the halls of Congress (a skill Dr. DeBakey excelled in) led to the creation of a federally sponsored network of clinical centers that would combine research, training, and patient care. These regional medical centers, with Baylor and Methodist involved in leadership roles, became part of LBJ's Great Society legislation in 1965.

. . .

Of course, not all Methodist stories from the 1960s represent medical advancements. Some involve social advancement. The 1960s represent a troubling time marred by the bullets of assassins who tragically took the lives of a U.S. president, his brother, a very special humanitarian named King, and other civil rights activists. The decade was a roller coaster of emotions—divided by Vietnam, puzzled by a summer of love, and elated as Neil Armstrong set foot on the moon.

Uncomfortable as it is to remember, in less enlightened times racial segregation was commonplace in U.S. hospitals well into the twentieth century. That changed in 1964 with the passing of the Civil Rights Act. As mentioned, the hospital's Blue Bird Clinic for Neurological Disorders on the fourth floor of the new hospital in the early 1950s had continued to accept both black and white children as it had as an orthopedic clinic in the "little cottage" on Rosalie in the 1940s. Baylor chairman of pediatrics Dr. Russell Blattner along with the program's director, Dr. Peter Kellaway, championed breaking this color barrier. When Dr. Kellaway informed Josie Roberts in 1952 that he "would resign [from] the Blue Bird Circle Clinic if black children were excluded" in the new medical center hospital, Roberts responded angrily, telling Dr. Kellaway, "You easterners come down here and tell us how to run our lives." Dr. Kellaway was actually from South Africa and change did come.[29]

Late in 1955 Dr. Blattner brought the application of Dr. Clarence R. Higgins to the Jefferson Davis Medical Board for acceptance as a third-year pediatric resident. Dr. Higgins became the first black resident for Baylor's affiliated hospitals (working primarily at Jeff Davis Hospital), and he noted years later that Ben Taub, the hospital's chairman, had personally underwritten his monthly salary out-of-pocket.[30] Dr. Stuart Yudofsky, a 1970 Baylor graduate, noted acceptance came easier among the patients. "Such homogeneity [predominantly white medical staffs and administrations throughout the Texas Medical Center] stood in striking contrast to the beloved patients whom we care for at the Ben

Taub [General Hospital], the Jefferson Davis, the VA; and even Methodist and St. Luke's hospitals, where all ethnicities were abundantly represented."[31] In this way progress was made as diversity in administration, the hospital board, and medical staff followed on the heels of these students who broke difficult ground and should not be lost in these stories.

• • •

Five years after President Johnson signed the Civil Rights Act, Dr. DeBakey was in Washington not to appeal for research funding but to receive the Presidential Medal of Freedom. As a medical statesman Dr. DeBakey walked the halls of Congress with Mary Lasker to the benefit of cardiovascular research and health care funding nationwide. That his patients and his sphere of surgery was based at Methodist meant that the hospital's name was known far and wide as Methodist patient outcomes supported in important ways the DeBakey–Lasker statesmanship that transcended institutional identity. Consider the numbers: the budget for the NIH was $3.4 million in 1946, $50 million in 1960, and surpassed $1 billion in 1965.[32]

On May 2, 1965, Dr. DeBakey appeared in the first live television broadcast from Methodist Hospital on all three national networks and around the world via satellite as he inserted an artificial aortic valve into the left chamber of a patient's heart. The next year he was first to successfully implant a partial artificial heart (left ventricular assist device) in a patient.

In 1968 he performed the first heart transplant at Methodist Hospital. True to style, it was not just a heart but four organs (heart, lung, two kidneys) transplanted by teams of surgeons from one donor to four recipients. Nurse Ruth Abeles was there that day tending to the lung recipient. Little did she realize she would still be caring for patients at the hospital in 2018 when the Houston Methodist J.C. Walter Jr. Transplant Center performed its one thousandth heart transplant. That milestone was "an incredible accomplishment and testament to the world-class expertise and dedication of the multitude of physicians, researchers, coordinators, nurses, social workers, managers, dietitians and everyone else who makes heart transplantation at Houston Methodist possible," wrote Houston Methodist president Dr. Marc L. Boom, in his message to all employees on January 2, 2018.[33]

Difficult to please in the operating room, Dr. DeBakey did let down his guard at times to brag about his Methodist-based colleagues. "In the first place, they were damn good surgeons. ... In the early days, the fellow I depended on most was Denton Cooley. He was my first appointment, and he was well trained and he was a hell of a good surgeon, too—damn good one. So, I was lucky because he worked very closely with me on many of the 'firsts' that we did. Denton Cooley was with me on all of them. ... All the others that followed also were exceptionally good."[34]

Given the need for space, Dr. Cooley in the early 1960s was doing more and more surgery at St. Luke's and Texas Children's hospitals down the street. As Dr. Cooley's reputation as a pediatric cardiovascular surgeon grew, he gravitated away from the surgical suites of Methodist Hospital and in 1962 established the Texas Heart Institute between St. Luke's Episcopal and Texas Children's hospitals.

Said Dr. DeBakey, "He had more space there. ... Because I had so many patients in the hospital here at Methodist—I was actually creating a problem for the hospital because some of the doctors couldn't get their patients in here. ... We talked about it and I urged him to do it."[35]

The real split took place on April 4, 1969, when Dr. Cooley, still a Baylor faculty member and a member of Dr. DeBakey's team, performed the first artificial heart implant using a half-pound device made of plastic and Dacron linked by tubes to a bedside control console. The original device was developed by Drs. DeBakey and Domingo Liotta, who was recruited to Baylor as a fellow in 1961. Dr. DeBakey heard about the procedure on the news while attending a meeting at the National Heart Institute. "It was a shock. I didn't know anything about it. It created a serious problem because all of our work was supported by the NIH. We had to explain to them how this had been done when it hadn't been approved by them or by the hospital review board."[36] Dr. Cooley claimed he was justified in attempting to save the life of a forty-seven-year-old patient, Haskell Karp. The artificial device kept Karp alive for three days until a human heart was available. Karp lived less than two days after the human heart was implanted. It would not be until the early 1980s that a new immunosuppressant medication, cyclosporin, proved effective in preventing organ rejection and rejuvenated heart transplant programs worldwide.

Dr. Lawrence K. Altman, writing for *The New York Times*, noted that during legal proceedings Dr. Cooley was asked whether he considered himself the best heart surgeon in the world. "Yes," Dr. Cooley replied. And when asked whether he was being rather immodest Dr. Cooley responded, "Perhaps, but remember I'm under oath."[37] Dr. DeBakey refused to testify against his colleague and the case ended there.

However, the debacle led to the famous rift between the two multitalented heart surgeons. Dr. Cooley resigned his Baylor faculty appointment and moved permanently to his Texas Heart Institute to pursue many more "firsts" and assemble one of the great heart institutes in the world. Dr. DeBakey and his team soon moved their attention away from the artificial heart to the LVAD and by 1973 were focused on cardiac assistance as opposed to artificial hearts.

While books have been written about the two surgeons who did not speak to each other for four decades, what is certain is that in the end they shook hands and complimented each other for a job well done. In 2008, a few days after Dr. DeBakey received the Congressional Gold Medal, he shook hands with Dr. Cooley in Houston and accepted a lifetime achievement award from the Denton A. Cooley Cardiovascular Surgical Society. A video of the meeting at St. Luke's Episcopal Hospital shows Dr. Cooley stepping down from the stage to kneel next to Dr. DeBakey in his motorized scooter. Always competitive, Dr. Cooley suggested it must be a heavy burden "for one person to be honored by a Congressional Gold Medal and membership in the Cooley Society all in one week." Dr. DeBakey noted his Congressional medal was solid gold and assumed the Cooley award was the same. Dr. Cooley replied with a chuckle that his was fourteen karats.[38]

Sometimes humor is the best medicine. Another book has a story that makes one smile: "There is the apocryphal story of DeBakey arriving at the hospital parking lot only to find it completely full. When he pressured the attendant to find him a place, and pointed out that he was Michael DeBakey, the attendant reportedly replied, 'I don't care who you are. I couldn't find you a place even if you were Denton Cooley.'"[39]

In hindsight, perhaps the two giants of cardiovascular surgery were just too big for any one institution and their separation over the years only gave the world two great heart programs and provided a double dose of renown that made Baylor College of Medicine, Houston Methodist, the Texas Heart Institute, and the Texas Medical Center household names. Dr. DeBakey died at The Methodist Hospital on July 11, 2008, two months short of his one hundredth birthday. Dr. Cooley died eight years later, on November 18, 2016, at age ninety-six.

SEVEN

FIVE BUILDINGS AND A FLOOD
1970-1980

During the 1970s:
Population of Houston approaches 1.25 million (1970)
One Shell Plaza is completed in downtown Houston, the tallest building west of
the Mississippi River (1971)
Voting age in the United States is lowered from twenty-one to eighteen (1971)
Terrorist massacre mars Munich Olympics (1972)
Houston Community College System established (1972)
Watergate break-in (1972)
U.S. prisoners of war return from Vietnam (1973)
President Richard Nixon resigns and Gerald Ford assumes office (1974)
Gallon of gas costs 44 cents (1975)
United States celebrates its bicentennial (1976)
Steve Jobs and Steve Wozniak build their first computer and start a company named
Apple in Cupertino, California (1976)
Jimmy Carter is elected president (1976)
Lucasfilm releases Star Wars (1977)
Houston voters approve the Metropolitan Transportation Authority (1978)
The first test tube baby, Louise Joy Brown, is born in Oldham, England (1978)
Three Mile Island nuclear plant accident (1979)

On February 15, 1968, Ted Bowen approached the podium for an event celebrating the fortieth anniversary of the Women's Auxiliary to Methodist Hospital. Over the years, the Auxiliary had established itself as an invaluable resource. "With you we have succeeded, without you we would have failed," Bowen said. His talk was a walk through the hospital's history as well as an overview of the present, including the Annex and new Fondren-Brown Building. The numbers presented were impressive.

> The hospital has 945,632 square feet of floor space in operation, the equivalent of 22 acres, and its 903 beds makes it one of the largest hospitals in the nation. To operate the Methodist Hospital requires a staff that will approach 2,500 to 2,700 people by the end of 1968. At present the annual payroll is over $11 million. Each month the electric bill is approximately $12,000 and the telephone bill is around $13,000. For the year, the food bill is almost $750,000. A portion of this large dietary bill is the 7,000 cups of coffee we serve each day. Each month the hospital uses 1.7 million gallons of water and its laundry, one of the largest in the state, processes more than 600,000 pounds of linen each month. Our pharmacy fills more than 600,000 prescriptions each year. [1]

Attempting some humor that may have made a few in the audience blush, Bowen added, "To top it off or to bottom it out in the statistical arena, the hospital requires 50,000 rolls of toilet tissue a year."

To understand Houston Methodist in these years of Watergate is to understand the many factors impacting society and medicine. While the nation put a man on the moon in 1969, it also saw a growing distrust of big government exacerbated by the Vietnam War and the August 9, 1974, resignation of President Richard Nixon. Although Rachel Carson's environmental treatise *Silent Spring*[2] was released in the mid-1960s, it was in the 1970s that the modern environmental movement began in earnest. Words like *carcinogen* emerged in the national consciousness, and a new questioning of the ethics of science and technology demanded both answers and accountability. A national war on cancer was announced in Washington, D.C. and the phrase *preventive medicine* gained long overdue recognition. The hospital with a soul understood precisely that total health care involved much more than simply treating disease. Across the spectrum of medical specialties, research increasingly addressed prevention of disease, offering both behavioral interventions and a new understanding of disease processes at the molecular level. This in turn required facilities to house new technology and the ever-increasing number of patients who sought their care at the hospital the Methodists built.

In 1968, while the hospital was growing by leaps and bounds, its academic partner, Baylor, was addressing challenges of their own—financial shortfalls, faculty departures, limitations to accept federal funding, and the impending arrival of a new University of Texas medical school with lower state-supported tuition. Medical schools at the time were under increasing pressure to increase class sizes to resolve a predicted national shortage of physicians in coming years. Across the country medical schools also found themselves increasingly dependent on the clinical income of their faculty to support the financial bottom line of the schools. These national trends affecting the hospital's primary academic partner harbored important implications for both medical school and Methodist Hospital.

Dr. DeBakey summed up the situation in a report he penned for the Baptist General Convention of Texas titled *Current Status of the Baylor University College of Medicine*, dated September 1, 1968. His message for Baylor's medical school to break ties with the Baptist church was clear.

> Baylor University College of Medicine now faces a decisive moment in its history. … Because Baylor continues to operate at an increasing annual deficit, now amounting to almost one million dollars, and is constantly scrambling for funds to meet the deficits, it is unable to plan constructively for future expansion and development. … The only practical solution is to remove its identification in the public's mind as a Baptist responsibility and to re-establish it as a nonprofit institution, to permit its fair competition for funds and resources with all other institutions in the community and nation.[3]

He also recommended that "the head of each clinical department of a medical school must have control over the clinical services in the affiliated hospitals. Although Baylor has highly qualified and responsible persons actively engaged in medical education and research work, they do not enjoy the organizational control they need to function effectively."[4]

In this way, in 1969 the hospital's academic partner separated from the Baptist General Convention of Texas and became an independent entity, doubled its class size, began to receive state appropriations for medical education, and named Dr. Michael DeBakey president while changing the school's name to Baylor College of Medicine.

Methodist Hospital at this time was on solid financial ground. Many in the early 1970s credited Ted Bowen's adept management and tight-knit administrative team for the hospital's healthy position. Between 1951 and 1971 hospital beds had increased from 300 to 1,040 and assets from $4,813,413 to $40,050,402.[5]

As the 1970s began, Methodist and Baylor worked together behind the scenes to strengthen their relationship and plan the future. At the request of the school, Bowen and his team analyzed Baylor's basic administrative and service departments. They found them in "a rather chaotic state" and suggested constructive changes and cooperative strategies between the two partners with mutual benefits in mind. For example, in food services he offered a proposal to save Baylor $100,000 annually.[6]

The hospital and medical school also worked together at the board level, linked by overlapping membership and ensuring both partners were united. Ella Fondren and A. Frank Smith, Jr. (son of Bishop Smith and a future hospital board chair, 1977–1991) accepted appointments to the new Baylor board as the school separated from Baylor University. Seven other Methodist board members joined the medical school's board. Leonard F.

McCollum, president of Continental Oil Company, resigned from the Methodist board to accept the chairmanship of the Baylor board.

Perhaps Bowen captured the hospital's outlook best: "I am and always have been of the opinion that the hospital and the medical school are both improved by a good working relationship. Neither should dominate the other. On the contrary, each should support and complement the other; for in the long run their aims in total are the same. In my opinion, now is the time for an equitable, enduring agreement."[7]

Dr. Edward C. Lynch, a hematologist and member of the hospital's medical staff and Baylor faculty for forty-six years, provides additional insight: "There were some conflicts between the Baylor central administration and the administration at Methodist in the '70s. They signed this affiliation agreement in 1970 and not always did they agree on things. The driving thing that helped from the Methodist side was that Ted Bowen had the vision of an academically oriented hospital of the model that was true at Washington University-Barnes Hospital [where he trained in hospital administration]. … That affiliation was established in the early 1900s [and] they were tied in so closely, that they mutually supported each other. That model was a very good one, in my opinion."[8]

To accomplish the expanding needs of the academically oriented hospital, the hospital administration and board diligently worked together, adding along the way to Bowen's administrative team. If the Washington University-Barnes Hospital in St. Louis provided a good model for academic hospital management, then its master's program in hospital administration would be the best place to seek new administrative talent. Larry Mathis arrived in August 1971 from St. Louis. Just as Ella Fondren and Josie Roberts had vetted Bowen himself at a train station in St. Louis, Bowen traveled to St. Louis to meet Mathis.

During the early 1970s the two institutions moved forward together. They updated their affiliation agreement to further tighten the bond with an agreement that the chairman of a department at Baylor would also serve as chief of the corresponding service at Methodist and that a staff member appointed at Methodist first become a member of the Baylor faculty with the understanding that the medical staff "*shall*" (important distinction) contribute financially to the support of the institutions. By the end of January 1970, both boards had signed off.

The appointment of a new chairman of internal medicine in the early 1970s serving both the medical school and the hospital presented a test of the new alliance. At the time, Dr. Hatch Cummings, Jr., a strong proponent of the original Baylor affiliation and head of internal medicine at the hospital since 1946, announced his retirement. A grateful patient, R. E. "Bob" Smith, agreed to endow a chair for internal medicine with a gift of $2 million under the condition that the person occupying it would serve both as chairman of the department of internal medicine at Baylor and chief of the corresponding service at Methodist.

The need had arisen when longtime Baylor chair Dr. Raymond Pruitt (1959–1967) was recruited from Houston to become the dean of the new Mayo Clinic Medical School. Dr.

Henry D. McIntosh, a noted cardiologist, arrived from Duke University in 1970 as the first holder of the internal medicine chair with a mission to build stronger ties between Baylor and Methodist. This in turn further added to the concerns of the private physicians who wondered if this was the beginning of a "closed" system that would limit entirely their privileges to admit and care for patients in the hospital and have any voice in hospital matters.

The hospital's leadership soon recognized their misstep. They had neglected to fully communicate the new 1970 agreement with the clinical staff, those private doctors loyal to the hospital, who, in fact, referred a majority of the patients. Like Dr. DeBakey just months earlier hearing about Dr. Cooley's controversial artificial heart implant from the media, many on the clinical staff learned of the new Methodist–Baylor agreement in similar fashion.

Dr. Mavis Kelsey recalled the misstep in his memoirs: "Problems erupted immediately because Methodist and Baylor reached this agreement without consulting the clinical staff. From the time Baylor first relocated to Houston, Kelsey-Seybold doctors and other private physicians played an important role in the school's survival by voluntarily serving as teaching faculty. The high-handed manner of the negotiations left private practice physicians with the empty feeling of being cast aside." Dr. Kelsey expressed his dismay and concern in a letter to Curtis B. Delhomme, chairman of the Methodist board, saying that "private physicians practicing outside of Methodist Hospital will be gradually removed from the staff, and there will be no new staff appointments for doctors who practice outside of Methodist Hospital."[9]

Seventy-five physicians attended a meeting on February 9, 1970, and appointed Dr. Kelsey to a five-physician task force to represent them. In turn, the Methodist Hospital board appointed an Ad Hoc Committee on Implementation of Principles Approved by the Boards of Methodist and Baylor to resolve the dispute. Noted Dr. Kelsey, "Issues were resolved in June by recommending that the financial contributions become *voluntary* and that additional clinical staff members [private practice physicians] be appointed to the executive committee, which would establish a balance of power between hospital and school. However, the entire episode caused most of the Kelsey-Seybold doctors to begin referring most of their patients to St. Luke's Hospital."[10]

. . .

With these events behind the two affiliated partners, the hospital moved into a significant building phase that would define the 1970s. Whereas once the measure of a hospital was in the number of beds, the hospital and its board had their eyes on the future. And that future was about prevention, wellness programs, strengthening facilities to support medical education, increasing outpatient care, and supporting the ever-growing research enterprise that the hospital and medical school shared.

These were forward-thinking times as Americans walked on the moon and the United States celebrated its bicentennial. The hospital and affiliated medical school continued to command the national and international spotlight as an epicenter for heart care and research while adding resources to support the medical staff's talent across the spectrum of disciplines. Research linking Methodist, Baylor, and NASA ensured that Methodist-based care and research were now both firmly planted on the ground in Houston as well as international and out-of-this-world in reach.

Patient care and research aside, the need for additional training facilities in the hospital is best illustrated by the success of Dr. McIntosh, chief of medicine, and his medical staff, who rigorously expanded training opportunities throughout the hospital. The numbers are telling. In 1971 he had eighty-six trainees in his department. Six years later, when he departed Houston to return to private practice in Florida, the program had grown to more than 185 trainees and was nationally recognized.[11] The rapidly expanding training programs throughout the hospital (his department is but one example), along with the ever-growing need for new facilities to support research grants and federally funded centers of excellence, meant that hospital leadership had to plan big and keep a constant eye not on what was needed at the moment but what would be needed in the future.

To accomplish this took bold ideas and generous pocketbooks, and Methodist Hospital had both. Four major construction projects in the 1970s with a total $100 million budget constituted the game plan. During the 1970s the hospital would develop with Baylor College of Medicine a Neurosensory Center to house three institutes—ophthalmology, neurology, and otolaryngology (ear, nose, and throat, and communicative disorders).

Ophthalmology is a program that should not be overlooked. It was back in 1943 when Baylor arrived in Houston that they established an eye department and appointed Dr. Everett Goar as chairman (1943–1958). While strong women like Josie Roberts and Ella Fondren were essential to the growth of the hospital itself, Dr. Alice R. McPherson would prove essential to the growth of ophthalmology. A native of Saskatchewan, she earned her medical degree at the University of Wisconsin in 1951 and was recruited to Houston in 1960 by Dr. Goar's successor, Dr. Louis Girard. She is considered the world's first female full-time vitreoretinal specialist who pioneered the use of the first ophthalmic lasers and cryopexy. In Houston, Dr. McPherson founded the retina service at Baylor while further refining ophthalmology, a specialty, into subspecialties.

In addition, she pioneered fellowship programs that have trained generations of eye specialists. These McPherson fellows use procedures she introduced that are accepted to this day as basic elements in retinal-detachment surgery. The Retina Research Foundation she founded in 1969 has funded almost $35 million in pilot study grants, chairs, and professorships, major research awards, and more while launching or elevating the careers of many leading vision researchers in the U.S. and abroad. Her more than fifty-year association with Houston Methodist led Dr. William L. Winters, Jr., president of the hospital's medical staff 1981–1982, to refer to her in his book *Reflections* as "the grande dame of the Houston Methodist medical staff."[12]

. . .

Just as the physicians of the day were innovative within their specialties, the hospital itself innovated on a broad scale. Being family-oriented and holistic in approach in a time when preventive medicine was gaining a foothold in American medicine, the hospital planned an innovative Total Health Care Center to support the needs of patients and their families outside the hospital. Additional projects included a four-floor addition to the Brown Building (Alkek Tower) for expanding research facilities and cardiovascular inpatient services. Also on the books was a six-floor expansion of the Fondren Building for additional patient beds, research, and medical service. Each project defines the hospital's future in important ways.

The Neurosensory Center

Since the time the hospital opened in the Texas Medical Center, the Blue Bird Clinic established a strong reputation as an international leader in the diagnosis, treatment, teaching, and research of neurological disorders of children. It was a one-of-a kind program in the Southwest. Dr. James Greenwood, the longtime head of the hospital's neurosurgery department, championed the concept of an institute for years while Alice and David C. Bintliff, dedicated friends of the Blue Bird Circle Children's Clinic, made it happen with a gift of $2 million in the spring of 1969.

Dr. Greenwood was actually thinking about an institute for the neurosciences back in the early 1950s when the hospital arrived in the medical center. The concept made perfect sense for a hospital that believes in a synergistic approach combining all related resources to tackle the most difficult medical problems. He was well aware that an American–Canadian neurosurgeon, Dr. Wilder Penfield, persuaded the Rockefeller Foundation to endow and fund construction of the Montreal Neurological Institute, which opened in 1934.[13] Here, clinicians and scientists from different disciplines worked side by side, focusing their talent and expertise on cutting-edge questions revolving around the complexities of the human brain. Dr. Penfield was a Rhodes Scholar who trained with the legendary Sir William Osler and is considered a giant in his field and a visionary to this day.

Dr. Greenwood recognized that a multidisciplinary focus was not only a good idea but was essential. Dr. Bill Fields, a Harvard-educated neurologist who arrived at Baylor in 1949 and worked with Dr. Greenwood at the hospital on Rosalie and in the medical center, recalled, "Early in 1952, Milton McGinty, architect of Methodist Hospital, had prepared for Jim Greenwood and myself detailed plans for a neurological institute such as the one in Montreal to be built on part of that parking lot behind the hospital (West Wing expansion footprint)."[14]

Dr. Fields in his memoirs added, "Mrs. Roberts, several members of the Methodist Hospital board, the dean of Baylor College of Medicine, Dr. Walter Moursund, and Dr. Brown [Dr. Warren Brown, chairman of neuropsychiatry] felt very keenly that this additional structure should be called 'The Neurological Institute of the Methodist Hospital.'"[15] While a good idea at the time, the building would have to wait until the 1970s to come to fruition.

. . .

With 1.8 acres adjoining the Fondren and Brown buildings provided by the Texas Medical Center, new hospital board member Corby Robertson, Jr. (grandson of Hugh Roy Cullen) accepted the chairmanship of the fundraising committee and worked tirelessly on behalf of the hospital and medical school. The project would be a jointly funded and owned by the hospital and Baylor College of Medicine with costs shared 50–50. The three-tower structure was designed to house institutes for Ophthalmology, Neurology, and Otorhinolaryngology/Communicative Disorders. Once again generous Houstonians rallied. The Cullen Foundation gave $1 million to establish the Cullen Eye Institute. The Stella Wolters Russell and Willard Russell estate contributed to the Otorhinolaryngology/ Communicative Disorders Institute. Houston Endowment contributed to the Jones Patient Tower in honor of former hospital board member Jesse H. Jones and his wife, Mary Gibbs Jones. What began as an estimated $24 million project ended up costing $35 million.[16] With groundbreaking on January 30, 1975, the Bintliff Blue Bird Building opened to patients on June 1, 1977.

Ron Girotto, who in the years ahead would work closely with Larry Mathis, Houston Methodist's president and CEO (1983-1997), and who served as president of the hospital himself from 2001–2011, recalls that he arrived in Houston in 1977 to serve as administrator for the new Otorhinolaryngology Institute (Oto for short) under the direction of Dr. Bobby R. Alford: "I was one of the first joint employees of Baylor College of Medicine and the Methodist Hospital [paid fifty percent by each] . ... Oto had a need for someone with a financial background. Dr. Alford had research, education, operating rooms, and a lot of debt to repay given there was a significant expansion of the clinical, research, and educational facilities with initial funds loaned by Baylor. While the plan had been to pay back the school's investment in the program in five years, it was actually accomplished in 18 months. After about 19 months or so, Ted Bowen asked me to become a full-time employee of the hospital and work for him on special projects including Scurlock Tower."[17]

Total Health Care Center (Scurlock Tower)

The special project Ron Girotto was asked to assist with in 1979 was the planned Total Health Care Center, a twenty-one-story office tower across the street on Fannin and later renamed Scurlock Tower. The story behind the property is vintage Houston Methodist.

Bill Williams arrived in Houston in 1929—not as a physician but as a cook. He was nineteen and had less than two dollars in his pocket. His original plan to join a cousin in

Hollywood never came to be as he went to work at a popular restaurant downtown known as One's-A-Meal and decided to stay. After five years he was ready to leave Houston after being turned down for a promotion. He found a job in Chicago and prepared to move but not before mentioning his situation to one of his loyal patrons, L. B. Hamilton. Hamilton, a local oilman, had other ideas and talked him out of leaving while reaching into his billfold. Williams could not believe his eyes as Hamilton peeled off five $100 bills and suggested Williams open his own restaurant a few blocks over on Clay Street.[18] Williams did just that. In time he would own several restaurants but none more popular than his Bill Williams Chicken House, opened in 1936 at the very address where Houston Methodist's Scurlock Tower stands today.

For years Rice University students considered the restaurant their cafeteria since the Rice campus had no dining halls in those days. Williams's chicken restaurant, including the two hundred-seat upstairs banquet room, was a place Houstonians visited in droves until fast food chicken franchises arrived in the late 1950s and cooled Williams's receipts. He added an oyster bar and kept the business going, recognizing that the new medical center across the street was making his property very valuable.

Josie Roberts's proclamation that seven acres was not enough for a hospital like Methodist in the late 1940s proved true again. In the months before O'Banion Williams retired as chairman of the hospital board in 1963, he looked into buying Bill Williams's property for the hospital but considered the asking price inflated and unreasonable. By 1971 Curtis B. Delhomme, chairman of the board (1963–1977), decided to take another look at purchasing the property. Born in Scott, Louisiana, Delhomme was one of the founders of the Houston Boat Show and the South's largest boat distributor.

The Delhomme hunting lodge on Trinity Bay near Galveston was a favorite gathering place for hospital board members, administrators, and medical staff to bond and compare notes far from the formalities of the boardroom and big city. At one such gathering Delhomme turned his attention from hunting ducks to hunting chickens. He asked board member Eddy Scurlock to lead a committee to test the waters and see if the chicken king would sell. Of course, as Scurlock and his committee soon learned, the price was now higher as Williams demanded $3.3 million in cash with no further discussion (chicken fryers included).[19]

Again, the prospect went on hold but only briefly as Scurlock was not easily discouraged. Raised in the small East Texas town of Tenaha, he borrowed money to get into the oil business and by the 1980s had built one of the largest crude oil gathering and transportation businesses in the country. Getting Bill Williams to sell seemed an easy challenge, but Williams was a bulldog when it came to parting with his chicken palace. When Scurlock learned of other offers on the table, he quickly picked up the phone. Surprisingly, Williams was now willing to negotiate and lowered the price to $3 million with terms for cash up front, twenty-nine percent of the total by year's end, and the full balance paid in three years.[20]

To speed the process, Scurlock simply purchased the property himself and offered it to the hospital at his cost. In this way Houston Methodist could expand across Fannin

Street—or not. Losing land directly across the street was not something Scurlock wanted to gamble on. While the board agreed to the deal, not all approved of Scurlock's free-handed protocol that left them in the dark until after the purchase. The story harkens back to Will Hogg, who had purchased the very land the Texas Medical Center occupies and sold it to the city at his cost to ensure it would not be lost. It is a story repeated time after time in which generous Houstonians with means do whatever necessary to selflessly benefit their community. It defines the city and Houston Methodist to this day.

To honor the many contributions of Eddy Scurlock and his wife, Elizabeth, the hospital's board unanimously voted to name the building Scurlock Tower. Their only daughter, Laura Lee, married Jack Blanton, who became a Scurlock Oil and Eddy Refinery executive and served the community for years as a highly respected business leader and member of the hospital's board (1967–1988; 1991–2008).

The twenty-one-story Scurlock Tower was designed to accommodate outpatient operating rooms and services (floors three through six), physician offices, and expanded radiology and laboratory services. The fourth floor housed the Sid W. Richardson Institute for Preventive Medicine, made possible by the Sid W. Richardson Foundation of Fort Worth, which provided a $1.46 million grant to build and furnish an innovative facility dedicated to the prevention of disease, including cardiac rehabilitation, weight control, and a nutrition clinic. The Chapman Group (those cardiologists once known as the Dawn Patrol) became the building's first occupant by relocating on December 30, 1979, even before toilet seats were fully installed.[21]

In the late 1970s a fifth building was on the drawing board for the 1980s. Next to Scurlock Tower the board leased property to the Marriott Corporation to build a twenty-four-story hotel with four hundred rooms, giving patients and family members convenient accommodations and access to the growing Methodist Hospital complex, including the new outpatient facilities of Scurlock Tower. The hotel and conference center were dedicated on September 13, 1984.

In a great twist of irony, what had been ground zero for fried chicken and high cholesterol was now a mecca for preventive medicine and wellness programs supported by new research to discover, prevent, and even reverse the impact of harmful lifestyle choices on health. In fact, for many years, until 1993, a gourmet restaurant championed by Dr. Antonio Gotto, Jr. and appropriately named Chez Eddy was on the fourth floor to serve wholesome food and model healthy diets—even inspiring a *Chez Eddy Living Heart Cookbook* as well as *The Living Heart* book series, which both Drs. Gotto and DeBakey had an important hand in. Both restaurant and cookbook alike featured foods low in salt, cholesterol, and calories. Fried chicken, not so much.

From an administrative standpoint, Scurlock Tower also provided an important training ground for hospital leadership, including future hospital president Ron Girotto. Ted Bowen assigned him there to negotiate leases for office space with individual physicians and large practice groups alike. Years later, in retirement, Girotto recalled that the experience he gained built a deep trust and understanding as he worked closely with both academic and private practice physicians, benefiting both the hospital and his future tenure as president.

Alkek Tower and Fondren Additions

In the early 1970s Albert A. and Margaret Alkek provided a $3 million gift for a four-floor addition to the Brown Building. It was back in the 1930s that Albert Alkek dropped out of college to get into the oil business. Working with his mentor Harry Sinclair, he started his own oil company and the state's first petroleum products pipeline, making a fortune that he redistributed as a patron of health care, education, and the arts. Starting on April 1, 1976, the $7.3 million tower was a joint project of the hospital and Baylor. The tower's seventy thousand square feet would provide space for the expansion and consolidation of the cardiovascular patient care and research program, including sixty-eight additional beds. Dedication took place on May 12, 1978, with Princess Lilian of Belgium returning to Houston to dedicate the bust of Dr. DeBakey that she and her husband commissioned. Accompanying her were friends Ann Landers, the syndicated advice columnist, and Mary Lasker.[22]

The following year a six-story addition to the Fondren Building was completed, expanding patient care facilities, research, and laboratories. The top floor featured twenty-six luxury patient suites. A $7.4 million grant from the Fondren Foundation made the addition possible. David M. Underwood, grandson of Walter and Ella Fondren, and a dedicated member of the hospital's board (1963–2015) and chairman of the Texas Medical Center board for twenty-three years, requested the Fondren Building be rededicated to honor both his grandparents. Other major gifts for the new expansion included gifts from the Catherine Fondren Underwood Trust and the Houston Endowment. Another major gift from the Fondren trusts furnished the twelfth floor in memory of Sue Fondren Trammell.[23]

The Flood of 1976

Throughout the 1970s construction cranes crowded the Texas Medical Center's emerging skyline. It was evident to all who flew into one of Houston's two airports that Houston now had two skylines—downtown and the Texas Medical Center. If you were in Houston on June 15, 1976, looking to the sky you would see something else—dark skies, rain, and lots of it. The flood of 1976 was the first major flood to devastate the Texas Medical Center, the precursor of disasters to come, including Tropical Storm Allison (June 9, 2001) and Hurricane Harvey (August 25–27, 2017).

Even the Allen brothers realized that their new city was not immune to flooding. A deluge in April 1837 was followed by another six months later when a hurricane hit and Buffalo Bayou rose four feet on Main Street. A seventeen-inch rainfall on December 6, 1935, flooded two-thirds of the county, and residents at Jesse Jones's Rice Hotel fished from the mezzanine level of the hotel for their meals.[24]

Closer to home, in 1976 it was the Texas Medical Center's turn to take the brunt of the 10.47 inches of rain that fell that day, most of it recorded in just six hours directly over the Rice University and the Texas Medical Center area.

. . .

Houston is the Bayou City. On average the city is fifty feet above sea level with only about a four-foot variation defining the topography of the nation's fourth-largest city. There are exceptions, and Daniel Denton Cooley (Dr. Denton Cooley's grandfather) found one when he came to Houston from Nebraska in 1891 to purchase and develop 1,765 acres for the Omaha and South Texas Land Company. Today we know his purchase as the Houston Heights at seventy-five feet above sea level and situated just a few miles to the northwest of downtown.

What Abbe Emmanuel Domenech in 1848 did not know (that Frenchman who traveled up the "Buffalo River" from Galveston to find Methodists and ants) was that it was a *bayou*, not a *river*. Buffalo Bayou is the largest natural drainage Mother Nature provides the city and is intersected by numerous other smaller bayous whose primary job is to move rainwater out of the city and south to the Gulf of Mexico. Domenech also did not know that Spanish explorers beat him to the city by three hundred years and carefully marked this family of bayous on their maps.

Of primary interest to the Texas Medical Center is Brays Bayou, which snakes right through the medical center, providing critical drainage. At its end, the Brays meets the Buffalo at a junction that once was the site of a small town named Harrisburg. In 1836 Santa Anna and his army burned Harrisburg to the ground but did not erase the name. From Harrisburg and its founder, John R. Harris, we get our county name—Harris.

Heavy rain in an urban environment tests even the best of bayous, and rain that falls to the west of the Texas Medical Center, say over the Rice University area, drains down the Harris Gully (now large boxed culverts buried from sight) through the Texas Medical Center in search of Brays Bayou. When the bayou fills, the Harris Gully has nowhere to go but up and into the streets and structures above. And that, on June 15, 1976, is exactly what happened faster than anyone could have anticipated.

Dr. Phil Migliore, a pathologist, was in the hospital that day and remembers it well. In 2001 he recorded his memories:

> It was like a battle zone. … The disaster really became apparent to everyone at about 5 in the afternoon. It had been raining all day, very hard. And of course, the water began to rise. At Methodist Hospital, the emergency generators are in the sub-basement. The tunnel system that existed at that time was open—so there were no barriers and the waters began to come into the basement.
>
> The first thing that was lost was the city power, so the hospital switched to emergency power, but the generators became flooded, so by 5 all the

lights were out [and] we had people on the surgery table. They finished under flashlights. For the next week, there were no lights and no power available. … During the night they had to evacuate the patients, and there were no elevators, so they had to be brought down stairs.

We were living in the laboratories. There were maybe a few fans around but the temperature in the labs was about 90 degrees, close to the limit that these instruments would operate and get accurate results. The basement was where the autopsy room was. … Anyone who had gone into the basement had to get a tetanus shot. We were able to provide for the better part of the week some semblance of medical care for the patients still in the hospital at that time, but it was an experience that I or I don't think anyone else will ever forget.[25]

Future hospital CEO Larry Mathis had to rent a canoe that night when his car could go no farther due to high water. He arrived at the hospital by paddle power, dodging a waterfall of water on Fannin cascading into a large hole in the ground that was the early basement of Scurlock Tower then under construction.

Michael V. Williamson, an administrator who joined the hospital in 1964 as assistant director of personnel and retired in 1997, also recalls the flood of '76. He certainly knew his way around the basement that day given his first office was in the basement of the West Wing directly across from the morgue, which was "not an ideal location for job applicants," he recalls. "[During the flood] I was surveying damage in the sub-basement. Water was still waist deep and I was standing near an electrical bus bar when it exploded and began smoking. I found a fire extinguisher and began spraying [which] probably was not the smartest thing to do. Dozens of electricians worked around the clock to restore permanent power. Within one week we were admitting new patients."[26]

· · ·

Throughout the Texas Medical Center similar stories were told. At the Jesse Jones Library archivists raced to move rare books to higher ground. At the new University of Texas Medical School nearby, their seven-story building that connected on every floor to Hermann Hospital had just been completed and was being readied for fall medical students. New microscopes and textbooks were still in their crates carefully stored in the basement along with cadavers awaiting their teachable moment when the rains came and set them free. Those students who were asked to dive into that basement to retrieve whatever they could find received an early medical education with images few would forget.

The 1976 flood can be considered a disaster but also a rite of passage for those who joined hands and persevered. Such disasters, like a good story, provide the glue that binds institutional character and collective pride. In its purest form such events illuminate those theological virtues that are the very foundation upon which the hospital is built—faith, hope, and charity.

Ask Dr. Marc Boom, president of Houston Methodist during the centennial year, about such moments and you'll hear little about the structural and financial losses compared to the invaluable lessons learned to prevent such events in the future and the renewed appreciation of employees who put patients and institution first. You'll hear about new programs to train, prepare, prevent, mitigate, and care (about patients and the employee family) going forward. Henry Ford put it this way: "Obstacles are those frightful things you see when you take your eyes off your goal." Houston Methodist's goal—leading medicine—proved fixed and firm.

The 1970s included five big buildings and one unforgettable flood. The hospital that attracted so many famous names in the 1960s—dukes, kings, and Hollywood royalty—continued to draw patients from around the world. One celebrity arrived on April 5, 1976, two months before the flood, and not by the front door. Howard Hughes, who was delivered as a newborn back in 1905 by Dr. Oscar Norsworthy, arrived in Houston on a private jet. Destined for Methodist Hospital, the mysterious, eccentric billionaire attracted an army of news reporters.

Larry Mathis and Michael Williamson were there that day as well, both recalling that Dr. Henry McIntosh boarded the plane to find Hughes deceased. The body, by request of the family, was taken to Methodist Hospital rather than the Harris County morgue. Williamson found himself once again in the basement, this time with a Houston police officer and instructions from Ted Bowen to guard the body from unauthorized visitors, especially those with a camera. A chaotic press conference ensued as Mathis announced that Howard Robard Hughes had died at 1:27 p.m. Recalled Williamson, "It was a long night, but without incident." The autopsy the next day was conducted by the county medical examiner and Dr. Jack Titus, chief of pathology, with Williamson attending. "To my knowledge no photographs were taken of the body while at the hospital and I can say I met the famous Howard Hughes even though it was a one-sided meeting."[27] In life and in death, Hughes seemed always to be cloaked in mystery, with Houston Methodist providing the final chapter. Although no clandestine photo was taken, a rogue sketch destined for the shredder is rumored to have drawn Bowen's ire.

• • •

The 1970s offered challenges, opportunities, and a few unexpected guests. The hospital grew and matured in ways Dr. Oscar Norsworthy and the early board could never have imagined. Yet the decade ahead would offer its own challenges and opportunities along with federally mandated changes in health care that demanded the attention of every hospital in the country.

EIGHT

CHANGING OF THE GUARD
1980-1990

During the 1980s:

Ronald Reagan is elected president (1980)

"Raiders of the Lost Ark," starring Harrison Ford, is released (1981)

Kathryn J. Whitmire becomes Houston's first woman mayor (1981)

The nation's first AIDS clinic opens in San Francisco (1983)

Hurricane Alicia strikes the Houston-Galveston area, causing $2 billion in damage (1983)

Apple releases the Macintosh computer (1984)

Average price for a new car is $9,005 (1985)

Mikhail Gorbachev is chosen as new leader of the Soviet Union (1985)

Space shuttle Challenger explodes shortly after liftoff (1986)

Chernobyl nuclear plant disaster occurs (1986)

Houston and the nation experience an economic recession (1987)

George R. Brown Convention Center and the Wortham Theatre open (1987)

Phillips 66 plant in Pasadena, Texas, explodes, killing 23 (1988)

The Berlin Wall comes down (1989)

At 8:32 a.m. on the morning of May 18, 1980, Mount St. Helens erupted in southwestern Washington state with a force that seized the attention of the nation. The event was not entirely unexpected, given the ground had been rumbling for months. Yet the outcome exceeded the worst predictions as the entire north face of the mountain exploded in minutes, devastating lives and pristine forest for miles around. It was a force of nature that literally changed the landscape while depositing ash across eleven states.

In health care, the ground was also rumbling in 1980 with signs of the change to come. Ted Bowen, now in his twenty-fifth year at the helm, suspected dire consequences for large teaching hospitals like Methodist. Noted medical historian Dr. Kenneth Ludmerer explained, "The term 'teaching hospital' was reserved for a select group of institutions—100–150 of the roughly 6,800 hospitals in existence—that served as major clinical facilities for medical schools. Though few in number, teaching hospitals were indispensable to medical education as the most important sites of clinical education and research."[1]

Teaching hospitals like Methodist, capable of treating the sickest of the sick, armed with the latest technology, and supported by a large professional workforce, also shouldered the added responsibility, expense, and privilege of educating at the bedside the next generation of health care professionals. Prestige and privilege aside, large modern teaching hospitals are expensive to run, maintain, and continuously upgrade in support of the patient care, research, and educational mission. Even nonprofit hospitals like Methodist have to make a margin of profit to stay out of debt and reinvest for the future—always prepared for unplanned events such as a 1976 flood, a hurricane named Harvey, or governmental mandates limiting hospital reimbursements for care. In the early 1980s those mandates were at the doorstep.

Three years before the new decade began, on April 25, 1977, a press release crossed Bowen's desk from the White House concerning the proposed Hospital Cost Containment Act of 1977. Bowen immediately requested Jim Henderson on his staff to work with him to develop a position paper for the hospital's board, medical staff, and key hospital constituents to analyze in detail the bill under consideration by Congress that would place new price controls on the hospital industry.

In Bowen's words: "This proposed legislation causes me great concern in both the immediate and long-range time frames. My immediate concern is that the discriminatory price controls proposed will be extremely harmful to the vast majority of high quality hospitals throughout the country. Most importantly, my long-range concern is that the enactment of this legislation would represent a giant stride toward socialized medicine."[2]

Copies of Bowen's 1977 report were sent to the medical staff and members of the board, including A. Frank Smith, Jr., who in August 1977 was named chairman of the board following the death of Curtis B. Delhomme at age seventy-seven. Smith was the son of beloved Bishop A. Frank Smith and managing partner of the law firm Vinson & Elkins. In this way it was A. Frank Smith, Jr., not Delhomme, who found himself on the podium dedicating the twenty-one-story Scurlock Tower on October 5, 1980. Frank Smith's love of his father and the institution could not be denied as he reminded the crowd that fifty-three years earlier, in 1927, his father officiated over the marriage of Eddy and Elizabeth Scurlock at Houston's First Methodist Church.

Also present that day was the chairman's brother William Randolph Smith ("Randy"), who should not be lost in this story given his many contributions to the hospital's board (1970–2001). Fast-forward to Randy Smith's death in 2004. Board members will search for a way to honor this beloved board member whose service to the hospital was as consistent and dedicated as his faith. In 2004 sculptor Willy Wang was commissioned to create a statue of Jesus that can be found prominently placed in the Crain Garden atrium of Dunn Tower.

. . .

In 1977 both Frank and Randy Smith along with the entire Methodist board were busy reading Bowen's report and learning about transformational changes in health care reimbursement that would impact hospitals across the country. Dr. Raymond Pruitt, who left Baylor to become dean of Mayo Clinic's new medical school, also received a copy of the report. "I found this an excellent analysis of this very complex problem. I took the liberty of sharing a copy of it with several members of the administrative staff of the Mayo Clinic." At the bottom of the letter, Pruitt penned a personal note, "I rejoice in the reports of your progress toward recovery."[3] Pruitt was referring to Bowen's recent, not-so-publicized heart attack. Despite that Bowen was being treated in one of the elite heart centers in the world, the very hospital he helped build, his active days as administrator were numbered.

Five years later, on the morning of October 20, 1982, the *Houston Post* announced Bowen's early retirement. "Ted Bowen, long considered the dean of Houston hospital executives, abruptly retired Tuesday as president of the Methodist Hospital. Bowen, 60, cited health reasons for his decision to relinquish the top administrative post he's held for 29 years. More than two dozen of his associates, including several key physicians at Methodist, expressed surprise at the seemingly sudden retirement, although all acknowledged Bowen had been advised to slow down after suffering two serious heart attacks and having coronary bypass surgery."[4] Dr. William Winters, then president of the hospital's medical staff, rushed a message conveying "the enormous admiration this medical staff has for his leadership."[5]

Bowen had seen the hospital grow from a 90-bed facility on Rosalie to the largest health care institution in Houston and the largest Methodist-affiliated medical complex in the world with 1,040 beds. The *Post* added, "Last year [1981] Methodist had an annual operating budget of nearly $180 million ... and lists 600 physicians and scientists on the active staff and in excess of 5,400 employees [who care for] approximately 43,000 patients who were admitted for services and another 144,000 outpatient visits recorded."[6]

For all his accomplishments, during his last five years at the helm Ted Bowen was not without his critics who accused him of spending lavishly, including excessive perks and administrative retreats that bordered on inappropriate. His supporters pointed out that he and his entire administrative team, no matter how it looked, were bonded like family and would literally wade through high water on a moment's notice to save the hospital and patients. Few could argue with their abilities and dedication.

Despite his failing health, during those five years prior to retirement Bowen recognized the very concerns expressed in his 1977 analysis of impending change in hospital reimbursements were coming true. Across the country hospital census figures had been dropping since the mid-1970s. Hospital costs were on the rise and patients were favoring outpatient facilities. Methodist costs for a private room over the years had lagged slightly behind comparable institutions in the area[7] and speak to the point. When the hospital moved to the Texas Medical Center in 1951, a private room cost from $12 to $20 a day; by 1970, the cost rose to $36 and by 1983, to $167.[8]

The year 1982 certainly marked a changing of the guard when Bowen stepped down. Chairman A. Frank Smith, Jr. stepped in and assumed the added responsibilities, serving as acting president while a national search for Bowen's replacement began. Five months following Bowen's retirement, Ella Fondren died on May 3 in the hospital she called home the last five years of her life. Just four months later the city learned of Ben Taub's death. Fondren was only a month short of her 102nd birthday and a hushed silence fell over the hospital with news of her passing. She outlived her husband and children with the exception, some would say, of the hospital that she loved like a child. Buried next to her husband in Houston's Forest Park Lawndale Cemetery, she left behind a generous foundation and an extended family who have contributed in gifts and service to help make the hospital and the city of Houston what it is to this day.

As secretary of the board, Randy Smith drafted a special resolution added to the minutes of the board's May 25, 1982, meeting, honoring Fondren as "a gracious lady with pioneer spirit and courage, [who] endowed the world with all the benefits of her creative vision, best expressed in her personal credo: 'No individual is honored as an individual. His life takes on dignity as the causes to which he attaches himself take on dignity.'"[9] Fellow board member Henry J. N. Taub likewise provided that September a tribute to his uncle, who did not live to see the renewed and modernized Ben Taub General Hospital open in the Texas Medical Center in 1989 that replaced the aging facility first named for Ben Taub in 1963.

1982 was also the year A. Frank Smith, Jr. appointed board member Jack Blanton to lead the search for a new hospital president. Needless to say, Bowen's 1977 concerns about impending health care reform were not lost on the hospital's leadership. This would be only the fifth administrative head of the institution and all were well aware that running one of the largest academic teaching hospitals in the country would take exceptional organizational skills and business sense to address the complex climate of health care reform.

The 1980 Total Health Care initiative, including Scurlock Tower, signaled a new tack for the hospital and demonstrated proactive leadership as the winds of change in health care shifted. Already local media were acknowledging the hospital as "a national leader in striving to offer more ambulatory care programs and focus on preventive medicine."[10] As Bowen prepared to step away, he left the board additional food for thought: "With the cutbacks in government funds and the tax changes relative to philanthropy, individual hospitals will need to mount continuous fund-raising programs. New technological advancements in medical science expected soon will require even more expensive equipment, and so many of the machines we use now become obsolete after only two years."[11]

Already, as of 1983, the concept of diagnosis-related groups (DRGs) had been introduced to place price controls on the cost of hospital care by classifying patients (especially

Medicare patients) for the purpose of reimbursing hospitals with a fixed fee regardless of the actual costs incurred based on specific diagnostic criteria. Across the country, large teaching hospitals like Methodist with the latest technology to care for difficult and complex medical needs would now be reimbursed with the same fee a smaller community hospital with less investment in facilities, technology, and expertise would receive. Yet the hospital board continued to support added facilities, new technology, and a mission to lead medicine through quality of care at all costs. It would prove to be a difficult task but true to the hospital's mission and values.

DRGs would be just the first of a new alphabet soup of managed care, cost-control programs on the horizon that would challenge the best of hospitals in the decades ahead. A new medical language was emerging on the national tongue with now familiar terminology including HMO (health maintenance organization), PPO (preferred provider organization), PCP (primary care physician), point-of-service, fee-for-service, capitation, copayment, and network provider. Clearly, the ground was rumbling. One new term that did not sit well with the Methodist staff and most physicians throughout the nation was use of the word *client* in place of *patient*. More than a few physicians in the hospital were heard to say, "I treat patients, not clients—and always will!"

The line was reminiscent of the great humanistic physician Sir William Osler (1849–1919), who reminded his students they were treating patients, not a disease. He also preached that "medicine is a calling, not a business." Dr. Oscar Norsworthy sold his small hospital to the Methodists with an intuition that times change and medicine in the years ahead would be *both* a calling and a business. Dr. Norsworthy wanted both ingrained in his hospital going forward, and the board, comprising church leaders complemented by experienced business leaders, gave the hospital exactly what the 1980s and thereafter required. The question at the moment was, whom would the board choose to replace Ted Bowen as the winds of change stiffened?

. . .

At the young age of twenty-eight, Larry Mathis was recruited by Bowen as an administrative resident reporting directly to Bowen. "During my first week [1971] I was assigned to Mr. Bowen as a prelude to rotating through the departments. He invited me to join him at a breakfast meeting. There were four people at the meeting: Mr. Bowen, Dr. DeBakey, former Texas Governor [and hospital board member] John Connally—and me! I do not remember the subject of the meeting; I do remember the heady sensation of being included in such an intimate and august group. I knew what was to come in the weeks, months, and years ahead would be incredible."[12]

By age thirty-four Mathis was senior vice president. How that was accomplished is an interesting story within the story best told by the future president himself:

> Ted Bowen's heart attack brought significant changes in the
> organization. … He divided the organization into three functional
> areas: Financial Services, Nursing Services, and Ancillary Services. …

I was named senior VP and assigned to lead Ancillary Services, which I quickly nicknamed the Third Division. The division was a significant operating responsibility. It contained the big revenue generating services of radiology, pathology, and pharmacy; with the exception of surgery, all of Methodist's clinical services and related entities; and the main staff departments including human resources and public affairs. My executive team included, among others, vice presidents Ronald G. Girotto, M. James Henderson, and Michael V. Williamson. As a team, our challenge was difficult. First, we had to learn to work together rather than for Mr. Bowen. Because departmental budgets had always been handed down from finance … we had to create our own bottom-up expense and capital budgeting process. The team developed real *esprit de corps*, a visible pride in working in the Third Division, and significantly improved the operations and financial performance of its units.[13]

As an Army infantry captain assigned as an adviser to a Vietnamese battalion, Mathis spent seven months in the late 1960s in combat operations in the Iron Triangle, an enemy stronghold northwest of Saigon. On one unforgettable night he showered and climbed up on the roof of his bunker to relax from a stressful day on patrol. "Without warning, four 155-millimeter artillery shells burst in the air over my head. Shrapnel was everywhere. The smell of cordite and the cries of the wounded assaulted the senses."[14] It was a near-miss by friendly fire. Mathis learned an invaluable lesson that night: there is no substitute for good communications and well-planned, strategic teamwork. Both would define his leadership style as a future hospital chief executive officer.

The flood of 1976 was followed by a financial storm in the early 1980s largely attributed to the costs of equipping, furnishing, and staffing the new $34 million Neurosensory Center. It was also a time, as mentioned, when the patient census was dropping in hospitals across the country. Mathis relates: "And Mr. Bowen had a 'no debt' policy. The cash demands for capital equipment, furnishings, and startup costs inundated the senior vice present for finance. He did the best he could: he delayed payments to vendors by as much as nine months; he borrowed all existing restricted funds; and unfortunately, he also stopped funding the malpractice trust fund for two years. It wasn't enough. The board had to authorize borrowing $3 million to meet the hospital's payroll."[15]

These events embarrassed Bowen, recalls Mathis, and he reorganized again, turning to Mathis to become his chief operating officer. "I first assembled my team [with] Ron Girotto as my senior vice president and chief financial officer, and Mike Williamson and Jim Henderson as senior vice presidents and division heads."[16] With that done Mathis and Girotto boarded a plane to look at the organizational plans of other leading teaching hospitals to see how Methodist Hospital "stacked up" against two of the best: Massachusetts General in Boston and Johns Hopkins in Baltimore. "After the visits, we knew we could be better. … The plan was very simple. Reorganize operations. Create a stronger finance division. Enhance revenue. Rein in operating expenses. Control capital expenses. Manage cash."[17]

Girotto remembers those days. "They had just built the Neurosensory Center and had to borrow $3 million to make payroll. Internal borrowing of restricted funds is not something a hospital wants to do. That has to be repaid. And we were six to eight months in arrears to all vendors and suppliers for medical equipment, medication/pharmaceuticals, and medical supplies. When you add all that up its $25 million to $30 million. [So] I called all the suppliers and vendors into the auditorium of the Neurosensory Center. It was me and them in the room. And the communication was, 'I can't pay you. I can't pay you today. But if you give me six months to a year, you will be paid in full. If you decide to quit supplying me, I've got a major problem and you'll have a bad day.' It was kind of that way. It was really interesting after that a number of them came up and shook my hand. And we paid them inside of six months."[18]

Adds Mathis, "Within twelve months we had retired the $3 million bank loan. ... In eighteen months, we had fully refunded the malpractice trust fund and, at the two-year mark, we completed the recovery by fully repaying the ransacked restricted funds. Then, suddenly, our ailing leader retired [and] the Bowen era was stunningly over."[19]

A lengthy search for Bowen's successor commenced in 1983. Mathis recalls being last to interview with the search committee. When asked what he would do if named president, Mathis responded by outlining his goals: "a strong strategic planning process, financial strength, a better relationship with Baylor College of Medicine, a motivated and informed workforce, patient service excellence, and top-quality programs for patient care, teaching, and research."[20]

At the hospital's board meeting in July 1983 Larry Mathis was named president and chief executive officer. He promoted members of his Third Division team (Girotto, Henderson, and Williamson) to executive vice presidents. With an average age of forty-four, they were well experienced, each having on average thirteen years with the hospital. Bonded like brothers, each also received advanced training at Harvard and possessed an entrepreneurial mentality guided by Mathis's favorite mantra, "The best way to predict the future is to create it."

Additionally, they had a strong and supportive board and talented medical staff—that winning combination Josie Roberts proclaimed decades earlier was the very reason the hospital prospered when it could easily have failed. For example, the corporate business plan that Mathis built his fourteen-year tenure as president around was modeled after a plan initiated by board member John Bookout, president and chief executive officer of Shell Oil Company and future chairman of the hospital's board (1991–2007). As future decades will tell, Bookout's leadership literally shaped Houston Methodist's destiny into and beyond the centennial year.

Recalls Mathis, "We set an incredibly brisk management pace. ... We structured the strategic planning process; we addressed service problems, and we created a new relationship with our employees. ... Along the way, we reorganized our corporate structure.

We created The Methodist Hospital System. We built a large and successful network of owned, managed, and affiliated hospitals in Texas and Louisiana. We used the network to pursue growth in admissions among our foreign patients. We signed affiliation agreements with private hospitals in Mexico, Turkey, Greece, Guatemala, Italy, and Peru, as well as other countries. … At one point, four percent of Methodist's patients were foreign, but they accounted for twenty percent of its net income."[21]

The advantages of creating a multihospital system, as explained by Marilyn Sibley writing about the hospital in the 1980s, were many. "In order to cope with the changes [competition, government regulations, rising costs], many hospitals found it advantageous to band together around a major teaching institution such as The Methodist Hospital. The central institution shares management techniques, clinical facilities, medical expertise, and otherwise complemented the services offered by community hospitals. In return, it promoted a network for greater use of clinical resources. … The community also benefited from more efficient delivery of health care, a wider range of services, and improved accessibility to medical services and talents."[22]

The new regional hospital system, organized in 1980, was initially led by administrator Tom Fourqurean. By early 1982 nine hospitals representing about 1,600 beds had joined the system, including San Jacinto Methodist Hospital in Baytown (the first consolidated member of the system) along with management contracts with hospitals in Conroe, Jacksonville, The Woodlands, Victoria, Jasper, Orange, and Austin as well as the Hospital San Jose/Instituto Tecnologico in Monterrey, Mexico.[23]

Ron Girotto, who would be named president and CEO in 2001, recalls it was an impressive turnaround to go from the debt of 1980 to become "one of the most financially viable institutions in the United States."[24] Recalls Girotto, "In 1984, we sought board approval to borrow $200 million to build the Smith and Dunn Towers. With this request I acknowledged to the board that while we had significant financial issues a few years earlier and this was the largest such request in the history of the hospital, I was making a commitment to the board that upon completion of the two projects we would be able to write a check to pay all funds borrowed, including interest and principal. We had at the time $250 million in the bank already and we borrowed $200 million of it. The rest of it is kind of history."[25]

This was a pivotal period in the hospital's story. Josie Roberts defined the hospital's position in the 1930s and '40s that to retain the best medical staff required a commitment from the administration and board to provide the very best facilities and the technology necessary to be leaders in their specialties, leaders in medicine. Despite a new groundswell that would change hospital reimbursement for services, this was a hospital with no intention of retreating or reverting back to the small community-based hospital it once had been. The business at hand was to support the calling of medicine and continue the academic course that had been first formally defined through the hospital's 1950 affiliation with one of the great medical schools in the country. Quality of care mattered and would center the business approach as it had throughout the life of the institution.

Summarizing the board's approach, Mathis notes, "We recognized as an institution that the best way to build security for the institution looking ahead was to build our reserves, invest in outstanding facilities, and communicate with our growing employee base."[26]

. . .

With the new outpatient and preventive medicine dimension, the hospital was riding the wave of the future, combining the academic research dimension with the latest in technology and a strong business sense informed by the past that would help overcome future storms and challenges that every business must anticipate.

The aggressive building programs were made possible by approval to use $196.9 million in tax-exempt bonds. The nine-story Dunn Tower would be constructed on a footprint between the Fondren-Brown Building and original hospital and West Wing, adding 300 more beds and bringing the total of operating rooms managed by the hospital to seventy-six.[27] When completed in 1989, Dunn Tower would increase the hospital's total bed capacity to 1,527, making Methodist the largest private teaching hospital in the country.

Of note, the tower honors John S. Dunn, a successful and respected Houston businessman whose community service knew no institutional boundaries. In 1963 his son, Steve, was severely burned in a West Houston plane crash that nearly took his life. A trustee of the Hermann Hospital Estate, Dunn had Steve transferred to Methodist for the successful lifesaving burn care needed. Given the excruciating pain the father witnessed as his son was transferred across town from Spring Branch in an old ambulance whose every bump elicited cries of pain, the father vowed that there had to be a better way.

In 1973 Dunn had the foresight to fund a heliport above the emergency room of Hermann Hospital, where in 1976 trauma surgeon Dr. Red Duke was tasked with building Hermann's trauma care services and launched Life Flight, the second hospital-based air ambulance service in the nation.[28] Both father and son never forgot that lifesaving care received at Methodist, giving special meaning to Dunn Tower and the Dunn Foundation's generosity. Steve Dunn serves on the Methodist Foundation board to this day, carrying forward the Dunn family's service and support spanning three decades and including milestone investments in brain cancer research and innovative advancements in reconstructive and plastic surgery. The John S. Dunn Foundation's support over the years to fund eight endowed chairs (at the time the most funded by a single philanthropic organization) proved transformational and trendsetting.

Dunn Tower's ground floor atrium, made possible by the late Dr. E. Lillo Crain[29] in honor of his mother and first wife, Betty, provides a large, airy, and elegant setting for staff, visitors, and patients alike. In the hospital's Crain Garden guest musicians frequently perform as part of the hospital's Center for Performing Arts Medicine program that integrates arts into the institution's holistic patient care approach. In 2017 the Margaret Alkek Williams Crain Garden Performance Series presented 125 performances for patients, families, and employees.[30] The immense Crain Garden atrium also provides soaring wall space to acknowledge the many generous foundations and individuals who have supported the hospital and its growth over the years. The scale is large to match the generosity of the community throughout the hospital's first century.

It should not be overlooked that the building, especially the soaring atrium lobby, received its share of criticism. Critics said The Methodist Hospital and its décor looked like an expensive hotel and was inappropriate for a hospital setting. Over time, however, hospitals across the country have come to recognize The Methodist Hospital's soaring atriums and welcoming ambience (now integrated into all new designs for Houston Methodist hospitals) have a holistic, healing value that is part of a bigger picture of patient care. What was once considered inappropriate is today a recognized and valued trend in hospital design emulated by hospitals across the country to enhance both patient and family care.

Phase two of the mid-1980s building initiative included Smith Tower connected to both Scurlock Tower and the new Marriott Hotel complex via skybridge walkways for direct access to the original hospital across the street. The hotel opened on October 4, 1984, with four hundred rooms made possible through an innovative lease agreement between the hospital and Marriott International. The twenty-five-story Smith Tower welcomed its first tenant on July 4, 1989, while adding more outpatient services and a new home for the hospital's internal medicine and cardiology departments as well as a 1,400-car parking garage.[31]

In June 2005, following the death of his brother A. Frank Smith, Jr., Randy Smith gazed proudly at the tower honoring his family name and reflected, "Whenever I see Smith Tower, I don't just think of my mom and dad. I also think of my brother Frank. He gave so many years to the hospital and loved his involvement with Methodist. Pausing for a moment he added a sentiment that links all board members, employees, and donors—past and present. "Methodist has a mission you just can't walk away from."[32]

Some would say it was an aggressive move to launch such a large building program in the mid-1980s close on the heels of the financial hurdles just a few years earlier. Others recognized that the added buildings and the centers of excellence they housed were essential to meet the needs of a growing international community that Houston had become. While the hospital witnessed a major changing of the guard on the administrative side, one key aspect of the overall enterprise had not changed. The medical staff based at Methodist and throughout the affiliated system had never been better.

. . .

Step back in time to 1957. Hugh Roy Cullen was laid to rest in Houston's Forest Park Cemetery, and Russia launched a satellite called Sputnik I. Who could have imagined the impact that small, beach ball-sized space-age innovation would have on the future? In hindsight it served as the catalyst for an international space race and technological revolution that forever changed the planet we inhabit right down to the smartphone in your pocket.

This was also the year that a then-small pharmaceutical company in Switzerland known as Sandoz handed out plastic bags to their employees and asked them to bring back soil samples from family vacations.[33] The company was looking for fungi that might hold medicinal properties. Searching in the dark they tested all the samples, and one bag of soil from Norway held the golden ticket—*Tolypocladium inflatum*. This fungus proved unique, yielding a drug that could suppress the immune system without the typical toxic side effects.

In 1983 that new immunosuppression drug known as cyclosporine was approved for clinical use to prevent rejection following organ transplantation. Seemingly overnight heart transplant programs that had screeched to a halt in the late 1960s were resumed with renewed confidence thanks to the new drug. Fourteen years after Dr. Michael DeBakey turned his attention away from heart transplants, he and teams of Methodist surgeons were back in business generating a new round of transplant firsts at the hospital. Advancements in transplanting multiple organs, including heart, kidney, cornea, pancreas, liver, combined heart and lungs, and single lungs, made great strides in the 1980s thanks to cyclosporine and the modern facilities the hospital provided its talented medical staff.

The hospital's new Multi-Organ Transplant Center that opened in 1984 supported some thirty-five physicians and support staff. By 1985 Methodist was the first hospital in Texas to perform a heart-lung transplant, followed in 1987 with the nation's first successful single lung transplant.[34] A Methodist-based hospital helicopter service was introduced in 1984 to support Methodist physicians who were among the first to administer clot-dissolving drugs directly to the coronary artery to treat heart attack patients. By 1987 the Methodist-based air ambulance program was transporting cardiac patients and providing support for organ procurement as the number of transplant procedures increased. By 2018, as mentioned, Houston Methodist's J.C. Walter Jr. Transplant Center reached an impressive milestone— its one thousandth heart transplant.

· · ·

Perhaps no one medical procedure captured the attention of the media in the mid-1980s more than the story of Tracy Baird, a seventeen-year-old high school student from Mansfield, Texas, just outside Fort Worth. An extremely rare disease, bronchiolitis obliterans, was literally destroying her lungs. By the time she was referred to Methodist in early October 1985 she required a respirator to breathe and was in desperate need of a new heart and lungs—the sooner the better. On October 27 she received a new heart and lungs from a deceased donor in Tennessee.

When she walked out of Methodist on a bright sunny day in April 1986 the media attention and celebration were reminiscent of the Duke of Windsor smiling before a sea of cameras two decades earlier. Only Tracy's procedure was far from routine. It was the first successful heart-lung transplant in Texas—something few individuals in the history of mankind could claim. "I'm nervous, but I'm ready to get out," she said as she got in a car with her mother and headed for a nearby hotel where she would spend the next few months. She walked out of the hospital with a working heart and lungs despite the serious complications she had survived in recovery, including kidney failure, infections, and an often-fatal form of pneumonia. Her smile that day was a testament to the entire team of researchers, surgeons, and support staff (more than a hundred strong) who lined the sidewalk outside the hospital with more than a few tears of joy.

It was a moment not to be lost in the hospital's centennial history as it speaks directly to leading medicine and the research and clinical expertise the hospital and its medical school affiliate honed to excellence over the years, along with a powerful dose of compassion that could not be missed as hundreds gathered and cheered for the young patient. At the time, only a handful of such transplant procedures had been attempted worldwide, and even fewer patients survived. Tracy would attend her high school graduation the following year. By the end of the decade more than four hundred lung transplant procedures were performed worldwide, building upon the knowledge Methodist and other leading transplant programs in the country were developing. In recent years as the hospital's centennial approached, more than two thousand patients a year are estimated to receive lung transplants.[35]

While such surgical innovations commanded the spotlight at the time, other work within the hospital was gaining far less attention yet had the long-range potential to improve the health of millions—even prevent or perhaps reverse disease processes before surgery or other medical interventions would be needed.

. . .

Few can argue with what Benjamin Franklin said: "An ounce of prevention is worth a pound of cure." Medical statisticians are very good at quantifying outcomes. They can analyze exactly how many procedures are performed and the patient outcomes. What is much harder to calculate is how many procedures were prevented and never needed in the first place. The benefits of prevention are not to be overlooked by institutions intent on leading medicine. Prevention was very much on the mind of the hospital and its academic partner in the 1980s going forward.

For example, if you're interested in the difference between good cholesterol and bad, Dr. Antonio Gotto, Jr. is someone you would want to talk to. Prevention of disease has commanded his attention since he was a 1957 Rhodes Scholar at Oxford studying with Dr. Hans Kornberg and Nobel Laureate Sir Hans Krebs. A graduate of Vanderbilt University School of Medicine, Dr. Gotto was recruited by Baylor College of Medicine in 1971 and immediately initiated a section of atherosclerosis and lipoprotein research. He also served as chairman of medicine 1977–1997, replacing Dr. Henry McIntosh.

During the mid-1970s, Dr. Gotto notes, "we put together this specialized center of research in arteriosclerosis in Dr. DeBakey's Cardiovascular Research and Training Center and called that the Super Center." In 1982, the National Heart, Lung, and Blood Institute awarded $14 million to revive the Super Center's funding and expand the mission to form the National Research and Demonstration Center at Baylor and Methodist. "We were awarded the only one [in the nation] in heart and blood vessel disease," he recalls with more than a hint of pride.

In 1985 Methodist established the Michael E. DeBakey Heart Center with support from the newly established Michael E. DeBakey Heart Center Foundation, and Dr. Gotto was named scientific director. In other words, The Methodist Hospital and Baylor College of Medicine became the epicenter for leading research designed to understand cardiovascular disease at the molecular level with a strong focus on prevention. Here, on the site that once sold fried chicken, the first clinical trial to show that reducing cholesterol would lower the risk of coronary events was performed and published by Dr. Gotto and his team.[36]

In 1983 he was elected president of the American Heart Association, only intensifying the national and international spotlight on the good work of the hospital and its academic partner. Emphasizing the importance of prevention, including good nutrition, exercise, and other lifestyle choices such as smoking cessation, the Sid Richardson Institute of Preventive Medicine in Scurlock Tower opened in the early 1980s along with a heart-healthy restaurant named Chez Eddy.

Step forward to 1996. After twenty-six years serving Baylor College of Medicine and The Methodist Hospital, Dr. Gotto was recruited as dean and provost of Cornell University's medical school, Weill Cornell Medical College, in New York City. The significance of that move should not be overlooked given that on June 24, 2004, Houston Methodist would change its primary academic affiliation from Baylor College of Medicine to Weill Cornell Medical College and New York-Presbyterian Hospital as future stories will tell.

. . .

The 1980s saw a changing of the guard as Ted Bowen retired and Larry Mathis assumed leadership. The death of Eddy Scurlock in 1988 darkened these times of change that also saw the loss of Ella Fondren, whose role in the hospital's history is legendary. In contrast to the losses were the gains in new facilities, new technologies, and medical advances made throughout the hospital across all specialties of medicine during the decade.

For example, Dr. Peter Scardino pioneered the use of ultrasonography for the imaging of prostate tumors; Dr. Stanley Appel, an internationally recognized authority on ALS (amyotrophic lateral sclerosis), added research addressing the chemical treatment of Alzheimer's to his clinical interests; Dr. Robin Roberts experimented with tissue plasminogen activator (tPA); Dr. William Winters introduced a new technique known as angioplasty as cardiologists expanded their role from diagnosticians to interventionalists, using catheters to repair cardiovascular problems once only accessible by surgeons opening the chest. With that in mind, Dr. Nadim Zacca performed the first atherectomy (an alternative procedure to angioplasty for opening up blocked blood vessels). During this period surgeons at Methodist also performed the first successful piggyback heart surgery, sewing a second heart with a Dacron graft alongside a patient's native heart.

Marilyn Sibley summarized the momentum of the decade, writing: "The same physician who remembered the primitive oxygen tent [at the original hospital on Rosalie] lived to see the hospital offer such marvels as nuclear magnetic resonance imaging, CT scans, laser microsurgery, computerized anesthesia monitoring, a lithotripter for nonsurgical treatment of kidney stones [one of six devices in the nation at the time], and the array of technology that made possible Tracy Baird's heart-lung transplant."[37] The hospital's growing reputation as one of the best in the country was further sealed by decade's end with receipt of the 1989 Commitment to Quality Award, then the nation's only quality award for health care delivery.[38]

Throughout the 1980s the reputations of the hospital's medical staff, executive team, and resulting patient care innovations drew increased national attention. Likewise, the hospital was gaining a reputation for developing administrative leaders who would advance in the years ahead within the Methodist system or find themselves highly sought after by leading hospitals throughout the country. In this way, senior vice president Mark Wallace, only thirty-six, was recruited in 1989 as president and chief executive officer of Texas Children's Hospital—a position he capably holds during Methodist's centennial year.

The 1980s also brought important changes in hospital administration and how costs for care would be addressed as new governmental relations collectively referred to as "managed care" approached. These new guidelines and regulations affecting reimbursement for medical services would bring challenges as well as opportunities. No hospital in the country could ignore the impact of these changes on the horizon and all would discover that no one magic formula exists for how hospitals and hospital systems should best respond.

Neither could the hospital ignore Texas Attorney General Jim Mattox, who in the mid-1980s alleged the hospital did not provide enough charity care. Specifically, he questioned whether the amount of charity care provided "is in keeping with the purpose of The Methodist Hospital" and "whether Methodist is exempt from disclosing its financial records as required by the Texas Non-profit Corporation Act."[39] As the next chapter will tell, Larry Mathis and the hospital board were more than ready to respond and did so with the determination of an army combat leader under fire. The outcome in support of the hospital's position would have to wait until 1993, but the public airing of laundry was not pleasant. Like all other challenges the hospital faced over the years, this would prove to be an important learning experience with hospital leadership helping the state develop new standards of charity care impacting all hospitals and benefiting communities throughout Texas to the present day.

• • •

Cost containment versus quality of care. Could the two live together harmoniously in a managed care world? How much charity care is appropriate for a nonprofit hospital to provide? How much is too little? These key questions will be addressed head-on in the decade ahead.

NINE

WEATHERING THE STORM
1990-2000

During the 1990s:
  Population of Houston is 1.7 million (1990)
  Operation Desert Storm (1991)
  William J. Clinton is elected president (1992)
  Federal agents raid Branch Davidian cult in Waco, Texas (1993)
  Houston Rockets win NBA Finals (1994, 1995)
  Nelson Mandela is elected president of South Africa (1994)
  O.J. Simpson is found not guilty (1995)
  Dolly the sheep, the world's first cloned mammal, is born (1996)
  Princess Diana dies in Paris car crash (1997)
  First Harry Potter book arrives in bookstores (1997)
  Exxon and Mobil merge to create the world's largest petroleum company (1998)
  John F. Kennedy, Jr. dies in small plane crash off Martha's Vineyard (1999)
  Two students kill twelve students and a teacher at Columbine High School (1999)

Hospitals have long been regarded as centers of healing for individuals from all walks of life. In the 1700s the United States witnessed the emergence of isolation houses known as alms houses to provide custodial care for the poor and destitute. Throughout the 1800s medical care for the poor or isolated was provided in institutions while the middle and upper classes with means received care at home. That changed as modern medicine evolved and hospitals transformed in the public perception from places associated with dying to modern facilities associated with care and cure regardless of social status or financial means.

The very word *hospital* comes from the Latin *hospes*, signifying a stranger or foreigner—a guest. Another noun derived from this, *hospitium*, came to signify hospitality—the relation between guest and shelterer, hospitality, friendliness, and hospitable reception. In more recent history, policies encouraged hospitals to continue the provision of uncompensated care in the face of rising health care costs. Think of uncompensated care as charity care, bad debt, and hospitals covering shortfalls in reimbursement for government-sponsored care, including Medicare and Medicaid. Charity care itself has many interpretations but summarized here as unbilled, discounted, and uncollected expenditures for disadvantaged patients.

Throughout the history of Houston Methodist, charity care has been a central tenet of the hospital's faith-based mission. Even during the Great Depression when the hospital on Rosalie struggled to find its feet, Rev. D. H. Hotchkiss advised the board that $8,877 in "charity work" had been provided to children alone, noting, "Care for the deformed and needy children sponsored by the Shrine is a privilege that brings joy. To bring health to some, to make more nearly normal the deformed, and to bring comfort to all is a Christly ministry."[1]

The Christian concept of *caritas* (charity) has never lost its momentum throughout the hospital's first ten decades. Compare then and now. In 2017 Houston Methodist reported uncompensated and charity care for the community (internal and external care provided directly or through sponsored organizations) in excess of $236 million.[2]

With that in mind it may be surprising that in the mid-1980s Texas Attorney General Jim Mattox announced he was investigating The Methodist Hospital for an alleged lack of sufficient charity care. Speaking before delegates to the annual meeting of the United Methodist Church's Texas Annual Conference in May 1986, hospital president Larry Mathis stated his position with no apologies, "The hospital is conducted ethically, in full compliance with the law and with the great Christian spirit that you would expect from this conference."[3] Mathis also pointed out that the attorney general's charges seemed overly political[4] and that no standardized formula even existed to define how much charity care was the appropriate amount.

By the early 1990s the Texas attorney general formally sued the hospital, prompting Internal Revenue Service audits and the media's undivided attention, including investigative reporting by ABC's *Prime Time Live* and CBS's *60 Minutes*. Mathis and the board countered that the hospital provided large amounts of charity care, noting, "We provided in excess of $100 million in uncompensated care last year [1989]."[5] He also noted that while Methodist is a charitable institution, "it was never intended to be a charity hospital" and has always relied on patient income, not tax dollars, to fund the enterprise.[6]

After all, nonprofit hospitals must still make a profit in order to stay in business, grow, and invest in the future. During the 1980s Methodist had become the largest nonprofit hospital in the United States, amassing reserves to carry it through difficult times and unseen storms. In January 1993 Jim Henderson, executive vice president of The Methodist Hospital System, explained to *Houston Chronicle* reporter Debra Beachy that the hospital's excess profits from revenues "could be misleading because all the money is plowed back into the institution. … As our work force grows and ages, requirements for pension funds grow over time. And in our business, malpractice liability is a fact of life."[7]

For nine long years the dispute over charity care continued. Then, on February 20, 1993, District Judge Pete Lowry's decision appeared in the headlines of the day: "Judge sides with Methodist Hospital." In ruling, Judge Lowry said, as reported in the morning *Houston Post*, "In my opinion the attorney general of the state of Texas does not have the power to tell charitable organizations how to allocate their resources."[8]

Throughout the extended ordeal, hospital leadership recognized the state's suit had implications much bigger than the hospital itself. As *Houston Post* reporter D. J. Wilson wrote two months prior to the judge's ruling, "The outcome of a clash between two heavyweights—the state of Texas and the largest nonprofit hospital in America—may have long-lasting effects on what role such hospitals will play in the nation's growing health care crisis. … Mathis contends any concession by Methodist could further darken the future of hospitals in Texas, a state that already leads the nation in hospital closings. 'We must hold the line on this for the good of the industry,' he insisted.'"[9] Mathis spoke with authority given that in 1993 he had been named chairman of the American Hospital Association with a vested interest in the bigger picture for all hospitals across the country.

In the end, Methodist leadership worked with state officials to write new standards of charity care for nonprofit hospitals in Texas—standards establishing thresholds of charity care and community benefits that Houston Methodist well exceeds on every measure as the hospital celebrates its centennial year in 2019.[10]

Managed Care—Changing the Landscape

To understand why the hospital was challenged in the first place on charity care requires some insight on managed care, because managed care literally defined the 1990s for large teaching hospitals like Methodist.

References to hospital closings relate directly to changes in health care reimbursement ongoing across the country—changes that began in the early 1980s and accelerated in the 1990s. Mentioned in the previous chapter, the federal government passed legislation establishing "prospective payment" of hospital bills with costs fixed by diagnosis-related groups, or DRGs. The landscape of how health care would be delivered and paid for would never be the same. Even management guru Peter Drucker suggested at the time that the challenges of leadership in a modern hospital surpassed those most corporate executives would encounter.

While textbooks have been written on managed care and its impact on large teaching hospitals, a brief and simplified review is important to understand how and why the hospital navigated the uncharted waters of the 1990s. The term *managed care* refers to a large variety of reimbursement plans in which third-party payers attempted to control costs by limiting the utilization of medical services. Prior to managed care we had a fee-for-service health insurance in which fees were set by providers (hospitals and physicians). Managed care organizations in the 1990s used a variety of strategies to exercise strong control over their doctors and hospitals, but they achieved most of their savings by reducing the number of hospitalizations and the use of specialists. Fortunately, managed care then is not managed care now, as over time it has evolved from a primary focus on cost cutting to value-based reimbursement that recognizes quality and safety outcomes.

In the 1990s health maintenance organizations, or HMOs, were perhaps the most extreme in their cost-reduction approach. While the earliest HMOs such as Kaiser Permanente were nonprofits, beginning in the 1980s the HMO industry came to be dominated by for-profit corporations that would soon be accused of limiting medical access and procedures in the interest of profits. By the mid-1990s for-profit organizations dominated the field with eight of the ten largest HMOs investor-owned; their sole legal responsibility was to increase shareholder value.[11]

Explained Dr. Kenneth Ludmerer, a physician and recognized historian on the topic of managed care and its impact on academic teaching hospitals: "By 1995, over 50 million Americans received their health care in HMOs, compared with less than 9 million in 1980, and tens of millions more were in 'looser' forms of managed care, such as preferred provider organizations (PPO) and discounted fee-for-service."[12]

The dynamics, he explained, were like this: "In the new (and still evolving) system, there was marked skepticism toward the professional authority of physicians, unprecedented external oversight and review of medical decision-making, intense price-based competition among doctors and hospitals, and unparalleled opportunities for large, profit-seeking corporations in health care. Control shifted from the 'providers' (doctors and hospitals) to the 'payers' (insurance companies and managed care organizations), whose power resulted from their control of the flow of patients and their skill at exploiting the oversupply of doctors and hospital beds."[13]

Regarding charity care, he added, "Out of economic necessity, most nonprofit community hospitals greatly reduced the amount of charity care they provided. ... This left teaching hospitals, together with municipal and veterans' hospitals, as the primary dispensers of charity care."[14] By the early 1980s teaching hospitals, including Methodist, with 5.6 percent of the acute care beds in the nation, were providing 47.2 percent of the free care in the country.[15]

The rapid spread of managed care in the 1980s and 1990s proved a formidable challenge for large, nonprofit teaching hospitals. Throughout the Texas Medical Center, Methodist and other hospitals struggled to adjust. HMOs and other managed care organizations emphasized more ambulatory care (outpatients), less hospitalization, and the substitution of primary care physicians for specialists whenever possible—trends that directly worked against the strengths of academic health centers like Methodist.

Noted Dr. Ludmerer: "When hospitalization was required, price-sensitive HMOs tried to avoid teaching hospitals because of their higher costs, even though these typically had the highest reputations for clinical excellence. Particularly after 1993, when the spread of managed care accelerated, the number of admissions to teaching hospitals fell, occupancy rates plummeted, and many teaching hospitals began closing beds."[16]

With the addition of Scurlock and Smith towers with new outpatient facilities and preventive medicine programs in addition to a newly emerging network of area hospitals, Methodist had already begun to adjust to the times. Yet in the early 1990s, to attract patients from managed care organizations, academic health centers had to compete with community hospitals on the basis of price, which was not an easy task given community hospitals did not have to support education, research, charity care, and the sicker case mix of patients that large teaching hospitals invested in and ably addressed. Some estimates at the time noted that teaching hospital costs ran on average thirty percent higher than those of community hospitals.[17] In a managed care world, the margins Methodist depended on were quickly disappearing.

Managed care in the 1990s was all about both cutting costs and competing for large blocks of patients at the lowest price. Recalls Mathis, "Until that time, our successful strategy had been to be the high-quality alternative to managed care."[18] He felt strongly that one of the most respected institutions in health care shouldn't jump to discount its prices as it would cheapen the hospital and the medical staff. That St. Luke's Episcopal Hospital next door took a different stance and discounted early added more pressure to Mathis's position.[19] Methodist held strong only to find the hospital's strategy soon overpowered by marketplace demands.

Looking back Mathis recalls, "In 1993, our planning process provoked a mission conference. A mission conference is usually necessary when momentous change is occurring. That change was the growth of managed care in the Houston market and our physicians' perceived need to contract for it. … Over the course of several months, key stakeholders [with the help of consultants] met and struggled with the issues."

1993 had proved to be a year of significant change as Judge Lowry threw out the state's lawsuit against Methodist regarding charity care. Mathis announced in July his cost-cutting moves with job reductions and the hospital's planned entry into the managed care market. Also, in 1993 he announced the hospital's purchase of the 297-bed Diagnostic Hospital in the Texas Medical Center next door to Smith Tower. Across the street Baylor College of Medicine was celebrating its fiftieth anniversary and Dr. DeBakey retired as chairman of Baylor's department of surgery but not from surgery.

In May 1994 the Methodist board made the formal decision to change to a health care system configured for lower-cost managed care. Adds Mathis, "Over the course of fifteen months, we reduced the workforce from 7,025 to 4,900. … Over twelve months, we went from no managed care contracts to thirty-one and moved the city's largest HMO's business to Methodist from Hermann Hospital. We created a primary care physician group, acquired Houston's largest visiting nurse association, and began building community health centers. We created MethodistCare, our own health maintenance organization. That much change, that fast, is very hard on an organization."[20]

Two years later, in 1996, twenty-four months after the hospital celebrated its seventy-fifth anniversary, Methodist was in negotiations to merge with St. Luke's Episcopal Hospital. Methodist had moved slowly and cautiously into managed care but now was all in. 1996 is also remembered as the year Dr. DeBakey and his team, including Dr. George Noon, found themselves on the world stage in Russia consulting on bypass surgery for President Boris Yeltsin. Not to be overlooked, Dr. Antonio Gotto, Jr. left Baylor and Methodist that year to become dean of Cornell's medical school in New York with future transformational implications for Houston Methodist.

Dr. DeBakey, always the medical statesman, was outspoken regarding his concerns that managed care (focused on cost savings) was endangering patient safety and access to care. His well-read editorials appearing in *The New York Times* and numerous medical journals stated his position that no insurance executive sitting in the back of a stretch limo would tell him he could not admit a patient and perform surgery when his expertise said otherwise.

Methodist, like all other hospitals in Houston, was on a steep learning curve throughout the decade as it attempted to understand and address the demands of managed care. There simply was no single formula for success for large, nonprofit teaching hospitals in this rapidly evolving environment. To complicate matters, what worked for one community did not necessarily work for another. One might look back to the medical profession in the early 1900s when there were few cures and no antibiotics. It was a time when doing the right thing for a patient often required trying one approach after another until progress in the patient's condition revealed itself. Addressing the new concept of managed care provided a similar challenge as hospital administrators and boards worked with consultants in search of the right approach to best serve the patient and community while navigating difficult financial waters ahead.

The reserves the hospital board was building through investments certainly proved to be a strong lifeline as some teaching hospitals in the nation merged, sold out, or closed. For example, in 1998 the $1.3 billion Allegheny Health, Education and Research Foundation, a nonprofit hospital chain, declared bankruptcy, sending a shock wave of concern throughout the nation's academic medical centers. Which of them would be next?[21]

Merging Methodist with St. Luke's Episcopal Hospital was another option to consider in these difficult times. On September 28, 1994, Larry Mathis and his St. Luke's counterpart, Dr. John Burdine, filed a letter of intent to merge the hospitals.[22] By 1996 the merger was abandoned. Recalls future chairman of the board Judge Ewing Werlein, Jr., the merger failed due to governance issues that complicated the process.[23] Adds Mathis, "Methodist's considerably higher value of its assets additionally created an imbalance and a further complicating factor in the merger."

Methodist, in turn, negotiated thirty-nine additional managed care plans covering 2.5 million patients. While this merger did not come to fruition, just down the street at Hermann Hospital merger talks were also underway between Hermann CEO David R. Page and Memorial Healthcare System administrator Dan Wilford. Influenced by changes managed care presented, the Memorial Hermann Health System was born in 1997.

In 1996 Larry Mathis also announced his retirement, noting he had accomplished much during his twenty-six years at the hospital, fourteen as president and CEO. The *Houston Chronicle* headline of September 26, 1996, announced, "Methodist's CEO Stepping Down: Mathis to head hospital until successor found." Board chairman John Bookout noted in the article that the board would look for a new chief executive experienced in running a system that integrates health care and finances.[24]

The hospital's board had moved purposely slow into the managed care market while building reserves of more than $800 million and reducing annual operating costs by $100 million.[25] Moreover, leadership had been trendsetters in hospital management, recognized for patient service above all else by bringing elements of the hospitality industry into the hospital. From concierge service and valet parking to upscale hospital lobbies, the service approach of the hospital was as bold as the hospital's mission statement "to provide the best care and service in the world." As mentioned, starting with the new Dunn Tower atrium in 1989, Methodist Hospital was innovating hospital design in ways that were new to the hospital industry—innovations then that are acknowledged today as hospital standards.[26]

Peter Butler and Integrated Medical Delivery Systems

The board's challenge was now to find a new leader who had direct, hands-on experience working in a managed care environment. John Bookout recalled it was a most difficult search with numerous candidates reviewed. While the board originally looked for a physician with the leadership skills to navigate large hospital systems through the uncharted waters of managed care, there were only a handful of such physician leaders and of those few willing to interview, none seemed to fit the bill or the salary the board was willing to pay.

In September 1997, after a yearlong effort to find a new CEO, Peter W. Butler was named Mathis's successor. Butler previously served as senior vice president and chief administrative officer of Henry Ford Health System in Detroit and held a Master of Health Services Administration degree from the University of Michigan School of Public Health. Butler would be the first (and only to date) administrative head in the history of Methodist to be recruited from outside the organization.

Prior to Butler's arrival the hospital had launched two physician strategies: a joint venture primary care network with Baylor called Baylor/Methodist Primary Care Associates and an independent practice association called the Methodist Medical Group that was developed to contract with independent physicians and provide services to managed care organizations.

By the end of the decade both programs would prove ineffective. Yet in hindsight they were important learning experiences and brought into the spotlight the leadership abilities of Dr. Marc Boom, who in 2012 would be named president and CEO of Houston Methodist. Dr. Boom, with administrative skills honed during the difficult managed care era of the 1990s, would apply lessons learned to steer the hospital well beyond the challenges of the decade.

Dr. Boom, a 1992 graduate of Baylor College of Medicine, joined Methodist as the Baylor administrator assigned to the joint network Baylor/Methodist Primary Care Associates. His Methodist counterpart was Randy Wright and together they began developing the joint venture. The program represented a $44 million investment over five years. In the first six months 142 community physicians signed letters of intent to affiliate with the joint venture.[27] By mid-1998, Dr. Boom, a primary care physician himself with an MBA from the Wharton School of Business, was a full-time Methodist employee reporting to Butler and running the program. Boom would in 2000 be named president of the hospital's 1993 acquisition, Diagnostic Hospital. He assumed that leadership role following the 1999 retirement of Diagnostic's CEO, who had come to Methodist as part of the transaction.

Dr. Boom recalls, "It was while I was in medical school that I became interested in the business side. … I owe a lot to Dr. Ralph Feigin, a major mentor for me." Dr. Feigin chaired Baylor's department of pediatrics 1977–2003 and became president of the medical school in 1996. From 1977 until his death in 2008 he was physician-in-chief at Texas Children's Hospital.

During Dr. Boom's fourth year in medical school he spent six weeks on an administrative rotation with Dr. Feigin. "I followed him around. I remember going to board meetings, city council meetings, helping him write book chapters. … He had it all, from a leadership, academic, and pediatric base," said Dr. Boom.[28] The Feigin model was not only impressive but also inspiring, and to this day Dr. Boom maintains his own medical practice while involved in hospital leadership at the highest level. Little could he know at the time how much was to be learned during the 1990s as his new president, Peter Butler, addressed the financial challenges at hand. As a new Methodist administrator in 1997 it did not take Dr. Boom long to realize that the hospital's physician strategies (the joint venture with Baylor and the independent practice association) were not working well.[29] Both would be disbanded within four years.

· · ·

Methodist, like all other hospitals in Houston, was on a steep learning curve searching out strategies. At the time Butler arrived from Detroit in 1997, The Methodist Hospital was no longer that small hospital Josie Roberts and Ted Bowen along with the medical staff built to international status. By the late 1990s it had redesigned itself as The Methodist Health Care System with four licensed hospitals, a managed care organization with over eighty thousand members, an annual operating budget of more than $900 million, assets totaling

$2.8 billion, and two large affiliated multispecialty group practices, in addition to serving as the principal teaching affiliate for Baylor College of Medicine.[30] About half of the system's annual revenues were generated by The Methodist Hospital in the Texas Medical Center, the flagship of the enterprise.[31] It had grown into a large, complex institution, and like any large ship in the uncharted waters of managed care, turning the vessel quickly was no easy task.

As chairman of the hospital's board, John Bookout noted in the announcement of Larry Mathis's retirement that the board was looking for someone with managed care experience who understood and could manage an integrated medical delivery system (IDS). So, what exactly is an IDS?

Dr. Ludmerer described it in this way: "An IDS represented an interlocking bottom-to-top health care system that offered a complete continuum of health care services from primary care to complex surgery to home health care and did so for a defined population at a preset price. … [Typically, they] contained not only an academic health center but primary and secondary hospitals, individual medical practices, nursing homes, rehabilitation centers, hospices, psychiatric facilities, and home health care programs. … To assure enough referrals to the teaching hospital in an era of declining hospitalization rates, an academic IDS had to be responsible for a huge number of patient lives—as many as one million or more."[32]

Ron Girotto, who continued to serve as chief operating and financial officer following Mathis's retirement, noted that to have an integrated delivery system you must have three essential components: physicians, hospital, and financing system—all integrated as one. The physicians, he noted, become full-time employees of the hospital paid by the hospital like every other employee. "So there began to be a rub with the IDS theory from the beginning given that both the private physicians and the full-time faculty at Baylor were not interested in it. It just didn't work. … It was better for Peter Butler for me not to be here in charge of operations and not advocating the concept. It was time for me to move on."[33]

At age fifty, Butler knew a great deal about integrated systems from his leadership role at Henry Ford Health System, which was well versed in IDS implementation. What he did not know was Houston, and he was on a fast learning curve to learn the lay of the land in the world's largest medical center and the nation's fourth-largest city. To assist him, he brought from Henry Ford Health a senior colleague and trusted adviser, Richard Wittrup.

After Girotto's departure, Butler recruited former Hermann Hospital administrator Dr. Lynn Schroth to serve as an executive vice president and chief operating officer. Dr. Schroth served as vice president of clinical services at the University of Pittsburgh Medical Center prior to joining Hermann Hospital with a key role in the merger that created Memorial Hermann Health System. She knew the Houston community and had board experience working with the University Health System Consortium, a national organization that provided a big picture perspective of how other large teaching hospitals around the country were adapting to managed care and reorganizing services with cost and quality control measures in place.

Dr. Schroth, who holds a doctorate in public health and is in recent years a professor in health management at the UTHealth School of Public Health in Houston, remembered well the challenges she accepted when joining Butler in 1997. That very year Congress passed the Balanced Budget Act to reduce health care spending by $160 billion with Medicare cuts of $112 billion to be achieved by reducing payments to hospitals, doctors, and nurse practitioners.[34] The effects were dramatic. Methodist alone saw its funding cut by $127.3 million over five years.[35] For the first time in its history the hospital ended 1999 in the red, and the tension between Methodist and Baylor that had always been a given now seemed to heighten longtime differences due to the dire financial circumstances.

"So, when Peter Butler hired me," Dr. Schroth recalls, "I didn't realize they were losing money. I thought I was going to go to a place that had more money than God and that I was going to get to grow stuff rather than counting every penny. But when I was there I found out they were going to lose $20 million that year and I was going to be helping fix that.[36] Peter had been charged with bringing Methodist kind of out of the '70s and '80s era into the world of managed care. You can argue all day long that he didn't go about it the right way but he definitely was a change agent that came in, shook the place up, and got them moving on the right path."[37]

Adds Dr. Schroth: "So I think you don't change until you have to. Nobody likes change. … I give John Bookout all the credit in the world. As Judge [Ewing] Werlein [future board chair 2007–2017] always said, John Bookout has an ability to see around corners. He knew what they were doing. … So it was a period of drastic change and having to go in and involve physicians in a way they had never been involved because they were used to decisions being made behind closed doors. They had their own in-house quality program, which is fine but if you don't benchmark our quality against anybody it is real easy to look good."[38]

Many of the employee layoffs in the late 1990s were achieved by offering early retirement packages. "Those who couldn't change or couldn't adapt to changes at Methodist are the ones that went," notes Dr. Schroth. "The ones who realized there was a different way of doing it are the ones that stayed. It was kind of interesting. We did a retreat with the director level, one hundred directors, and we had a facilitator come in, and one of the exercises that she asked them to do was to draw a picture of how they perceived Methodist in the past and how they perceived what Methodist was going to have to be in the future to survive."

Those executives, she adds, "depicted Methodist's past with a picture of the *Titanic*, the doomed ocean liner. Its future took the form of a World Cup-winning racing yacht. Over the years Methodist had tended to fund Baylor projects while requiring little in the way of accountability." Times had to change, recalls Dr. Schroth. "We changed the way we started relating to Baylor. … You had to convince people that the way they were doing things, just because they'd done it for twenty years, wasn't particularly the right way to do it. I'd say to them [Baylor], 'If I give you $10 million a year, what are you going to do for me and how will I hold you accountable?' Obviously, that caused a crack in the relationship."[39]

In addition to overhauling her own team and cutting costs across the institution, Dr. Schroth and her team addressed the development of a global hospital network along with a reorganization of the hospital infrastructure to benchmark patient care quality and outcome measures—institutionalizing rigorous standards of accountability, which is a hallmark of Houston Methodist to this day.

Among those vice presidents joining Dr. Schroth's team from within the organization were Dr. Debbie Sukin (Ph.D.), who in the hospital's centennial year serves as a regional senior vice president of Houston Methodist and CEO of Methodist's Woodlands hospital, and Dr. Ann Scanlon McGinity (Ph.D.) to lead nursing. Also joining Dr. Schroth's team were Dr. Marc Boom and Dr. Roberta Schwartz (Ph.D.). Dr. Sukin, who now holds a doctorate in health policy, took on the job of benchmarking costs and outcomes across departments while integrating services to successfully create the Methodist DeBakey Heart & Vascular Center.

Dr. Albert E. Raizner, a longtime cardiologist at Methodist, spearheaded the effort with Dr. Sukin and became the center's first director in 2001. In a 2012 interview he recalled that assembling the various heart-related components into one unified center was no easy job but long overdue.

> You had the Baylor people, you had the Methodist people, you had the private practitioners, you had the surgeons, you had the cardiologists, and nobody was in charge. There was no one person to bring it all together. ... The coup de grâce was when *U.S. News & World Report* came out ... and The Methodist Hospital was not on this [in the national rankings]. So I said to the board, "Here's the list. See if you can find your heart center and your hospital on this list. You may view our institution as one of the top heart centers in the world, but that's not how it is viewed by the public." We then had an honest discussion about what our strengths were and what our weaknesses were—most notably the lack of a single identity. [40]

While Dr. Denton Cooley had been the architect of the Texas Heart Institute one block down the street with a unified heart institute capable of tracking all costs and outcomes across all services and cost centers, Methodist was missing the unified approach that a managed care world demanded. The Methodist DeBakey Heart & Vascular Center represents an important model of integrated accountability that has been successfully replicated throughout Houston Methodist and born in large part in response to the changes managed care demanded.

During the year of the hospital's centennial, one can open the latest issue of *U.S. News & World Report* hospital rankings and find Houston Methodist not just listed among the best of the nation's hospital systems but also as the best or among the best across a long list of clinical specialties and services in addition to being ranked the number-one hospital in Texas. Additionally, Houston Methodist is listed in the publication's Honor

Roll, a distinguished list of the top twenty hospitals in the nation. Three times as of this writing, the hospital has been recognized with this national accolade. For all the uncertainty managed care presented administration during the decade, it should not be overlooked that the commitment to the highest standards of patient care never waned across all medical specialties and the growing number of community-based hospitals and service centers that are Houston Methodist today.

While Houston Methodist made great strides in integrating cost centers and programs as evidenced by the Methodist DeBakey Heart & Vascular Center, not all initiatives were as successful. Under Peter Butler's leadership the hospital also created the Texas Medical Group and contracted to provide management services (billing, collection, accounting) for the MacGregor physician group while purchasing half ownership with St. Luke's Episcopal Hospital in the management company of Kelsey Seybold. In time Kelsey Seybold physicians would buy back the full practice. Both failed initiatives would be disbanded within a few short years.

Ed Tyrrell, senior vice president for corporate financial services at Houston Methodist, remembers the 1990s well given his three-plus decades of service to the institution. "We had a lot going on and not all of it was working out. I think the Peter Butler legacy was the opening of the Sugar Land hospital in Fort Bend County in early 1998 and Willowbrook hospital in northwest Houston in December 2000."[41] During this period Houston Methodist expanded rapidly into the community with a network of outstanding community-based hospitals and services that continue to grow and serve the expanding Greater Houston Area in ways no one Methodist hospital in the Texas Medical Center could ever achieve. The appendices of this book include a historical listing of the eight hospitals that constitute Houston Methodist in 2019.

Tyrrell, like so many other senior administrators, is quick to credit former finance chair of the hospital board David Underwood, the grandson of Ella and Walter Fondren. "He did a tremendous job helping us navigate through some rough waters at times."[42] Tyrrell recalls the credit crisis of 2008–2009 and John Hagale's (CFO at the time) discussion with Underwood about the free fall in the equity markets and board members wanting to sell equities. "David calmly remarked with a smile, 'If our board members want us to sell some of our equities, it's the best news I've heard in a long time because when smart guys are ready to capitulate, the bottom must be there.' After patiently listening to much discussion at the next Finance Committee (February 2009) Mr. Underwood, always the teacher, summarized the discussion and then shared three rules that I will never forget saying, 'I am loath to sell equities at market low; you have to be present to win; and never bet against the U.S. economy.'" Underwood, who passed away in 2015, served the Methodist board for fifty-two years (1963–2015) in addition to his many years leading the Texas Medical Center board. He is forever remembered for his service that contributed in many ways to the international renown that both Houston and the medical community enjoy to this day.

• • •

Managed care in the 1990s had tested the hospital in important ways. It was a painful period of cost cutting and learning, but looking back, it was an important period in the growth of Houston Methodist. Recalls Dr. Boom, "We retrenched in the early 2000s. Not just retrenched from doing managed care but the whole world changed. … So we figured it out—these weren't the right things to do—and then started winding it back."[43]

• • •

Managed care as it was in the late 1990s was not a good fit for Houston Methodist but an important teaching moment. Houston Methodist was not alone. Across the Houston health care landscape, managed care in the late 1990s took its toll on both hospitals and patient–physician relationships. Sometimes you just can't see the rainbow until the storm has passed. Lord Byron, the English nobleman and poet, put it this way: "Be thou the rainbow in the storms of life. The evening beam that smiles the clouds away, and tints tomorrow with prophetic ray."

Numerous rainbows emerged from the 1990s that were prophetic. Lessons learned during the decade brought a new sense of equilibrium, enabling hospital management to address change and uncertain times with newfound patience and confidence.

• • •

Dr. Marc Boom, who leads Houston Methodist during this centennial year, has an appreciation of the hospital's history and a physician's sense of confidence and equanimity honed during the '90s. "I watched us cling to the old so tightly that we missed it and didn't shift. But then we shifted too hard and the pendulum swung the other way."[44] These were invaluable lessons learned and now applied with a renewed appreciation that good leadership is informed by institutional successes as well as failures that sometimes only reveal themselves in the most challenging of times.

Clearly the storms of managed care experienced in the '90s strengthened the enterprise in many important and positive ways. The next decade would reveal storms of a different nature (both man-made and by Mother Nature's hand) along with new opportunities for the hospital to grow in ways Dr. Oscar Norsworthy and the early leadership never dreamed possible.

TEN

STEERING A NEW COURSE

2000-2010

During the 2000s:

Population of Houston is 1.9 million (2000)

9/11 terrorist attacks on the United States claim lives of 2,977, including 2,753 in the destruction of World Trade Center's Twin Towers (2001)

Enron files for bankruptcy (2001)

European Monetary Union introduces euro banknotes and coins (2002)

Iraqi President Saddam Hussein is captured (2003)

Human genome project launched in 1990 declared complete (2003)

Houston METRO opens light rail service (2004)

Former President Ronald Reagan dies (2004)

Super Bowl XXXVIII is played in Houston's Reliant Stadium (2004)

As Hurricane Katrina devastates New Orleans, 200,000 evacuate to Houston (2005)

Hurricane Rita causes 2.5 million Houstonians to evacuate and makes landfall near Sabine Pass on the Texas-Louisiana coast (2005)

Steve Jobs, co-founder of Apple Computer, announces the first iPhone (2007)

Hurricane Ike makes a direct hit on Galveston and Houston (2008)

Barack Obama is elected as the 44th president (2008)

Singer Michael Jackson dies in Los Angeles (2009)

The year 2000 did not come easy. While Josie Roberts started her career logging the business of the hospital with pencil and paper, the world was now computerized and the question of the moment was how computers around the world would handle the transition from the last day of 1999 to the first of 2000. Fear swept the nation that computers would not recognize "00" as "2000" and all banking, hospitals, government records, and utility systems would grind to a halt. An estimated $150 billion was spent in the United States alone to upgrade computers and application programs to be Y2K compliant.[1] After a year of international alarm, few major failures actually occurred as the new millennium arrived.

Throughout the growing Methodist system attention was focused beyond the fears of Y2K to the reality of managed care. While Peter Butler and his team made strides expanding the Methodist system into the community and cutting the hospital's large operating deficits, programs initiated to create an integrated delivery system were not working. Both Baylor and Methodist engaged consultants Kurt Salmon Associates to help. At Baylor the consultants helped develop clinical program priorities and requirements.[2] At Methodist they simultaneously developed a five-year plan for clinical space expansion in Sugar Land. The Sugar Land hospital opened in 1998 and a decade later would triple in size. The consultants also worked with hospital leadership to address expansion into Houston's Willowbrook area.[3]

Already the board understood that the integrated delivery system strategies of the previous decade needed to be abandoned. By 2000 the hospital board set a new course to get back to doing what Methodist does best—focus on excellence in patient care with centers of excellence defined. Also, in 2001 a Methodist Health Care Master Plan Steering Committee comprising both Baylor and Methodist representatives was at work developing a master facility plan for the future. The early 2000s were a time of comprehensive strategic planning for both institutions—planning that would affect in important ways the future of both Baylor and Methodist, together and apart. Changes in leadership were happening as well.

In 2000 Dr. Ralph Feigin, Baylor's president, was asked to choose between his Baylor presidency or his position as physician-in-chief at Texas Children's Hospital. Dr. Feigin's divided attention between the two was a point of concern. He chose, to the surprise of many, to hand in his resignation as president of Baylor. In response to key trustees and faculty who passionately called for Dr. Feigin to reconsider, his departure was postponed until 2003, when he would turn sixty-five. Meanwhile, in 2001 Corby Robertson, Jr., president of Quintana Minerals, Inc. and grandson of Hugh Roy Cullen, was named to lead Baylor's board to replace local businessman Daniel "Dan" C. Arnold, who had served as chairman of Baylor's board since 1996.

The arrival of the new millennium also signaled the need to renew the Methodist–Baylor affiliation agreement scheduled to expire on June 12, 2000. Given the changes in leadership at the time, both institutions approved extending the agreement until 2002 and put joint facilities planning activities on hold. Clearly, there were strains between the two institutions that leaders of both had seen coming for years.

Changes in health care delivery and reimbursement, as previously discussed, were challenging the financial viability of even the best medical schools in the nation, like Baylor, that increasingly depended on clinical revenue streams to support education and research missions. Early in the decade the terms of the new affiliation were already shaping up as the primary topic of discussion by both boards with the media and community watching. While difficult affiliation discussions loomed, a tropical storm named Allison was about to take center stage and wreak havoc.

Tropical Storm Allison

Houstonians are no strangers to floods as the 1976 disaster ably demonstrated. Yet in general, tropical storms command little respect compared to hurricanes. Tropical Storm Allison changed that perspective. The storm first arrived in Houston on the night of June 5, 2001, as a rain event soaking the ground and filling bayous before heading north. All seemed well until Allison took a U-turn, recharged in the warm Gulf waters, and three days later parked directly over the Rice University and the Texas Medical Center community. It was a cats-and-dogs rain event that dropped a lake of water the likes of which the area had never seen—up to 37 inches in the medical center area—causing the worst flooding at that time in the city's history.[4]

Imagine all this water, literally billions of gallons, racing across the Rice campus and surrounding neighborhoods in search of a bayou. The Texas Medical Center stood between Rice University and Brays Bayou and as the saying goes, you can't stop water; you can only move it. The bayou left its banks and water rose rapidly throughout the Texas Medical Center. It filled basements, blew out walls where corridors connected buildings, destroyed research labs and animal care facilities, knocked out power, and flooded streets throughout the night as most employees slept at home with little idea of the unfolding disaster.

Allison would be the costliest tropical storm in U.S. history at the time, and even its name was retired, a first for a tropical storm. When it was over, the storm had caused twenty-four deaths and $5 billion in damage.[5] Dr. Marc Boom was a Methodist senior vice president at the time and enjoying a summer vacation with his family away from home, like many Houstonians, when he got word and returned immediately. At the time, he was running Diagnostic Hospital for Methodist and was in the process of closing that facility and folding it into the main hospital. In hindsight, it was fortunate the Diagnostic Hospital facilities were still in operation. Recalls Dr. Boom:

> Diagnostic was actually a pop-off valve providing unflooded space
> and backup services for Methodist, so it was good we had it and
> could help. Tropical Storm Allison was devastating to Methodist and
> the entire Texas Medical Center. It took us five years or more to get
> our Methodist facilities in the medical center back to normal. The
> basement had to be shut down entirely. The cafeteria and conference
> areas on the first floor all became supply chain. It was a hospital-wide
> effort and our goal was to go beyond fixing damage to mitigation—
> doing everything humanly possible to prevent this from ever happening

again. We put in true flood doors and gates and overhauled our emergency procedures to streamline the decision-making process, assuring the right resources are in the right place at the right time to ensure the safety of all. Tropical Storm Allison provided us a teachable moment and the efforts invested paid off. During Hurricane Harvey [2017] these systems were tested and worked well. I'm told Walter Tower has the second-largest flood door in the nation, perhaps the world. For Harvey we kept eight hospitals high and dry. The difference between Allison and Harvey was night and day.[6]

For new hospital administrator Roberta Schwartz, Allison was her welcoming committee. As a new employee accustomed to the blizzards of the Northeast, tropical storms and hurricanes were a whole new challenge. "I arrived in Houston the day after Tropical Storm Allison. I was on one of three flights to arrive in Houston and the rental cars were under water. We were taken in by some incredibly hospitable folks. I started work the day after that. I was put into the war room as a junior executive where we were trying to work to move the rest of the patients out of the hospital and then shut down all of those beds safely. And then get our employees to the institutions that could take care of patients, all while trying to figure out where our employees were because they were completely displaced. It was quite an interesting start to my Houston Methodist career."[7] Since those early days in the wake of Allison, Dr. Schwartz has continued to impress and serves at the time of this writing as executive vice president of Houston Methodist with oversight for hospital facilities in the Texas Medical Center—well versed in making the most out of even the greatest challenges.

Dr. Michael W. Lieberman, who chaired pathology at Baylor and oversaw the busy pathology service for Methodist in 2001, provides a departmental perspective. "We were fortunate Texas Children's never went down. They operated on emergency power, so we could get things cut [tissue samples for pathology slides], mounted, and stained there. ... We just lugged microscopes across the bridge from Methodist to the ballroom [of the Marriott Hotel] and plugged them in. Then we cannibalized some stuff from Baylor and some stuff from Methodist and put it all together." On the bright side, he recalls, "the hospital was in the midst of doing a total reassessment of its space needs and planning for the future, but this, of course, really accelerated the process."[8]

Nearly two decades later, Ed Tyrrell, senior vice president for finance at Houston Methodist, readily recalls the monetary loss—numbers he will never forget. "With Allison we had $250 million in combined property and business interruption losses. We covered that with $100 million in insurance proceeds. ... I think we got about $75 million in FEMA monies to help with our property damage. So, $175 million in FEMA and insurance just in round dollars bumped up against $250 million in losses. The silver lining from Tropical Storm Allison was that we were able to recapitalize (rebuild and improve) and put protections in place for all of our space that was below ground on our medical center campus. Harvey put those protections to a test of Biblical proportions, and we passed with flying colors."[9]

Just a block from Methodist, the Harris Gully that transports rain runoff from the Rice University area through a large box culvert to the bayou runs directly beneath Baylor's red-tiled Cullen Building. During Allison, the sub-basement and basement were inundated, destroying years of research, including more than thirty thousand rodents supporting research trials.[10] Losses totaled $282.9 million.[11] Throughout the Texas Medical Center that scene of destruction repeated itself. For the first time in eighty years Memorial Hermann Hospital closed its doors as military and civilian helicopters hovered over parking lots to evacuate patients.

That night as Methodist basements filled and power was lost, all attention went to patients and getting them safely down dark stairways. While nature's fury destroyed bricks and mortar with ease, the resourcefulness and dedication of hospital employees proved impenetrable. It made no difference whether you were a student or head of surgery, all hands were on deck. With flashlights and great care, volunteers evacuated patients from the eleventh floor skilled nursing unit in the Neurosensory building until their arms gave out. Even clerical employees who rarely encountered patients found themselves helping move patients down dark stairwells—returning into the darkness to retrieve patient belongings.[12] Throughout the hospital similar scenes unfolded.

Other employees heard shouts for help and found themselves involved in a dramatic rescue pulling a lone co-worker through the ceiling of an elevator car that had stalled in the basement as water rose. It was a scene right out of a Hollywood movie and in all probability the rescued employee took the stairs for months thereafter.

Not every patient could be evacuated. Family members of one woman awaiting a heart transplant pitched in, moving equipment and bringing in sandwiches and other donated items. Many staff left their own flooded homes to help. Esteemed physicians found themselves loading shopping carts at big box stores with food and bottled water.

Dr. Gustavo Ayala,[13] a pathologist, recalls the teamwork it took to save priceless research housed in the Fondren-Brown Building's tissue bank on the fourth floor, where thirty thousand frozen prostate specimens representing twelve years of work were about to be lost. Power cabled from a distant building provided hit-and-miss electricity, "so we started a rotation to stand in front of the freezers to save the tissue ... and the rotation lasted for two weeks. It was over ninety degrees inside, sometimes a hundred and the freezers were supposed to go to minus eighty."[14]

In many ways the difficulties of managed care in the 1990s followed by Tropical Storm Allison forged a renewed strength and appreciation that Methodist was a family capable of weathering any storm. Just months after Tropical Storm Allison, a tragedy affected the entire nation as four passenger jets commandeered by terrorists destroyed the World Trade Center, struck the Pentagon, and crashed in a Pennsylvania field on a day that will forever be known as 9/11.

· · ·

At Methodist John Bookout, who joined the hospital's board in 1979, chaired the board working with hospital CEO Peter Butler. Bookout recalls it was his neighbor, Jack Blanton, who first urged him to join the Methodist board. For five years he held off, noting his many other business responsibilities. Yet Blanton was patient, eventually telling Bookout in 1979 that he had just turned in Bookout's acceptance to join the board. It was a bold move and it worked.[15] Bookout's addition to the board and chairmanship during the first seven years of the new millennium held transformational value—shaping the very character and direction of Houston Methodist in the years ahead.

The aftermath of Allison was not the only problem Bookout and the hospital board were addressing. It was time for new leadership, and that leadership change, notes Bookout, had nothing to do with Tropical Storm Allison and everything to do with managed care. Many of the initiatives launched before and after Butler's arrival were to be walked back and discontinued in the early 2000s. On September 29, 2001, Butler was removed from his leadership role.[16] He moved to Chicago, retiring in 2016 as president of Rush University Medical Center with numerous accolades. It was a painful period of cost cutting and learning but looking back, it was an important period in the growth of Houston Methodist.

Following Butler's departure, Bookout called Ron Girotto and asked him to consider coming back and filling the leadership role on an interim basis. Whether the interim would be a few months or a year was neither defined nor known at the time, recalls Bookout.[17] The trust Girotto earned through personal relationships over the years with both Baylor physicians and private physicians would prove invaluable in the coming decades as Houston Methodist transformed into the major academic medical center it is today.

Times had changed, the IDS approach was out, and Girotto, with decades of hospital experience along with trusted relationships with both academic and private physicians at Methodist, was in. "One condition [for coming back] from my perspective was I didn't want to be the one to appear to make the decision to move out of integrated care. The answer came back that decision had been made but it hadn't been implemented, so from October 1 to May 31 of 2002, that's when we turned out the lights on IDS programs. We shut them down."[18] Girotto sums up the failed IDS approach this way: "There was a fairly significant move to integrate, where you tried to amalgamate yourself into a financing institution, physician organization, and then a health care provider. We failed significantly in about every aspect of that, but we weren't the only system in the U.S to fail; most failed."[19]

A year to the day following his interim appointment, Girotto was named Methodist's president and CEO. While he had retired in 1999 as Methodist's chief financial and operating officer, noting an IDS was neither his strength nor his interest, he was now at the helm and reinvigorated to work with the board going forward. While Allison and the difficult years of managed care would soon be memories, they would forever be important teaching moments guiding leadership decisions going forward.

Building the Culture – I CARE Values

Across the entire Methodist system employees endured a great deal during the first three years of the new millennium as impending deadlines to renew the affiliation agreement with Baylor approached. The genesis of the I CARE values program actually traces its roots to 1999 when the System Spiritual Care and Values Integration Committee (SSCVIC) was created and the hospital's belief, mission, vision, and values statements were addressed across the growing Houston Methodist system of care facilities.

Recalls Judge Ewing Werlein, Jr., who chaired the board from 2007–2017, it was board member William "Bill" Hinson, senior pastor of Houston's First United Methodist Church, who insisted the hospital's mission statement would not be complete until "spirituality" was incorporated.[20] This led to the board's appointment of the spiritual care committee, which researched the topic and returned with two recommendations: integrate spiritual values across the entire system and hire someone to oversee that process.

In this way Rev. Thomas "Tom" Daugherty was appointed vice president of spiritual care and values integration by the newly formed committee chaired by Dr. Stuart M. Dobbs. The SSCVIC organized an employee committee comprising members from the then five hospitals in The Methodist Hospital System, hired a facilitator, and developed a vision statement around one central theme: the integration of spiritual values throughout the entire hospital system. Daugherty and consultant Cindy Wigglesworth mapped out an education and tracking strategy, and what is known today as I CARE values (Integrity, Compassion, Accountability, Respect, and Excellence) moved from concept to implementation.[21]

Recalls Fred Pluckhorn, who joined Methodist in March 2000 as vice president of human resources, the process reached a milestone in mid-2001 with the release of results from Methodist's first "cultural assessment" survey. Then Tropical Storm Allison struck. With the appointment of Ron Girotto as Methodist's interim CEO in 2001, implementation moved quickly. Pluckhorn recalled in a 2005 interview that Girotto "really championed the values effort." The team-building experience of Tropical Storm Allison provided ideal timing.[22]

Girotto inherited a plateful of complex issues at the time and drew from two strengths readily at hand: a supportive and capable hospital board under the leadership of John Bookout and a dedicated employee base that was tried, tested, and strengthened by Allison. Girotto was well known as a people person, and his wife, Judy, in 2018 summed up her husband's dedication to Houston Methodist: "I remember Ron saying so often, 'Life would be so much easier if I just gave in to various demands, but if it is not the best for Methodist, I will not do it.'"[23]

From the newest hire to senior members of the board, recalls Girotto, "we mandated that all ten thousand employees participate in a one half-day, four-hour session and do nothing but talk about what those values mean."[24] The hospital system introduced a series of training sessions: "Spiritual Integrity at Work," "Healing and Dying Across Cultures," and a four-hour "Living Methodist Values" class. Every Methodist employee, including physicians, was required to attend. Says Girotto, "Within sixteen months more than 170 such sessions had been conducted and every one initiated with a senior executive present—myself included. … Two to three years into it, the organization all of a sudden embraced that [and to this day] there's not a board meeting that goes by that somebody doesn't bring up the word 'values.' … We got our arms around it. We got our culture embedded back into us, and it's really made a huge difference in the organization."[25]

Within two years, in 2005, Houston Methodist was listed among *Fortune* magazine's "100 Best Companies to Work For," an honor complementing the institution's accolades in *U.S. News & World Report* naming Houston Methodist physicians and staff across numerous clinical specialties among the best of the best in the nation year after year.[26]

Step forward in time to Houston Methodist's centennial year and you'll learn the I CARE values have never wavered. Carole Hackett, senior vice president for human resources, is a registered nurse who spent 28 years working for Cleveland Clinic before making the move to Houston in 2007. "I interviewed in Houston and went home and told my husband, 'There's something very special about Methodist—you can feel it, it's the culture, it's the people.'"

By 2014 Hackett was overseeing systemwide human resources operations. "And I love it. It really is all about culture, how to create and structure that culture, and we've done it in a variety of ways across the system so you have that consistency. I CARE values are the foundation of our culture. Everybody talks about it, we train for it, we reward behaviors that support it, and we hold each other accountable for it."[27] To build that consistency, she adds, every newly opened Methodist facility starts with a percentage of experienced Methodist employees who have lived the culture and model it for new hires to ensure I CARE continuity.

In hindsight it all started in response to a tropical storm named Allison and the difficult years defined by 9/11, and further reinforced when a hurricane named Ike struck the Galveston–Houston area on September 13, 2008. Once again, dark clouds yielded rainbows of opportunity and Methodist employees made the most of it. In a city known for stepping up and helping others, Methodist employees can be found front and center in times good and bad. In fact, reminds Hackett, community service is now expected and recognized with paid time off given annually to every employee, assuring that the community is never short of helping hands. Looking back on his sixteen years as chairman, John Bookout proudly reflects on these culture-building programs and considers I CARE "one of the most effective things I've ever seen in my business career to the degree it was embraced, accepted, and is actually practiced today."[28]

Prior to retirement in 2011, Ron Girotto remembers being invited as the featured speaker at national meetings addressing workplace excellence. Here he addressed chief executive officers from other industries across the country who were more than interested in the culture of Methodist and how to duplicate the success of I CARE values.[29] Although overseeing the implementation of I CARE was successful and rewarding, it was hardly Girotto's greatest challenge. Another storm, not of Mother Nature's making, was about to take center stage.

Methodist and Baylor Part Ways

Friendship is the marriage of the soul and this marriage is liable to divorce.
– Voltaire (1694–1778)

In the new millennium the shifting landscape of health care that managed care introduced over a decade earlier presented both institutions (separately and together) numerous challenges and uncertainties. While one can easily argue all the reasons for the breakup of the Baylor–Methodist partnership, one fact cannot be disputed—both institutions to this day remain among the elite medical institutions in the nation, accomplishing over five decades great things together that would have been impossible apart.

In the 1950s Dr. Michael DeBakey and Methodist leadership shook hands and drafted a short, straightforward agreement. Short and simple had been the key. The world of health care in the new millennium was no longer conducive to short and simple. Times had changed, making renewal of the affiliation agreement much more challenging and complex compared to years gone by. In the past, tensions in the relationship over finances, medical authority, and shared facilities had always found a way to be resolved—or at least pushed under the surface for the time being.

In the early 2000s a new health care world squeezed revenue streams across the country in ways few medical school deans had ever seen. Most of the nation's 125 medical schools (at the time) leaned heavily on clinical income to make ends meet. This only exacerbated underlying tension and distrust between Baylor and Methodist. Not to be overlooked is the previously mentioned 1996 near merger between St. Luke's and Methodist that left Baylor feeling blindsided and minimalized. "Virtual exclusion" was Baylor president William Butler's take.[30] For those living in the middle of the relationship, it was a wound that never really healed, adding more tension to the mix.

By November 2001, in the wake of Tropical Storm Allison, both Baylor and Methodist regrouped to work on renewal of the affiliation agreement that was postponed in 2000 and was now due on July 1, 2002. Recalls Girotto:

> I worked hard with John Bookout. We worked incredibly hard on
> the Baylor affiliation. ... Since June 12, 2000, when the thirty-year
> agreement ended, we had been working with one-year extensions. By
> 2002 we came to an agreement, a new affiliation agreement that was to
> extend twenty-five years. We [both institutions] agreed we were going
> to go to our boards for approval.[31] It was in the fall of 2002 [October
> 23, 2002] that we were informed the school was uncomfortable in

signing a twenty-five-year agreement due to the transition of CEOs.
Dr. Ralph Feigin was scheduled to retire in 2003, so they preferred
to execute the agreement for a term of eighteen months. We were
reluctant to do that because we weren't sure what that meant. What
difference would the CEO make, as long as the two institutions agreed
on what the agreement was? But we did. We executed on that.[32]

As planned, Dr. Feigin retired from Baylor to return full time to his Texas Children's Hospital post. In March 2003, Baylor trustees named Dr. Peter G. Traber president of Baylor College of Medicine. The former CEO for the University of Pennsylvania Medical Center had more recently served as chief medical officer of pharmaceutical giant GlaxoSmithKline. Traber's tenure at Penn had been controversial, lasting less than six months, and he had become one of the primary figures in *Governance of Teaching Hospitals: Turmoil at Penn and Hopkins*,[33] a book detailing failed negotiations between the medical school and its hospital affiliate. In March 2003 Baylor trustees announced Traber as their new president—fourth in the line of previous Baylor presidents: Dr. Michael DeBakey (1969–1979), Dr. William Butler (1979–1996), and Dr. Ralph Feigin (1996–2003).

. . .

Strategically, Baylor's blueprint for the future had been defined just days before 9/11 when consultants Kurt Salmon Associates presented their report to the Baylor board. Titled *Clinical Program Development at Baylor, Strategies for National Leadership: 2001–2010*, the report noted that as respected and outstanding as Baylor College of Medicine was, they had work to do "to advance to national standing among the very top tier of medical schools." The Salmon report recommended six specific strategies for the medical school.[34]

Writing his own history of Baylor College of Medicine, the school's chancellor emeritus Dr. William Butler summarized, "The fifth strategy offered by the consultants sat at the heart of all other issues; to forge a more significant and interdependent partnership with Methodist." The report recommended, "This level of partnership involves the faculty being the dominant medical staff influence on the hospital, and the hospital being the dominant facility influence on the faculty. [Baylor] does not have such a relationship on the adult side [and] must renegotiate the role of clinical chairs [at Methodist], providing for greater medical authority – responsibility and accountability – over the critical diagnostic and treatment service areas of the hospital [and] define a strong set of institutional relationships."[35] As the new president of Baylor, Dr. Traber's directives had been largely defined a year and a half prior to his arrival. Some say that even before his arrival Baylor was already in discussions with St. Luke's.

Dr. Robert E. Jackson, a highly respected internist to this day who served as president of Methodist's medical staff in 2007–2008, knows the hospital well. His late father, Dr. Dan Jackson, brought his young family to Houston in 1949 and hitched his wagon to that little hospital on Rosalie that was going places. Dr. Robert Jackson, like his late father, has lived and breathed Methodist throughout his own professional career and recalls, "When Peter Traber came here, we went to greet him. ... After Dr. Michael Reardon and I left that meeting, I turned to Mike and said, 'Something is afoot.' The earth was beginning to wobble. The orbit was off kilter. I didn't understand what was actually coming at us. I don't think Methodist understood what was coming at us."[36]

Soon after Dr. Traber's arrival in March 2003, Ron Girotto recalls, "we were informed that several key elements in the affiliation agreement were not acceptable.[37] And I don't know exactly what happened, but things began to change very dramatically. Within about 120 days, we were informed that that agreement—the terms of that agreement that we had worked on for a year and a half—were not acceptable." The new demands, says Girotto, "basically called for a total renegotiation of the whole agreement."[38] Dr. Dan B. Jones, former Baylor dean of clinical affairs and chair of ophthalmology, put it this way: "There began to be conflicts between Methodist and Baylor about funds-flow. There were a lot of things that were locked in with regard to funding that was shared.[39] ... Yet we were getting nothing out of the deal. So the idea [was that] Baylor needed its own separate identifiable clinical practice site."[40] One Baylor board member summarized the sentiment that Baylor felt more like a mere *tenant* than a *partner*.[41]

As tensions grew, it is important to remember that each of these outstanding institutions had a mission and a strategic vision with certain tenets they were not willing to compromise. Each looked to the future and, in the end, could not agree to agree and chose a different path. The boards of these two Texas Medical Center cornerstone institutions included husbands and wives, and fathers and sons—many now on opposite sides of the table. It was difficult, complex, and painful for board members and medical staff alike who had lived at both institutions over the years yet now had hard, gut-wrenching decisions to make.

Like any divorce involving two good people, there are consequences for actions taken. In many ways the changing health care environment predestined the two institutions to pull apart. After all, fifty-year affiliations between medical schools and private hospitals across the country are rare to begin with. In simplistic terms, Baylor wanted their physicians to have more control in the hospital (in relation to the private physicians) along with new financial arrangements related to hospital space and distribution of diagnostic and clinical revenues. In Dr. Traber's words, Baylor was ready to "develop a multispecialty ambulatory clinic that will house the adult medical practices of clinical departments and create superb programs for patients, allow prominence and financial stability of clinical programs, and provide a value advantage for full-time faculty."[42] The *Houston Chronicle* on July 26, 2003, alerted the community with the headline, "A Rumbling in the Medical Center."[43] It would be the first of a long string of headlines that the community would follow in the years ahead.

In the simplest terms, Girotto summarized in a September 25, 2003, letter to Baylor's new president: "... our responsibility has been to provide and manage inpatient and outpatient ambulatory clinical facilities and services, including physician office space, and to support clinical research and education. Baylor's role has been to provide for and manage its basic teaching and scientific research facilities and services along with its professional clinical services. Baylor and Methodist's missions have complemented each other. Baylor is now challenging this relationship."[44]

Girotto further summarized Methodist's objections in a letter dated August 6, 2003, directed to Methodist medical staff, noting that Baylor's proposal was a "sharp departure" from the current affiliation. Baylor's clinic amounted to a competitive enterprise with a duplication of services. Speaking to the balance of power between Methodist-based private physicians and Baylor's full-time academic physicians, he added, "Methodist physicians also will continue their pivotal role in helping set the hospital agenda."[45] Methodist was built on the synergistic value of both the Baylor full-time clinical faculty and private physicians working together, and the hospital had no intention of discounting one for the other.

On November 19, 2003, Dr. Traber announced to his Baylor board ongoing collaborative discussions between Baylor and St. Luke's administrators. In a three-hour meeting he presented to the Baylor board a Memorandum of Understanding (MOU) and sought their approval to enter into a nonbinding agreement to work out the details to move Baylor's primary affiliation to St. Luke's. Baylor's published history notes it was the first time the entire Baylor board learned of Dr. Traber's ongoing discussions with St. Luke's.[46] On that very day Methodist presented an offer to build its medical school partner a clinic facility, and yet Baylor's board voted to support the MOU, giving Dr. Traber the next sixty days to work out the details of a primary affiliation with St. Luke's. Approval of the MOU also preempted Methodist and Baylor from further negotiations during the next two months.

While the Baylor board had approved Dr. Traber's efforts to work out a primary affiliation agreement with St. Luke's, it should be noted that a number of influential Baylor faculty (chairs and center directors) met and called for Dr. Traber's resignation—referring to his approach as "atrocious and very hostile."[47] Two Baylor board members, Dan Arnold (former Baylor chairman 1996–2001) and Morrie Abramson, would eventually lend their support to Methodist. Abramson joined the Methodist board, and the Arnold family along with many friends established the Beverly B. and Daniel C. Arnold Distinguished Chair in Cardiology in honor of William L. Winters, Jr., M.D. at Houston Methodist, the largest externally funded chair at the time.

On February 23, 2004, the sixty-day MOU expired, allowing Baylor to reopen discussions with Methodist while simultaneously continuing discussions with St. Luke's. Clearly Methodist's academic partner was shopping for the best offer as Dr. Traber touted the St. Luke's proposal to be "built on solid brick rather than the crumbling chalk of the Methodist Hospital affiliation."[48] Dr. DeBakey responded to the termination of the MOU in a different light, stating, "Indeed [it] was good news and opens the way for useful renewed discussions concerning the Baylor–Methodist affiliation. The importance of this relationship cannot be overstated, as I emphasized to you in my letter of June 5, 2002."[49]

Methodist had offered to build a clinical building for Baylor under a lease agreement in addition to increasing annual contributions to Baylor to nearly $75 million (an increase of $25 million over past annual support) along with the nearly $1.5 billion in Methodist facilities expansion that would benefit both institutions in many ways. An optimistic John Bookout presented the offer in a detailed letter dated April 13, 2004, noting it was "an agreement upon which our institutions can prosper together for the next 35 years in a primary relationship."[50] Still, among other issues, Methodist was not compromising on surrendering revenues from the hospital's clinical diagnostic and therapeutic services or diminishing the role of the hospital's private physicians. These private physicians helped build the hospital from day one and were key to the hospital's success then, now, and into the future.

Regarding the proposed annual contribution to Baylor approaching $75 million, Methodist wanted more accountability for how the funds were used—more documentation than annual contributions in years past had required. That annual contribution to the medical school, explains Girotto, included three components: 1) stipends for the 200-plus Baylor residents training at Methodist; 2) an Academic Services Agreement left to the medical school dean's discretion to appropriate for medical school research and educational purposes; and 3) support for the school's department chairs who were also the hospital's service chiefs (this earmark represented about half of the total appropriation). The amount varied year to year depending on the chairmen's budget requests.[51]

Discussions in the spring of 2004 went back and forth with pronouncements that the affiliation between Baylor and Methodist was coming together as late as March 30 when Baylor's board chair suggested there were "no deal breakers" in the document. Yet there were, as Dr. Peter Traber revealed on April 21, 2004, "I am pleased to announce that Baylor College of Medicine on April 24th will enter into a new affiliation with St. Luke's Episcopal Hospital, making them our primary private adult affiliated teaching hospital."[52] Recalls Ron Girotto, "We were informed that we were not the ones chosen. … We thought at the end of the day, we would end up being affiliated with Baylor, once all the negotiations had concluded."[53]

"Baylor Splits with Methodist, Picks St. Luke's" read the following morning's *Houston Chronicle* headline. The article quoted Dr. Traber, "Anytime you look to the future to change, you are going to shake the foundations of institutions because change is difficult. But if you don't change, you don't evolve and you don't develop." In the same front-page reporting, Dr. Mike Reardon, a former Baylor faculty member and president-elect of Methodist's medical staff, had a more cautionary take reflecting the sentiments of many throughout the hospital and the Texas Medical Center. "This ends a 50-year productive relationship for an unknown deviation in course that will have unknown consequences."[54]

Despite the efforts of many, including an outside mediation committee, signed petitions by numerous physicians to keep the marriage together, dinners hosted in the homes of prominent physicians who trained at Baylor and practiced at Methodist with strong appeals to maintain the partnership—despite it all—it was not to be.

Hospital board chairman John Bookout stood his ground, feeling the full weight of the responsibility invested in him, and *responsibility* is not a word he takes lightly. While some Methodist board members pressured him to just sign Baylor's demands, he noted that to do so would be giving the institution away. At one point, he recalls, "We were down to bare bones. I put the six conditions I would not sacrifice for Methodist on a blackboard and challenged those board members urging me to sign to step forward and check those issues they would sacrifice. None stepped forward."[55]

It was clearly time for Methodist to move forward on its own. Returning to a community hospital without research and education was never once considered an option. Since the early days of the small hospital on Rosalie, Josie Roberts and the board championed education and research even when funds were hard to find. Without Baylor, building an academic medical center was not going to be easy. Failure was not an option. It would require great faith and resolve going forward, not to mention risk. Not surprising, the process was already underway.

Building an Independent Academic Medical Center

When John Bookout was a young man, long before he was president and CEO of Shell Oil and heading other business ventures, he was a World War II bomber pilot flying the famed Boeing B-17 Flying Fortress. As lead pilot for the 413th squadron of the 96th Bomb Group stationed at RAF Snetterton Heath in Great Britain, not only his nine crewmen but the entire squad trusted him to lead them on bombing missions over the European theatre.[56] Flying in tight formation at thirty thousand feet where temperatures can drop to minus fifty (heated flight suits and oxygen required), Bookout and his crew faced the unknowns of enemy fighters and walls of flak that tore planes from the sky. At war's end he led his bomber squadron on his most rewarding mission, known as Operation Chowhound—dropping food rations in May 1945 to starving Dutch citizens.[57]

That life experience is part of who he is to this day. Whether in the Flying Fortress, running a large international company, or leading the Methodist board, Bookout understands the higher responsibility that leadership requires and takes it seriously. He once opted to miss an important corporate meeting out of state for which he was paid by retainer in order to chair a Methodist board meeting. When pressured that Methodist was voluntary work and should be a lower priority, he shot back that it made no difference—the responsibility of leadership and the trust invested in him was the same, paid or nonpaid. He stayed in Houston and led the Methodist board meeting as scheduled.[58] For him, a commitment is a commitment—pure and simple.

Even before Baylor's announcement to leave Methodist, hospital leadership with Bookout at the helm was at work addressing their every option. Site visits, recalls Ron Girotto, were made to UT Southwestern Medical Center in Dallas, Massachusetts General and Harvard in Boston, Cedars Sinai in Los Angeles, and Cleveland Clinic to study the academic medical center landscape and seek advice. Bookout recalls clearly one such meeting where he was told

Methodist was thirty-five years too late to become an academic medical center.[59] Others were not so negative. Recalls Girotto, guidance from Dr. Floyd Loop, a highly respected cardiac surgeon who was then head of Cleveland Clinic, was memorable. "Ron, you need to go home and get a good night's sleep. You've got the world by the tail. Clinically, you have one of the best hospitals in the world … but you have to decide if you want to be a research and education center … and get behind that. It will not be easy."[60]

In January 2004, three months before the Baylor–Methodist partnership ended, Girotto and his administrative team brought to the board a $50 million proposal to establish the Research Institute at Methodist. Showing their strong support (with or without Baylor) the board committed $100 million.[61]

With Baylor's departure in April 2004, Methodist moved with lightning speed and for good reason. At stake was the employee base and community of physicians and experienced support teams who were in search of direction following this divorce. Methodist employees at all levels, and especially the physicians who entrusted their patients and therefore their professional reputations to the hospital, watched carefully (some with one eye on the exit) to see how their hospital would respond.

With a new research building on the drawing board, Methodist needed a new academic partner as well as a new Methodist physician organization to replace the departing Baylor physicians (including residents) who literally were gone overnight. John Bookout recalls it was a conversation with Dr. Robert Grossman, chairman of neurosurgery at Baylor, that provided important direction. Dr. Grossman's prominence in neurosurgery at the national level led the American Board of Neurological Surgery to call Houston their home for more than fifteen years. His presence in Trauma Room 1 at Parkland Hospital that fateful day in Dallas when John F. Kennedy arrived[62] is just one chapter of many in an accomplished surgical career spanning six decades.

Dr. Grossman had been recruited jointly by Methodist and Baylor in 1980—effectively uniting the department. He explains, "It wasn't good to have the two positions separate. Dr. Jim Greenwood … was the chief of service at Methodist and Dr. George Ehni was the chairman at Baylor."[63] Dr. Ehni, it should be noted, was a highly respected and talented neurosurgeon who had served as president of the Neurosurgical Society of America in 1976 among many other national leadership roles. A 1940 graduate of Northwestern University Medical School, he had joined Baylor in 1949, the year after Dr. DeBakey arrived, and remained on the Baylor faculty until his death in 1986.

With experience running neurosurgery from a combined Baylor and Methodist perspective, Dr. Grossman was the ideal adviser to John Bookout at this time in the Baylor–Methodist relationship. Under his leadership, the department of neurosurgery developed into one of the top ten departments in the nation. He explained to Bookout that he and his academic colleagues built their careers around the importance of research and teaching combined with outstanding patient care. Methodist would need to affiliate not with a good medical school but with one of the highest caliber on the level of Baylor—top ten in the nation.[64]

Bookout listened carefully, noting that top ten certainly limited the field. Soon he was on the phone to consult with a trusted medical leader from Methodist's past. Dr. Antonio Gotto, Jr. was an old friend, Bookout's personal physician in years past, and a highly respected physician–scientist who left Houston in 1996 to become dean of Cornell University's medical school, Weill Cornell Medical College, in New York City.

Recalls Dr. Gotto: "I was very distressed when I heard that Baylor and Methodist were separating. … I had strong feelings for both Baylor and Methodist Hospital, but if we were in a position to collaborate with Methodist and help them on the road to becoming an academic medical center, then I would feel very good about it." [65]

Weill Cornell Medical College, established in 1898, had a long-established primary affiliation with New York Hospital, the second oldest hospital in the U.S., chartered in 1771 by King George III. The hospital was home to the first molded plaster splint and the first bedside patient chart. It was in the 1920s that Cornell's medical college and New York Hospital first affiliated. [66] On December 31, 1997, New York Hospital merged with Presbyterian Hospital, creating New York-Presbyterian Hospital, [67] the largest nonprofit hospital in the Northeast with 2,000 beds and sixteen percent of Manhattan's hospital patient market. [68] While the two hospitals merged, their respective medical schools (the Joan & Sanford I. Weill Medical College of Cornell University and the Columbia University Vagelos College of Physicians and Surgeons) remained separate with New York-Presbyterian having two campuses, a Weill Cornell and a Columbia campus.

Additionally, Weill Cornell had recently opened a medical school in the sovereign Arab state of Qatar recognizing in this new age of big data and telemedicine that distance and international boundaries no longer dictate how medical expertise and training are deployed. Methodist's Ron Girotto had served as a consultant on that venture during his brief retirement and understood that global medicine was more than a good idea for the future, it was already intrinsic in the forward thinking of both Weill Cornell and Methodist.

In short order the potential for a Methodist and Weill Cornell/New York-Presbyterian partnership was formed during Bookout's May 21, 2004, breakfast meeting at the Regency Hotel with Dr. Gotto. [69] Bookout outlined in some detail for Dr. Gotto the situation and Methodist's need to find a medical school of the highest caliber for affiliation. Dr. Gotto then asked a simple question nearly missed by Bookout in his quest for guidance. "What about Weill Cornell?" Bookout noted that he wanted to compare notes with leadership in Houston and would call Dr. Gotto after returning to Houston. The two would be in close contact in the weeks to come. That Monday (May 24) Bookout first briefed two trusted advisers, Judge Ewing Werlein, Jr. and D. Gibson "Gib" Walton. Both were experienced in matters of Methodist's board and the church. Both indicated their support. The next day Girotto and Methodist legal counsel Ramon "Mick" Cantu were briefed and made plans to travel to New York and get the agreement on paper.

After the initial breakfast meeting in New York, Dr. Gotto followed up with Sandy Weill, the school's namesake and chairman of the board, who was supportive. Soon, the full

Methodist board was involved as well as the Texas attorney general, who was briefed and provided his sign-off. By June 3, just thirteen days after the initial breakfast meeting, Girotto and Cantu were in New York meeting with Dr. Gotto and Weill. The former CEO of Citigroup, Sandy Weill proved a tough negotiator yet like-minded with Bookout in bringing the two institutions together quickly. Bookout and the board understood that time was of the essence to restore internal confidence among the medical staff and employee base. Weill agreed as did both boards. Says Bookout, "Sandy Weill deserves a great deal of credit for his part in seeing this affiliation to fruition."

Additionally, recalls Girotto, Bookout made it clear that certain things were not acceptable. "I don't want to take Methodist into any affiliation where Methodist is not fully in charge of its business and decision processes ... but rather, we want someone who is a partner that we can consult with. If we accept their advice, wonderful. If we don't, they're not going to get upset about it."[70] Discussions moved quickly and the affiliation was announced at a press conference in Houston on June 23, 2004—a mere eight weeks had elapsed since Baylor's April announcement to affiliate with St. Luke's. "Methodist Hospital Pairing with Cornell: New Partners Say Distance Not a Problem," read the *Houston Chronicle* lead front-page headline the following morning. A jointly prepared four-page press release announced the affiliation and outlined the details, including brief biographical sketches of each of the three partners.[71]

> New York, NY (June 23, 2004)—Weill Cornell Medical College and NewYork-Presbyterian Hospital in New York City and The Methodist Hospital in Houston jointly announced today that they have entered into an historic medical affiliation that will benefit residents of New York and Texas. Under the terms of the 30-year agreement ... the affiliation will enable the three internationally renowned institutions to collaborate in providing high-quality patient care, cutting-edge clinical and biomedical research, and the most innovative medical education and training of future physicians and biomedical scientists.

John Bookout noted, "Today marks an important, historic milestone for The Methodist Hospital. ... This new affiliation establishes new heights of collaboration and recognizes the strengths of all three partners. This relationship is the first of its kind and furthers our shared missions of excellence in patient care, research, and teaching."

Sandy Weill added, "Building a medical and scientific bridge between the North and South, this alliance offers unique opportunities to enhance health care for diverse patient populations and for fostering new initiatives across the spectrum of academic medicine, including clinical trials, international medicine, national health care policy, outcomes research, and graduate medical education."

Also adding remarks to the events of the day were Ron Girotto and Dr. Antonio Gotto, Jr. among others, including Jeffrey S. Lehman (J.D.), president of Cornell University, who noted, "We look forward to the opportunity to begin new collaborations with our new Weill Cornell faculty in Houston to the benefit not only of patients in our local communities but ultimately throughout the world."

Methodist's autonomy under the arrangement, and the fourteen hundred miles between the institutions, made the agreement unique and a first-of-its-kind "transcontinental affiliation."[72] Physicians at Methodist would be eligible for faculty appointments at Weill Cornell but such appointments would be neither automatic nor required. Weill Cornell students would have the option of serving as residents at New York-Presbyterian Hospital or joining a brand-new residency program that would be established at Methodist. Additionally, principal areas of collaboration were developed around education, research, quality improvement, information technology, and international program development.[73]

Enough credit cannot be given to John Bookout for his leadership. Those who know him well will tell you he will always be the last person in the room to seek credit. Ernest "Ernie" H. Cockrell, who has championed the Research Institute from conception to centennial, has a deep respect for how Bookout handled negotiations with Baylor while keeping the board informed and involved. "There was not intransigence, he was not throwing bombs, he was not being hard-headed, he was willing to negotiate anytime, anyplace."[74] His commitment to Methodist, adds a supporting chorus of hospital leadership, never wavered as he led Methodist to a renaissance in education, research, and patient care in the immediate years following Baylor's departure.

With the new Weill Cornell affiliation, Methodist had to move quickly to establish educational programs. Residencies, the important on-the-job training for postgraduate medical students, generally range from two to six years depending on the specialty. In critical care areas throughout the hospital, Baylor wasted no time transferring their residents to other programs outside Methodist—effectively leaving the hospital in a lurch. Ed Tyrrell summarized the situation noting, "When the divorce happened overnight—literally overnight—the students and the residents left. So one day we had several hundred. The next day we had zero. It was a cataclysmic event, not only from an educational standpoint, but from the standpoint of taking care of patients. All of a sudden, doctors who had residents working with them suddenly had nobody working with them."[75]

Adds Ron Girotto, "One of the great outcomes was that New York-Presbyterian and Weill Cornell gave us the expertise on how to go about building our own residency programs."[76] Dr. H. Dirk Sostman, a Weill Cornell radiologist with expertise in developing academic educational programs, provided invaluable guidance to get started and continues to serve as a key adviser for academic training programs with a new appointment in 2019 as president and chief academic officer of the Houston Methodist Academic Institute.

In 2004 Methodist also recruited Dr. Judy L. Paukert (Ph.D.) from The University of Texas San Antonio as vice president for the Methodist Hospital Education Institute led in-house by Dr. William Winters, a highly respected cardiologist with years of experience at both Baylor and Methodist. Dr. Paukert and her team, reporting to future CEO Dr.

Marc Boom, developed an unprecedented twenty-five accreditation programs in just seven years while transitioning to Methodist six other programs. Her work also resulted in a 2012 award from the Accreditation Council for Graduate Medical Education.[77]

The first accreditation for seven Methodist pathology residents included six subspecialties and was announced about a year after Dr. Paukert's arrival. Also in 2005, says Girotto, "It had to be divine intervention [when] St. Joseph's Hospital [in downtown Houston] called to say they had residency programs needing a home." Dr. Boom, reporting to Girotto, was tasked to oversee those negotiations. The *Houston Business Journal* announced the good news on July 20: "With Houston's Christus St. Joseph Hospital on the selling block, the hospital announced Wednesday that it will transfer five residency programs to The Methodist Hospital, allowing the hospital's 76 residents to continue their medical education."[78] From these early beginnings Methodist-based residency programs, strengthened by the new primary affiliation with Weill Cornell Medical College and New York-Presbyterian Hospital, grew steadily. By 2011 nearly two hundred residents were completing their advanced training at Methodist.[79] During the centennial year, that number exceeds three hundred.

The departure of Baylor in April 2004 included a seemingly endless cascade of difficult challenges. Given Baylor chairs were also the chiefs of service at Methodist at the time of the separation, physicians had to make difficult career choices between staying with Baylor or Methodist. Some immediately left for St. Luke's, the first of whom was Baylor's surgical chair, Dr. F. Charles Brunicardi, who left June 16. Seven years later he would leave Baylor to join the medical faculty of UCLA's David Geffen School of Medicine in Los Angeles. Others elected to stay with Methodist, including Dr. Michael W. Lieberman, who chaired Baylor's pathology department and brought with him nearly all of his faculty. His resignation was submitted to Dr. Peter Traber on July 8. He would also play a pivotal role planning and designing a new building to house the Houston Methodist Research Institute, to open in 2010.

With the departure of Baylor physicians, the hospital moved quickly to build its own in-house physician organization out of necessity given the split presented logistical hurdles with sobering financial implications. Approximately forty percent of Methodist admissions (sixteen thousand annually at the time)[80] came through Baylor's clinical faculty. Recalls Ed Tyrrell, "With our massive infrastructure and investment in capital assets and medical equipment, if you don't get the patient flow with your financials, all that capital investment becomes stranded."[81]

That winning combination of in-house physicians and private community physicians had carried the Methodist culture to this point and would carry it forward. Now leadership started building a Methodist organization of hospital physicians. During the hospital's centennial year, fifteen years after the two institutions parted ways, Houston Methodist's Specialty Physician Group comprises more than 630 Methodist-employed physicians (and growing) in addition to more than a hundred physicians serving patients through the Houston Methodist Primary Care Group[82] who work in concert with many of the community's best and brightest private physicians. Key to building the physician organization upon Baylor's departure was the trust factor Methodist and its leadership, particularly Ron Girotto, had established with Houston-area physicians over the years.

Trust is a currency that money cannot buy and is perhaps best illustrated by Dr. Stanley Appel, who left Baylor to join Methodist in 2005. Dr. Appel, one of the country's foremost experts on ALS and other neuromuscular diseases, was among many who faced the difficult decision to stay with Baylor and St. Luke's or join Methodist. He had been hired in 1977 to chair Baylor's neurology department and direct the operations of the new jointly owned Baylor–Methodist Neurosensory Center. Faced with the decision to stay at Baylor or join Methodist, he turned to his most trusted adviser—his ninety-six-year-old mother. Dr. Appel recalls one of the many important lessons his mother taught him before she passed away. She said, "Over the years, I've learned something. I don't have a great deal of trust in institutions, but I have a great deal of trust in people. You go with the people you trust, and you'll never be wrong in your decision." Dr. Appel went with Methodist.[83]

He was soon joined by Dr. Robert Grossman, chair of neurosurgery. While cardiovascular surgeon Dr. Joseph S. Coselli moved to St. Luke's, many other cardiovascular surgeons chose to stay.[84] Adds Dr. Boom, who in 2012 would be the first physician named president and CEO of Methodist, the relationships and trust with physicians that the administrative team established over the years with both private and full-time Baylor physicians went a long way in rebuilding the hospital's faculty.[85] Despite the protests of Baylor that Methodist was unfairly poaching their faculty, many more of the school's academic clinicians chose Methodist.

Dr. Boom adds: "You have to remember Methodist was home to many of these Baylor physicians. While they were Baylor faculty, they had offices in Methodist facilities, parked their cars here, cared for patients here, and many conducted research here. When faced with the choice they found joining Methodist had many advantages for their careers as well as their patients.[86] They were put in a very difficult position … and a vast majority of those individuals made the decision to stay at Methodist. But if you look at it, ninety percent of what they were doing didn't change."[87]

Looking back on her years of leadership at the hospital, Dr. Lynn Schroth notes, "Once the divorce happened and we were on our own, we had candidates we would never in a million years have had before. With our Cornell affiliation and the new Research Institute building [to open in 2010], we were able to recruit outstanding faculty around the country we never would have gotten before."[88]

For example, says Girotto, Dr. Barbara Bass was recruited as Methodist's new surgical chair and excelled. "When she arrived, I went up to see her the next day … she was on the sixteenth floor of Smith Tower. And she was sitting back in the corner and I felt so sorry for her. She must have been thinking, 'What have I gotten myself into?' I mean the whole floor was empty. [Like the other recruits] I told her if you execute, you make it happen—I'm going to give you the resources to make it happen. [Similarly] the cardiology guys were aware of what they had and what they were getting into, without exception. It was incredible. If you bring the people in, and give them the freedom to do—because they are good people, honest people, hardworking people and bright—great things can happen."[89] These were words right out of the Josie Roberts playbook—an ingrained institutional commitment to building excellence by recruiting the best and giving them the best.

Dr. Bass, who holds the John F., Jr. and Carolyn Bookout Presidential Distinguished Chair in the Department of Surgery, exemplifies Houston Methodist's success in recruiting at the highest level following Baylor's departure in 2004. A woman pioneer in surgery, mentor to many, and former president of the American College of Surgeons (among numerous national leadership roles), she is considered a star in academic circles. From a corner office with bare walls in July 2005, Dr. Bass built a surgical department that is today recognized as one of the best in the nation. How and why Dr. Bass came to Methodist is worth telling as it is one of many similar key recruitment stories that rapidly transformed Methodist in the mid-2000s. In Dr. Bass's words:

> Houston Methodist offered a clinical platform that is nearly unsurpassed in terms of capability, scope, scale of any hospital in this country. There were a lot of wonderful existing surgeons and clinical activity here already, but it was starting over in a new way in terms of recruiting faculty, building specific new programs that had not been part of the landscape here, and moving the hospital's departmental energies into centers. Centers are a new way of delivering health care, but really doing that from the get-go. … Without Mr. Bookout I would've said, "Is this really feasible?" With Mr. Bookout, this was all feasible and all part of the grand vision to really sustain what Houston Methodist had always been in terms of an academic, premier, clinical care research-driven, educationally focused institution. Others influential in my decision were Ron Girotto and Lynn Schroth.
>
> There are maybe ten hospitals I would say of this scope and scale in the nation [so this] was an exciting place to come and be a chair of surgery, because you get to leverage all that plus you get to build new things and faculty and programs including residency programs and educational pathways. If you're at a place that already has those things all set up, you can't be [as] creative or as innovative, which is another hallmark of the Methodist culture. … The beauty of this place is it was not stuck in the mud, we were running fast.[90]

"A century old and yet a startup" is the way Dr. Alan B. Lumsden summarized this rebirth of the hospital from 2004 to the centennial. His memorable line presented during a 2019 presentation for Houston Methodist DeBakey Heart & Vascular Center captures the very spirit of Houston Methodist in recent years.[91] Dr. Bass and other key clinical leadership recruits were central to this transformation. She began by recruiting surgical leaders in transplantation, gastrointestinal surgery, and cancer—each success stories of their own. She also came with a vision that would revolutionize surgical training—an idea presented in the next chapter.

In addition to the advances in surgery, the transition to academic medical center required an equally talented leader for the department of medicine. Dr. Richard J. Robbins was recruited to lead the department of medicine, "a cornerstone department to surgery in importance and in quality thanks to his strong leadership," says Dr. Boom.[92] Dr. Robbins, holder of the Charles and Anne Duncan Presidential Distinguished Chair in the Department of Medicine, is an internationally recognized endocrinologist renowned for his pioneering work with thyroid cancer. Like Dr. Bass, he has built a nationally recognized program and recruited top talent.

Another early recruit, notes John Bookout, now chairman emeritus of the board, was Dr. Stephen T. Wong (Ph.D.), who leads Houston Methodist's department of systems medicine and bioengineering and holds a John S. Dunn Foundation chair. Dr. Wong brought with him his team of nearly twenty researchers, decades of research and management experience in industry and academia, and experience at Bell Laboratories and Harvard. He was considered such a valued faculty member at Harvard that the *Boston Globe* announced his departure with the headline, "Houston 1, Boston 0."[93]

Add to these important recruitments Dr. Gavin Britz, who in the centennial year is chairman of neurosurgery at Houston Methodist and recognized as one of the most experienced cerebrovascular surgeons in the U.S. A native of South Africa, he came to Houston Methodist in 2013 from Duke University Medical Center. He recalls his father's spinal cord injury inspired him to seek a career in medicine with a special interest in neurosurgery. Today he leads a team that tackles some of the most challenging and life-threatening conditions known to mankind.

It should go without saying that a centennial book such as this cannot possibly list all of the outstanding faculty recruited in immediate years following the departure of Baylor. A list of departmental leadership (2004–2019) can be found in the appendices—each of whom has likewise recruited outstanding talent and accomplished important milestones. Names like Bass, Robbins, Wong, and Britz represent but the tip of the iceberg as Methodist transitioned from a large community hospital network of care facilities to a nationally recognized independent academic medical center.

That *independent* status is an important distinction, notes Dr. Boom, in that it "allows Houston Methodist full control (independent of medical school ownership or governance) to pick and choose affiliations that best further the institution's mission."[94] While there are just over six thousand hospitals in the U.S., the Alliance of Independent Academic Medical Centers notes there are only about seventy major academic medical centers and health systems in the country.[95]

It's Not Over Until It's Over

Throughout the remainder of the 2000s the hospital continued to be challenged by its former academic partner on a host of financial and academic issues, including disputed reimbursements and alleged unfair faculty recruitment. Even Houston Methodist's right to conduct independent research without a Texas Medical Center-based academic partner was challenged when Baylor informed trustees of the Texas Medical Center on April 27, 2005, that the medical center's deed restrictions seemed to allow Methodist use of their land for hospital services only and excluded internally generated educational or research uses.[96]

After a two-month review, the Texas Medical Center ruled in favor of Methodist's position and appealed to the two institutions to resolve their dispute. The *Houston Chronicle* reported the following day, "Baylor Fails in Bid to Stop Methodist: Medical Center Managers Say the Charter and Deed Are No Obstacle to Hospital's Plans."[97]

Texas Attorney General Greg Abbott's office had remained silent but now released a statement expressing hope that the two institutions would work out their differences. Abbott, who would be elected governor of Texas in 2015, was adamant that the two work together. He had received more than a few complaints that Baylor physicians were being unfairly recruited by Methodist, including dire concerns about the split voiced directly from Dr. DeBakey himself.[98] Some wrongly suggested Methodist was trying to put Baylor out of business.

Abbott responded by mandating in July 2005 a Joint Cooperation Committee (JCC) be formed with a specific directive. "The JCC should propose and eventually implement specific cooperative activities, renew the spirit of collaboration and cooperation within the TMC, set standards and parameters to govern the future relationship of the parties and set an example of the meaning of good faith and cooperation."[99] Topics were to include physician movement, privileges and expectations, residency programs, and other matters "to redefine and repair the relationship going forward." A 1942 Texas Supreme Court decision gave Abbott the right and the duty to represent the public interest in matters involving charitable trusts.[100]

Moreover, his interest in the welfare of the Texas Medical Center was personal. He had spent many weeks in recovery in the Texas Medical Center in the 1980s after an accident left him partially paralyzed and in a wheelchair. David Underwood, chairman of the TMC board and vice chair of the Methodist board, recalled in 2015 that Abbott made it crystal clear that the powers of his office gave him the right to fire both boards if necessary. Elizabeth Ghrist of the Texas Medical Center board was named to chair the new Abbott-directed committee that included Methodist board members Mary A. Daffin, Connie Dyer, and Dr. Stephen P. Wende (D.Min.), a member of the Methodist clergy as well as a board member. Baylor's board was represented by Robert H. Allen, Paul W. Hobby, and Terry Huffington.

Ultimately, on September 5, 2005, both Methodist and Baylor agreed in a thirteen-page Joint Cooperation Agreement to ten key features of cooperation, including an agreement that Baylor faculty may join the Methodist medical staff through Methodist's open staff model. They also agreed to have at least ninety Baylor students rotate through Methodist residency programs for five years and to a $16 million initiative to aid childhood immunization efforts and emergency room care throughout the community.[101] Daffin recalls of those meetings, "While at times the atmosphere in the room was unpleasant, both parties identified the sticking points as well as common ground that we could agree on. We focused on funds that would benefit the community and those areas we could agree on to support residency training opportunities and faculty movement."[102] By 2012 those funds designated for the community had been awarded to 223 nonprofits in the Greater Houston Area.

Richard Wainerdi, emeritus president of the Texas Medical Center, noted, "At the end of the [JCC] meetings, a decision was made by both parties that they would find their way into the future on their own. In my judgment, the outcome was better than I expected in the sense that both institutions could work together to the extent they wanted to, and both institutions had the freedom to chart a course."[103]

• • •

In 2007 John Bookout reached the term limit of his chairmanship. In 1996 he had called for revisions to the board's governance that resulted in ten-year term limits for board officers (members have no term limits). Reaching his term limit as chairman, he served as the board's senior chair until 2017, when he was named chair emeritus—a title he holds with distinction at the time of the hospital's centennial year.

In 2007 vice chair Judge Ewing Werlein, Jr., a senior judge for U.S. District Court for the Southern District of Texas (nominated by President George H.W. Bush in 1991), assumed the hospital board's chairmanship role. Judge Werlein, who first joined the board in 1990, had previously chaired the board's first committee on quality and patient safety and was well versed on all matters related to the board and the transformation underway at Methodist post-Baylor.

Knowing the hospital and its history is something Judge Werlein excels in, given he was born in the original Methodist hospital on Rosalie. "I come from a family who considers service to the community, the church, and Houston Methodist a high calling." Growing up, he remembers his mother was an active member of the Blue Bird Circle. When the new hospital opened in the Texas Medical Center, he remembers dining almost every Sunday after church with his family in the hospital's cafeteria. "The Methodists were so proud of the new hospital. It was a gathering place on Sundays for many of our Methodist friends and there was plenty of free parking on Bertner in those days."[104]

Judge Werlein stepped forward to lead the board in implementing the hospital's many ongoing initiatives. Two key activities on his list included facilities construction and expansion programs and the continued development of the education, research, and clinical programs to achieve Methodist's ambitious goal to transform itself into a top-ranked independent academic medical center. Additionally, he faced the ongoing challenge of addressing multiple and ongoing Baylor-generated disputes that followed in the wake of their 2004 departure.

Today, Judge Werlein remains as adept at addressing the many challenges and opportunities in detail as he was during his decade-long tenure as chairman of the board (2007–2017). Ask him for a favorite topic and he'll tell you about a program that remains close to his heart—quality of patient care. His committee's early work in this area is impressive. In fact, he will remind you Methodist was far from a leader in this field in the 1990s, prompting the board's immediate attention in creating a Quality Committee in 1999 that he chaired. Houston Methodist is now ranked in the highest tier when it comes to patient outcomes defined not by perception but rigorous systemwide processes for measuring patient satisfaction, patient safety, and quality of care metrics (to name three), which are in turn benchmarked against a cohort of peer hospitals.

Like John Bookout, Judge Werlein will defer any credit for this turnaround to the work of others, including the "terrific job" of board vice chair Mary Daffin, whose committee (now renamed Quality and Patient Safety) oversees a model program that has been the recipient of the highest honors in the nation among academic medical centers.[105] Judge Werlein also credits Dr. Boom's leadership, which supports a systems approach to quality of care and safety performance measures—a systemwide approach that measures and monitors metrics across every Methodist care facility. This systematic approach to quality improvement is essential to ensure that the highest standards of patient care are upheld across the entire Houston Methodist system and that patient care components throughout the network inform each other of successful initiatives that can be shared to continually improve the whole. This rigorous approach, notes Judge Werlein, and seconded by Daffin, is one more example of *leading medicine* that should not be overlooked.[106]

The judge also recalls Attorney General Abbott's fact-finding visit to his courthouse office back in 2005 after hearing community-wide concerns that the split from Baylor would damage irreparably both institutions along with the reputation of the Texas Medical Center. He notes he was pleased to report to the future governor how well things were going at Methodist with the new Weill Cornell affiliation, growing residency programs, a major Research Institute building in planning, expanded community and international outreach, a new Methodist physician organization, and newly created joint agreements with both the University of Houston and Rice University.

Abbott also learned that while Baylor, as the hospital's partner for half a century, had taken the lead in fundraising over the years, Methodist was quickly strengthening its own fundraising arm at the time. The newly revitalized Houston Methodist Hospital Foundation was on a fast track to generating invaluable community support for research and academic programs—demonstrating a community of support for Methodist. Recalls Judge Werlein of that meeting, "I remember outlining all we had going point by point only to hear the attorney general say repeatedly, 'No one told me about that.' I didn't know that."[107]

It should not be lost in the conversation that at the time of the future Texas governor's visit, the hospital's revitalized foundation had in planning its first-ever philanthropic campaign with a $200 million goal and chaired by David M. Underwood (*Giving Hope*, 2004–2012). The campaign, in fact, raised $212.5 million, resulting in twenty-six endowed chairs and professorships, twenty-seven fellowships, awards and scholarships, and nine major namings of facilities and programs.[108]

Today endowed chairs alone funded in the post-Baylor years are too many to list here but can be found in this book's appendices. Names on buildings, names on fellowships and scholarships, names on academic programs can be seen throughout Houston Methodist and proudly featured in hospital publications, websites, walls, and plaques. The generosity of the community continues through the centennial year with a new campaign chaired by Elizabeth Blanton Wareing and co-chaired by Rusty Walter (*Leading Medicine to the Power of M*) with a $500 million goal designed to "attract brilliance, accelerate research, train superstars, and promote healing."[109] Drs. Richard Harper and H. Dirk Sostman co-chaired the Faculty Campaign Steering Committee for the campaign.

Gifts over the years represent much more than dollars—they are personal and heartfelt as exemplified by the Nantz National Alzheimer Center (NNAC) at Houston Methodist. When the father of CBS sportscaster Jim Nantz died in 2008 following treatment at Houston Methodist for Alzheimer's, Jim and his wife, Courtney, met with Dr. Stanley Appel to develop their vision to create not a local but a national resource addressing the many complexities of Alzheimer's and associated dementia-based illnesses. Directed by Dr. Joseph C. Masdeu, a leading specialist in neurology, memory, and cognitive disorders, the NNAC is today one of the premier programs in the country, assisting patients and their families while coordinating research and training programs that attract health professionals worldwide.[110]

Without question, the hospital's transformation into a leading independent academic medical center that began in the mid-2000s owes an ongoing debt to the community of donors (generous individuals and foundations) who continue to shape and define Houston Methodist's *leading medicine* capabilities to this day.

· · ·

Similar to the aftershocks that follow large seismic events, arbitration between Baylor and Methodist continued for nearly five years after the two institutions separated in 2004. Apart from Abbott's 2005 Joint Cooperation Committee, on August 30, 2007, Baylor served Methodist an additional demand for arbitration. At stake were $47.5 million in funds deposited at Methodist that Baylor claimed as theirs. The arbitrator's final decision, delivered in November 2009, was to award all but $8.1 million to Methodist[111]—funds carefully invested in Houston Methodist's future.

The difficult period after the divorce challenged the entire board and administrative team. Looking back on the transformation of Houston Methodist as its own independent academic medical center, Judge Werlein notes with great pride all that has been accomplished since 2004 that might not otherwise have come to fruition.[112]

Key to navigating the difficult challenges of the decade, he notes, was that decision John Bookout made in 1996 during the early years of his chairmanship to revise the governance structure of the board. The implications were much greater than placing ten-year term limits on officers. Judge Werlein elaborates:

> While Mr. Bookout was chairman, he appointed a governance committee chaired by a Bishop Woodrow Hearn, who was the bishop of the Texas Annual Conference at that time. The objective was to get a board of size where it can operate and have full accountability for what is transpiring. So it was reduced to twenty-six [members] with the approval of the Texas Annual Conference.[113] Membership now includes four from the clergy including the bishop as well as two physicians (three when the CEO is a physician). Then a variety of others who come from the community.
>
> This really helped Houston Methodist when we got into that difficult period in 2003 and 2004. The board was small enough now to where they all were parts of the decision-making process. They were all informed and we were able to proceed [not always in agreement but] as a unified board in all of the important decision-making. To this day we have a fully involved and engaged board that works through committees ... most everybody in at least two or more committees. Everybody's involved in committee service [and] has a thorough and deep understanding of what is going on at the hospital and is instrumental in the formulation of our policies. We are today very much a *participatory* board as opposed to a *ceremonial* board.[114]

The new board requirements meant that those not able to commit to new attendance guidelines and expectations for committee assignments were replaced by new members who could. Houston Methodist board member Mary Daffin personifies what *participatory* means given her years of voluntary board service leading the Quality and Patient Safety Committee while also serving on the Heart Council.[115] Her voice is not alone when she says, "You feel an awesome burden for everyone who comes through these doors. You feel that responsibility to provide the best care, whoever that person is. They simply deserve the very best."[116]

Baylor and St. Luke's Path Forward

While Baylor changed course and affiliated with St. Luke's Episcopal Hospital in 2004, their new working relationship proved tenuous. Three years into the affiliation Baylor was already making plans to build their own hospital. On April 25, 2007, Baylor and St. Luke's negotiated a downgraded affiliation.[117] Baylor trustee Marc Shapiro summarized the situation in Dr. William Butler's history of Baylor College of Medicine in this way: "I think if you look behind it we didn't have congruent goals. St. Luke's goal was to provide faith-based care. Their goal was never particularly to be a great academic hospital. There's nothing wrong with that goal. It's just that we wanted a great academic hospital and that really wasn't their goal."[118]

Baylor's new hospital was to be a mile south of the main Texas Medical Center Campus on thirty-five acres they procured in 1988. Groundbreaking took place on May 23, 2007. Five months later the Parkwood site was named Baylor's McNair Campus. Financed by $400 million in bonds,[119] Baylor's trustees were forced to refinance the debt after the project went over budget, then on March 25, 2009, the trustees chose to pause construction altogether.

Dr. Peter Traber, who was instrumental in planning the new Baylor hospital, was not there to see it through. Six months after groundbreaking[120] on the McNair campus, he was dismissed from his leadership role on November 19, 2008.[121] Shapiro, Baylor's Finance Committee chairman, summarized, "He was asked to resign because of the significant operating losses that the school was having ... there were also ethical questions and interpersonal questions. ... But I would say the primary one was monetary."[122]

Rice and Baylor Merger Discussions

The 2009 potential merger of Rice University and Baylor that followed Dr. Traber's departure also generated a great deal of media attention, especially since many among the Rice faculty publicly opposed the idea for a number of reasons, including the potential downside of Rice University's much larger endowment being placed at risk. Judge Werlein, chairman of Methodist's board at the time, notes that in 2009 he was invited to a dinner at the home of Rice president David Leebron and was asked if Houston Methodist would entertain offering training opportunities at Methodist should Baylor's medical school merge with Rice. Leebron explained that establishing an adult hospital relationship was a precondition for a merger. The judge's answer was open and to the point—"yes."[123] Speaking for the board, Ron Girotto sent a memo to the Methodist medical staff noting the hospital would begin discussions about collaborating with Rice "after" any merger while making it clear that Methodist already had a primary affiliation with Weill Cornell.[124]

Yet the merger with Rice was not to be and ended with an announcement in early January 2010.[125] Girotto responded to the news, "Today we learned the merger negotiations between Rice University and Baylor College of Medicine ended. ... The Methodist Hospital is primarily affiliated with Weill Cornell's medical school and enjoys several ongoing programs with Rice and Baylor. We will continue to look for ways to expand our collaborations with each school."[126]

In July 2010, Dr. Paul Klotman, from the Mount Sinai School of Medicine in New York City, was named Baylor's new president and CEO, a position he remains in at the time of the Houston Methodist centennial year. Under Dr. Klotman's able leadership Baylor College of Medicine has moved forward as one of the outstanding medical schools in the nation.

For Sale: St. Luke's Episcopal Hospital

Early in Dr. Marc Boom's presidency of Houston Methodist, he recalls a note he received from David Fine, president and CEO of St. Luke's, asking if he would meet with some of their consultants. "It was May or early June 2012 that they asked if we would have any interest in acquiring them if they decided to sell. I told them we would consider it."[127]

Thus began a yearlong process discussing the pros and cons of acquiring St. Luke's. On the positive side was the opportunity to join forces with the Texas Heart Institute at St. Luke's—combining two of the nation's great cardiovascular programs while coming full circle on the legacies of Drs. DeBakey and Cooley. Likewise, such a union would combine two prestigious transplant programs, creating perhaps the largest whole organ transplant center in the world. Additionally, recalls Dr. Boom, purchasing St. Luke's would give Methodist an immediate presence in The Woodlands, which held strategic importance given the rapid growth of Houston to the north.[128]

Yet there were key reservations as well. St. Luke's facilities in the Texas Medical Center were in poor condition and a costly purchase on top of a major renovation gave pause to the idea. Also, St. Luke's facilities in Sugar Land would be duplicative of Methodist's campus. Other than St. Luke's presence in The Woodlands, St. Luke's community hospitals were considered underperforming.[129] Add to that the many complexities of the St. Luke's–Baylor affiliation in 2004.

Thus, the Methodist board had much to ponder and worked diligently addressing every detail. By December 2012 St. Luke's announced their process for bids. Recalls Dr. Boom, in the interest of transparency all Methodist staff and physicians were notified of the negotiations.[130] Moreover, Texas Children's Hospital (TCH) and Methodist would submit a joint bid as there were multiple advantages, especially given TCH's interest in the St. Luke's contiguous footprint to theirs. Adds Dr. Boom, "We knew Memorial Hermann was also bidding and that the third bidder to be selected was a Catholic system [unidentified at the time]. Larry Kellner, the former CEO of Continental Airlines, was then on our board and incredibly helpful as we worked through our bid, so we were comfortable that it was the right offer for us—a well-researched offer we would be comfortable with no matter what the outcome."[131]

In the end, St. Luke's announced on April 19, 2013, that the Episcopal-owned Houston-area hospitals would become part of Catholic Health Initiatives (CHI), then based in Englewood, Colorado. Looking back, Dr. Boom notes, "We had done our homework and had no regrets. In fact, the process proved to be an incredible learning opportunity for me and my entire team, including Kevin Burns, who at the time was our new chief financial officer. It solidified our interactions and working relationship with the board in ways that built a strong bond of trust while priming the pump for strategies going forward."[132] The rapid renewal of the north campus project including Walter Tower, then on hold, as well as planning for Methodist's new hospital in The Woodlands (built within four years of CHI's purchase of St. Luke's)—all benefited directly from the strategic discussions the St. Luke's sale generated.

Likewise, notes Dr. Boom, "We were in Dallas meeting with Christus just five days after St. Luke's sale to CHI was complete and moved quickly to acquire Christus St. John [renamed Methodist Clear Lake Hospital] and Christus St. Catherine [renamed Houston Methodist Continuing Care Hospital] to fulfill our need for a strategically placed hospital in the southern quadrant of Houston."[133] Thus, what might appear as an unsuccessful attempt to purchase St. Luke's was in fact a critically important strategic planning exercise that tightened the administrative team and accelerated the hospital's future trajectory. Once again, the word *resilience* comes to mind.

Four years later, in January 2017, Catholic Health Initiatives announced that CHI St. Luke's had partnered with Baylor College of Medicine in a joint venture for Baylor's new acute care hospital that had started, stopped, and restarted on Baylor's McNair Campus (Cambridge Street near the DeBakey Veterans Affairs Medical Center). The campus houses the Lee and Joe Jamail Specialty Care Center and the Baylor College of Medicine Medical Center with plans as of this writing for a new Baylor and CHI St. Luke's hospital on the site.[134]

Losing Dr. DeBakey

While Baylor and Methodist addressed their differences throughout the 2000s, they also shared a common bond that neither time nor new affiliations could ever erase. Together or apart, Dr. Michael DeBakey would always be a common link and beloved source of pride for the two institutions he called home. On the last day of 2005 Dr. DeBakey was stricken with a Type II dissection of the ascending aorta. He was 98. It was the very condition he had developed the classification system for and pioneered the surgical techniques to repair. Dr. George Noon, his former student and longtime surgical colleague, visited Dr. DeBakey daily as the decision was made initially to treat him medically. "He wanted to ride it out and see if he could get by." After several appeals, Dr. Noon finally got the approval he needed to perform surgery when Dr. DeBakey told his trusted colleague, "Well, do what you need to do."[135] Dr. DeBakey's life was extended nearly two years and scans showed the decision was made none too soon.

His recovery was slow, recalls Dr. Noon, "[but] when he recovered, he started coming to his office on a daily basis and doing his usual work. As a matter of fact, the day he died I went over to his house and we visited for about an hour. ... I ate some gumbo and got some peppers from his garden he used to spice up the gumbo, and he ate some ice cream. So we had a meal together and we had a great conversation [and] that's the last

I was able to talk to Dr. DeBakey."[136] From his arrival in 1948 until his death on July 11, 2008, just months short of his one hundredth birthday, Dr. DeBakey was the centerpiece of the Baylor–Methodist partnership. Days later he was laid to rest in Arlington National Cemetery across the Potomac from the nation's capital.[137]

While times and affiliations have changed, both institutions share a mutual admiration for the man who brought them together and pushed all who worked in his shadow to excel. His statue standing proudly in the lobby of Houston Methodist's Dunn Tower is a lasting reminder of the excellence he brought to Houston so many years ago.

• • •

Perhaps it is only fitting that a decade that started with Y2K, Allison, and 9/11 would yield a new, transformed Methodist with new academic partners, a robust educational program, a world-class research facility, and a blueprint to grow the hospital system across all quadrants of the city in ways the early founders could never have dreamed. The momentum did more than change the culture and the reach—it changed the name. What had once been *Norsworthy Hospital* had yielded to *Methodist Hospital, The Methodist Hospital,* and eventually *The Methodist Hospital System.* The newly transformed enterprise did not need to look far to draw from the city and the church that will always be the foundation for all the institution is and will be. Today one name seems to say it all for the global academic medical center the little hospital on Rosalie has become—*Houston Methodist.*[138]

Likewise, the new Houston Methodist had outgrown its former slogan, *Insist on Methodist.* It seems clear that the small hospital on Rosalie that once struggled to find its place in the new Texas Medical Center was now a rapidly transforming academic medical center, ranked the Best Hospital in Texas, and known for the highest standards in quality of care and patient safety. *Insist on Methodist* yielded in 2002 to two words every employee, whether physicians, research staff, or teams of medical professionals across the entire Methodist network, has a personal investment in—*Leading Medicine.*

In the end, what one calls the hospital the Methodists built is perhaps less important than what the institution accomplishes for its patients, the education of future health professionals, and the discovery of new treatments that indeed lead medicine forward. That reestablished synergy between the hospital's physician organization and private physicians working with I CARE values and some of the most rigorous patient safety and quality of care standards in the nation has not gone unnoticed. Just five years after the Baylor–Methodist affiliation ended and a new primary affiliation with Weill Cornell was established, Houston Methodist was named to the *2009 U.S. News & World Report*'s Honor Roll of America's Best Hospitals—the only hospital in Texas to receive the designation.[139] The distinction would be a sign of much more to come in the centennial decade ahead. Houston Methodist in one decade had accomplished what many experts in academic medicine had predicted would take thirty years. Yet they were just getting started.

ELEVEN

CELEBRATING THE CENTENNIAL
2010-2019

During 2010-2019:

> *Population of Houston is 2.1 million. Census for the Greater Houston Area*
> *(Houston-Woodlands-Sugar Land and nine counties) is 6.5 million (2010)*
>
> *Deepwater Horizon oil rig explodes in the Gulf of Mexico, causing the largest oil spill in*
> *U.S. history (2010)*
>
> *The Affordable Care Act becomes law (2010)*
>
> *U.S. Navy SEALS kill Osama bin Laden in Pakistan (2011)*
>
> *President Barack Obama is re-elected (2012)*
>
> *Superstorm Sandy makes landfall on the New Jersey coast near Atlantic City (2012)*
>
> *Scientists at Cornell University use a 3D printer to grow a living ear (2013)*
>
> *Boston Marathon bombing kills three and injures hundreds (2013)*
>
> *The first case of Ebola is certified in the United States (2014)*
>
> *Donald Trump is elected the 45th president (2016)*
>
> *Hurricane season brings Harvey to the Texas Gulf Coast, Irma to Florida, and Maria*
> *to Puerto Rico (2017)*

The first decade of the new millennium proved memorable including a historic tropical storm, the 9/11 attack, and a change in academic partners. Yet Methodist answered every challenge with a fixed focus and collective resilience. Who could have predicted that Dr. Oscar Norsworthy's little 30-bed hospital on Rosalie would transform into the Houston Methodist we know today? The small hospital that the Methodists bought in 1919 is now ranked the number-one hospital in Texas year after year[1] with eight hospitals forming an integrated and comprehensive network of care supported by more than twenty-four thousand employees. What was once a small community hospital is now a nationally recognized academic medical center with global reach, and not by accident.

Looking back to 2005, it was Sidney "Sid" Sanders, senior vice president for planning, capital construction, and real estate, who outlined the board's vision that would define Methodist into the next century. His report *Methodist Capital Construction Program 2005–2011*[2] provided a blueprint that was bold, perhaps risky, but pure Methodist. That plan would and did provide a comprehensive network of new and expanded community hospitals encircling the city while anchored in the Texas Medical Center with a research institute, a new inpatient hospital building (Walter Tower), and expanded outpatient facilities capable of handling the most complicated, acute medical needs known to man. Consider the many Houston Methodist facilities we know today as first seen on paper in that 2005 report (most clinical facilities listed here would be expanded one or more times in the decade ahead):

- Sugar Land expansion tripling the number of beds to 188 (completed 2008)
- Imaging Center near I-10 and Chimney Rock (new; opened 2009)
- Research Institute (new; opened 2010)
- A twenty-six-floor Methodist Outpatient Center in the Texas Medical Center adjacent to Smith Tower with two floors of operating rooms, an Imaging Center, Infusion/Oncology Center, Heart Center, Wellness Center, and parking garage (new; opened 2010)
- Willowbrook Hospital expansion to 240 beds (opened 2010)
- West Houston Hospital with 200 beds (new; opened 2010)
- A Data Center designed to withstand a Category 4 hurricane (new; opened 2011)
- Central Utility Plant Expansion (online 2011)
- A new North Tower replacement hospital (renamed Walter Tower) in the heart of the Texas Medical Center just north of the original hospital (placed on temporary hold in 1999 to study the impact of the Affordable Care Act; opened 2018)

It is important to note that considerable thought was given in 2005 to the hospital's aggressive expansion to add community hospitals throughout Houston. An important administrative consideration in 2005 was the potential impact on Methodist's flagship hospital in the Texas Medical Center. Would serving the community in all quadrants of the city cannibalize and diminish the importance of the Texas Medical Center campus—especially on the heels of Baylor's departure? The answer lies in levels of care and investment in the flagship hospital's capabilities in the Texas Medical Center to support the network of Methodist's community hospitals at the highest end of care (known as quaternary care). This was accomplished through large investments in the hospital's current six centers of excellence: Heart; Cancer; Neuroscience; Transplantation; Digestive Disorders; and Orthopedics/Sports Medicine.

In this way the community has access not just to excellent facilities in every part of the Houston area but to a network of care—all directly and seamlessly supported by the flagship's centers of excellence capable of addressing the most complex cases needing the most advanced expertise and facilities known to medicine. Transplant surgery is but one example of this transformational strategy for which Dr. Osama Gaber has assembled teams of expertise that in turn have built one of the most advanced and fastest-growing transplant programs in the world. Dr. Mark Ghobrial, one of Dr. Bass's earliest recruits post-Baylor, has built one of the nation's top-ranked liver transplant programs. While Dr. DeBakey first attracted the world's attention to innovations in heart surgery and cardiac transplants, today more than five hundred transplants of all types are accomplished annually at Houston Methodist—not to mention the world's first simultaneous skull and scalp transplant in 2015.

. . .

While John Bookout led the institution forward post-Baylor and orchestrated the transition of Methodist into an academic medical center, it was Judge Ewing Werlein, Jr. who followed Bookout as chairman in 2007 and inherited the daunting task of implementing this nearly $2 billion portfolio of projects. It was a monumental "to do" list—perhaps reminiscent on a much larger scale of the late 1940s when Ella Fondren and Josie Roberts went out on a limb planning a 300-bed hospital with air conditioning in the new, untested Texas Medical Center.

Consider that the leap of faith, post-Baylor, required embarking on such an extraordinary new course—developing and staffing a research institute, building a new physician organization, growing the hospital's community reach with expanded and new hospitals (and support facilities)—all while developing new primary and secondary academic affiliations and hospital-run teaching and residency programs. Now those seeds have bloomed, creating an impressive panorama worthy of a centennial celebration. Those who said Methodist was thirty-five years too late to transform itself into an independent academic medical center are now hard to find.

. . .

The retirement of Ron Girotto in 2011 gave Judge Werlein one more challenge—the recruitment of a new leader to oversee the growing Methodist enterprise. Interviewed in 2018, Judge Werlein notes without reservation, "I would say that the most important job that a board has is to select the right president and CEO. Midway through my ten-year term as chairman, Ron Girotto, who had been an outstanding president and CEO at Methodist during this troublesome time, took retirement." During the hospital's centennial year, he notes with satisfaction, "I think my proudest achievement during that time was the board's selection naming Dr. Marc Boom as our president and CEO in 2012."[3]

Dr. Boom at the time of his appointment was serving as executive vice president of the flagship hospital in the medical center. Now he assumed responsibility for the entire Methodist system. Seven years into the job, Dr. Boom reflects, "The board was not looking for radical change, things were going pretty well. ... And I will say the 1990s, at least for me, were informative years for future decision-making. ... It is important that we not cling so hard to the old that we end up missing opportunities or falling behind. But we also don't want to jump so hard or fast that we regret it. And I think so far we've threaded the needle."[4]

To thread that needle requires steady leadership and a strong sense of equanimity or calm in the face of a storm. It also requires strong appreciation of the institution's history. As Winston Churchill famously said, "The farther backward you can look, the farther forward you are likely to see." The book you hold was commissioned by Dr. Boom and the board with a Churchill-like understanding that knowing how the hospital got to where it is in the centennial year is essential for understanding where it is going.

Dr. Boom grew up in New Jersey, moved to Houston, and attended Memorial High School and The University of Texas in Austin. It was during high school that he fixed his sights on becoming a physician.[5] He met his wife, Julie, as a junior in pathophysiology class at UT Austin in 1986. Today, with three children, he leads Houston Methodist and Julie is a pediatrician at Texas Children's Hospital and a faculty member at Baylor College of Medicine.

Following medical school at Baylor College of Medicine and residency training in medicine at Massachusetts General Hospital, Dr. Boom attended Wharton School of Business in Philadelphia while working simultaneously as a general medicine and geriatrics fellow. His previously mentioned work with Dr. Ralph Feigin at Baylor during medical school provided an appreciation for combining both patient care and administrative leadership. As Methodist's president, his trademark report at each board meeting begins with the reading of one or more letters from patients followed not by the Finance Committee's report but by the Quality and Patient Safety Committee's report—another reminder that patients always come first.

Building a Research Institute

Houston Methodist's Research Institute building opened in 2010, more than a year prior to Dr. Boom becoming president and CEO. Yet its genesis dates back to 2003 when John Bookout and the board set into motion the plan for a focused research facility (with or without Baylor). In doing so the board took a genuine leap of faith hedged only by their confidence in Methodist's employees who have never failed to accomplish great things when provided opportunity and resources.

It was Dr. Michael Lieberman, that respected physician–scientist who brought his pathology department from Baylor to Methodist in 2005, who accepted the challenge to design a research institute from the ground up. Becoming an independent academic center hinged on the hospital's ability to coordinate research at the highest level. Ernie H. Cockrell notes he is among many on the board pleasantly surprised at how quickly things came together, noting, "Mike [Lieberman] literally had only a blank yellow pad and the board's commitment. … There was no building, no staff, no research board, nothing." [6]

Many recall seeing Dr. Lieberman with that yellow pad in hand as he made the rounds planning and sketching. Early plans to place the new building on a nearby site separate from the hospital soon yielded to a site arm-in-arm with the hospital's physicians and patients where it needed to be. With some persuasion, Ron Girotto convinced the architects to find a way to integrate the new building on that thin sliver of land that curves with the bend of Bertner Avenue in the heart of the Texas Medical Center. [7] They delivered.

Notes Cockrell, "While Mike Lieberman was responsible for planning the design and early recruitment of research faculty, I was responsible for developing the research board." [8] Spend a few minutes with Ernie Cockrell and you'll get an in-depth education in research funding mechanisms, intellectual property, research compliance and ethical guidelines, breaking silo mentalities, serial entrepreneurs, technology development, commercialization, and more. His knowledge seems boundless and is matched by the enthusiasm he has invested in seeing the research program to fruition.

His knowledge and pride regarding the institution's rapid transformation as a leader in translational research also includes cautionary advice looking forward. "As we get larger, we need to be careful not to institutionalize ourselves so much that we lose our hybrid vigor." With that in mind, the research board he first assembled was then and is today comprised of some of the most dedicated and bright business, legal, financial, and scientific minds to be found—all with an eye on the future. By design, each membership of the Research Institute board has established term limits on service to ensure that the continual rotation of new expertise matches the fast pace of today's medical research and technology development.

Board members completing their term typically remain involved and provide input long after their term ends. [9] Opened in 2010, the twelve-story, 444,000-square-foot Houston Methodist Research Institute signaled a new era for the hospital system, making a powerful statement that the little hospital on Rosalie was not just interested in research but was also committed to achieving international status. The building with its highly recognizable glass façade has six floors of laboratories, two floors of animal care facilities (vivarium), a two-hundred-seat auditorium named in honor of John Bookout, a boardroom named in honor of Ernie H. Cockrell, a cyclotron and floors of the latest technology, and much more.

Both Dr. Lieberman and Cockrell are revered to this day for the groundwork they established. It should be noted that The Cockrell Foundation endowed the first chair following the Baylor–Methodist split in honor of Cockrell's father and set the example for many others during the hospital's centennial year to reach the goal of one hundred endowed chairs in honor of the hospital's one hundredth birthday.

With the opening of the research building, Dr. Lieberman's work planning the framework of the research enterprise was complete as he announced plans for retirement.

Likewise, Cockrell stepped away from the board's leadership role (consistent with the term limits he established) and continues his support as a strong community advocate. Named to fill Cockrell's board leadership for the Research Institute was Gregory V. "Greg" Nelson, a highly respected Houston area attorney who leads the Houston office of Paul Hastings and is a former senior partner in the tax department of Baker Botts. Nelson had first joined the Methodist board in 2003 during the difficult period leading to the split with Baylor. Like Cockrell, he shared the enthusiasm and the challenge of starting an independent research enterprise and by 2017 was named chairman of the Houston Methodist board—a position he holds during the centennial year.

Nelson's first challenge in 2010 as chair of the research board was to find a new director. The search committee needed more than an experienced researcher to replace Dr. Lieberman; they needed an internationally recognized scientist with the leadership and entrepreneurial skills to build a nationally recognized research enterprise. Furthermore, they proposed an ambitious program with a stated and measurable goal to achieve defined national rankings within ten years. One candidate, Dr. Mauro Ferrari (Ph.D.), stood out and was named in 2010 president and CEO of the Research Institute. In medicine Dr. Ferrari is known for his leadership pioneering the field of nanomedicine at the National Cancer Institute.[10] As holder of the Ernest Cockrell, Jr., Presidential Distinguished Chair, Dr. Ferrari would lead the research enterprise for nearly a decade (2010–2019).

In addition to the more than one hundred research faculty he brought to Methodist, under Dr. Ferrari's leadership nearly two thousand researchers were recruited and credentialed during his decade of service—an impressive accomplishment by any measure. Within his first year alone Dr. Ferrari recruited from Harvard and Stanford research names few expected would ever come to Houston.

During his tenure Dr. Ferrari steered the Research Institute to national prominence, ranking fifth in the nation among hospital-based research productivity based on National Institutes of Health grants per faculty member. Looking back in 2018, Nelson recalls decisions made were critical.

> It was an expensive undertaking. [In 2003] we set out to build a $100 million research building with no research. So you're leading with your chin … we were taking a lot of risk [but] there was a healthy fear and a can-do attitude. … They decided early on there was no way you take on the basic research that has been done in huge levels in the Northeast. We needed a niche. The niche they were attracted to was translational research—research that is very close to becoming a product or device that we can apply to the clinic. That does several things. One is that it places your clinical side very close to your research side so you're not talking about basic research, pie in the sky, that will happen twenty years from now. You're talking about what is doable in the next five years and

our clinicians are very motivated by that. Even clinicians who don't do research want to be associated with an academic medical center where research is happening—specifically where it is happening in their area so they can apply the next innovation in medical care.

Hiring Mauro Ferrari in 2010 transformed who we are today. …We are a culture where performance in research is everything. What you did last week is more important than what you did five years ago. Dr. Ferrari was the right person at the right time and in less than a decade he has transformed in an unparalleled way a belief that we could attract the best scientists and build a great research enterprise into a reality.[11]

What had been a risky idea sketched on a yellow pad has become something much bigger. Dr. Ferrari explains the legacy he left in 2019: "In less than ten years [2010–2018] we went from [basically] zero basic science investigators to now more than two thousand research personnel … from zero clinical trials to now to more than one thousand clinical trials and protocols … from a situation where there was no grants office at Houston Methodist and no philanthropic fundraising to support research to an operation now that spends nearly $150 million in research every year."[12]

Today Houston Methodist researchers have at their disposal some of the most advanced technology available to focus on some of the most dangerous diseases of our time, including metastatic cancers, heart disease, neurological injury and neurodegenerative disease, diabetes, infectious diseases, and orthopedic injury. More specifically, adds Dr. Ferrari: "We have regulatory experts that help interface with the Food and Drug Administration. We have our own regulatory grade medical device pharmaceutical industry manufacturing which makes us very unique … and we have the clinical trials and the clinical practice so we can go the entire cycle. The next step involves greater involvement with the private sector and industry so that we can do large-scale distribution of our discoveries."[13]

The institute's cGMP Core (Current Good Manufacturing Practice) provides internal investigators and external academic or industry partners a cost-effective route for getting novel therapeutics to the bedside.[14] The Houston Methodist Institute for Technology, Innovation & Education (MITIE[SM]), the Cockrell Center for Advanced Therapeutics, and the Translational Research Initiative funds are all part of the Research Institute's bench-to-bedside formula for success that has created one of the fastest-growing research enterprises in the country. The role of generous community members defines the success of Houston Methodist's research enterprise in important ways. For example, in 2017 the Jerold B. Katz Foundation awarded $21 million to Houston Methodist (the largest gift in Houston Methodist's history at the time and the largest gift to the Research Institute to date) to support translational research, endow eight investigator positions, and provide an infrastructure fund to ensure the hospital's laboratories provide the latest technology.

Edward A. "Ed" Jones served as an early administrator for the research enterprise, ensuring the operational excellence of the facility itself while strengthening the translational research mission. In 2018 he was named president and CEO of the Research Institute and works closely with Dr. Dirk Sostman, president and chief academic officer of the newly formed (2019) Houston Methodist Academic Institute. Both the Research Institute and the Education Institute are components of the Academic Institute.

Not to be forgotten is former board member D. Gibson "Gib" Walton, who served the Methodist board for fifteen years and championed Methodist's research enterprise in important ways. He was a respected citizen of the community and a partner at Vinson & Elkins who died all too suddenly in 2013 at age 62. The Martha and D. Gibson Walton Lectureship honors his memory.

MITIE

Within two months of Dr. Barbara Bass's previously mentioned arrival in 2005, she went to the board with an idea. "OK, I'd like to build this education center, and it's going to be purpose-built to retrain surgeons in practice in new technologies so that we can safely adopt and disseminate new technologies in a safer, better way than we've done in the past. … And we're going to call the place MITIE, the Methodist Institute for Technology, Innovation & Education." She recalls that when she said "MITIE," there was a chuckle in the room. "I surmised they weren't quite sure what I was talking about." Yet it started a conversation. A few weeks later John Bookout responded, "Sounds good." Those two words were all she needed to know MITIE was a go.[15]

During the centennial year MITIE, housed in the Houston Methodist Research Institute, is considered one of the most advanced surgical training centers in the world. It's also, says Dr. Bass, one of her proudest accomplishments. The program was born out of pressing need she identified before arriving in Houston. "I was worried about those surgeons who were ten, twenty, thirty years in practice who really and truly had to scramble over years in practice to learn new skills, to adopt new technologies, to stay at the top of their game."[16] Her vision was to build a surgical training facility unlike any other in the world in size and scale to retrain surgeons in practice in new technologies in a setting that facilitates the safe adoption and dissemination of new technologies, including robotics. Houston Methodist proved to be the right place at the right time.

The $45 million investment dictated that the program needed a permanent home. Originally considered for placement in a renovated area of the West Pavilion, plans changed given the size of the investment and the perfect fit MITIE had with both research and education. The new Research Institute building proved ideal, and today MITIE is a recognized model teaching program for advanced surgical training where surgeons on a global scale come to learn new skills using the latest technology. "That technology is ever-evolving," says Dr. Bass, "and thematically it has converted surgery from an open discipline where we use our fingers and tools to precision surgery which includes image guidance, augmented reality and visualization, minimal access technology, and computer-enabled surgery [commonly referred to as robotic surgery]."[17]

Since the opening in 2011 and through 2018, more than fifty-five thousand health care providers in practice throughout the country and internationally came to MITIE for training.[18] "We've also leveraged MITIE for some really important surgical clinical trial work," Dr. Bass adds. "Those trials include training for new minimally invasive forms of heart valve replacement where much of the training was done in our MITIE facilities because of the sophisticated platform in place."[19]

Managing Big Data

In Josie Roberts's day, the hospital maintained a handwritten registry to record patient admission and discharge dates along with a chart with written notes (not always legible) clipped to the patient's bedside. Much has changed in this era of big data and computerized records. In recent years as Houston Methodist has transformed into a leading academic medical center with a systems approach, capabilities to manage big data—specifically electronic patient records—have transformed as well.

Today with the click of a mouse every detail of the patient care as well as safety and quality metrics is monitored electronically through a systemwide database called Epic. Efficiency of operations along with research and innovations is monitored as well and shared with health care providers following training and approved user access. Likewise, the system provides patients access to their appointments, records, medications, and more through a link that can connect a patient's care providers and records across multiple Epic-based care facilities inside and outside Houston Methodist. Time and cost efficiencies are but two obvious benefits.

On May 29, 2014, the first project team was formed to plan and implement the new Epic software. By choosing the Epic Corporation's software system, Houston Methodist joined a network of other hospitals with records-linking capabilities that benefit patients, care providers, and hospital alike. Following institution-wide training for more than twenty thousand staff (management included), Epic came online in the summer of 2017. Within a year, Houston Methodist held Epic's Star Level 8 rating (out of 10) demonstrating a systemwide proficiency rarely matched in the first year. Like the quality of patient care the system monitors, Epic management teams are constantly monitoring and enhancing the system to improve capabilities for patient and provider alike.[20]

Lessons from Harvey

When Dr. Marc Boom took the helm as CEO of Methodist in 2012, he already had over fifteen years of Houston Methodist leadership experience. He often shares the memory of Tropical Storm Allison (2001) as a lesson never to be forgotten or repeated. He will tell you the flood of 1976 presented an important wake-up call for crisis management requiring mitigation that did not get the full attention it deserved. Allison, he notes, was the catalyst for serious change in disaster preparedness. Hurricanes to follow, like Rita and Ike, provided important practice runs to further enhance crisis planning—practice runs and invaluable experience with flooding that would prove essential in 2017.

Five years into his leadership role a tropical wave surfaced off the west coast of Africa on the morning of August 12, 2017. By the next day the convection mass dissipated and what was to become Hurricane Harvey nearly ended right there. Yet it recovered, grew, and churned over the Texas Gulf coast, striking near Rockport on August 25, 2017, before drifting northeast over Houston. It was hopelessly stalled and did what trapped hurricanes do best—rain. Over four days, fifty inches of rain translated to twenty trillion gallons of water falling on the Houston area. The flooding event it created will be talked about into the hospital's next centennial.

Valuable lessons learned during Allison were employed and proved effective as all Houston Methodist hospitals remained operational. Adds Greg Nelson, "In those sixteen years we took steps including flood doors. That Sunday morning after Harvey [we had] water six feet up on the doors. If it wasn't for those doors, we'd have been flooded again and out of business for months."[21] Four business days poststorm, Houston Methodist physicians across the system were providing care to approximately four thousand ambulatory patients a day, which is on average consistent with typical patient volume at that time.[22]

The story of Harvey is not one of damaged buildings; it's the story of damaged and heartbroken people—the thousands of Houstonians, including Houston Methodist employees, who lost homes, cars, even loved ones. Yet employees in pain continued to help their patients and their neighbors. One young Texas A&M medical student flood-bound in her neighborhood found new teachable moments based on her clinical training at Houston Methodist by delivering a neighbor's baby in the bathtub. In all, over twenty percent of the Houston Methodist workforce then numbering twenty-three thousand were affected through loss of property or displacement. Hurricane Harvey upended the community, causing $125 billion in damage with an estimated 275,000 homes damaged and fifteen thousand destroyed.[23]

Stories of employee sacrifice and heroics that week were abundant. Every Houston Methodist employee has a story. Two are provided here:

> Nurse Julie Kaiser at Houston Methodist Sugar Land Hospital navigated around flooded streets, roadblocks, and detours to make it to work that Sunday, August 27. She was determined to help her coworkers despite concerns for her own home and family. The next morning she learned her neighborhood was subject to mandatory evacuation. Her family was able to make it to the hospital and find temporary shelter.

They were not alone. Some 200 families found refuge and safety there. Throughout the city, Houston Methodist hospitals opened their doors and demonstrated they were more than a *hospital* placed in the community but a *neighbor* ready to assist in times of need. [24]

Dr. Myung Park was on call the weekend Harvey hit. She woke to the sound of heavy rainfall and knew flooding was soon to follow. She was right. Her first concern as a heart specialist was not if, but how, she could get to her patients including one who had just received a heart transplant. Her husband tied a rope around his shoulder "so that I wouldn't just drift away." With her husband's help she made it despite one spot where the water came up to her eyes. Another colleague, she notes, had waded even further. When featured in the *Houston Chronicle* and praised for her heroics she deferred all credit to the nurses who helped so many noting their selfless sacrifice and hard work. "They were the lifeline in those hours of crisis." [25]

Recalls Dr. Boom:

We kept every hospital going. We had the right recovery teams at each hospital and coordinated well across the hospitals. Most of all we had the most amazing staff and dedicated physicians who gave their time and talent to help others, even when their own homes were damaged or lost. It was sobering on Monday when we really realized how many of our employees were impacted … we quickly started to figure how do we help. We had had this major donation, still unannounced at the time, from Rusty and Paula Walter. On Tuesday I texted both of them. Paula got back with me first and I noted that at the end of the day we could not lead medicine without great employees and our employees were suffering.

I asked if we could take $5 million of their $100 million pledge and help the employees. She said, "Let me talk to Rusty." Five minutes later the phone rings and Rusty says go ahead with the five … and we want to give you $1 million more [as a challenge gift to inspire additional gifts]. So, their $100 million donation became $101 million. … We put together a relief fund and an application process for our employees. It was very gratifying.[26]

More than 400 benefactors came together including medical staff, board members, employees, Houstonians throughout the community, current and former patients, hospital vendors, even Weill Cornell and New York-Presbyterian leadership and employees, to create an $8.4 million

Houston Methodist Employee Relief Fund. In turn that fund benefited 5,400 employees, nearly a fourth of the workforce who came to know I CARE is a two-way street with an appreciative institution caring back for its employees in times of need.[27]

Once again, the entire nation saw Houston at its very best as Houstonians and relief teams from states near and far stepped forward to help. For those many Houston Methodist employees directly assisted by the relief fund, their words of appreciation speak volumes. Feedback from two grateful employees stand out among many.[28]

OMG you have me crying right now. Thank you and the relief fund, the donors and Houston Methodist for all you have done for me and my children. This is why I have lived and breathed HMH for almost 15 years now. God bless this organization!

– Tray Tillman

I am so grateful for the privilege of working at Houston Methodist. When the time comes to move back into my home, I am going to name a new piece of furniture after Houston Methodist and I will keep it forever.

– Margaret Lamigan

Opening Walter Tower

The plans for a replacement hospital on the north side of the hospital's Texas Medical Center footprint were simply labeled, "North Tower." Dating back to the blueprint of 2005, those plans ended up on hold and for good reason. While the plans and budgets were drawn up and ready for implementation, President Obama's Affordable Care Act (ACA) signed into law March 27, 2010, changed those plans. The North Tower was placed on hold as the board assessed the impact of ACA on the hospital's business.

It was a precaution the board wisely took to better understand the impact of the act, which became known as Obamacare. Additionally, the board needed to focus attention on the pros and cons of purchasing St. Luke's Episcopal Hospital as previously noted. Recalls Judge Werlein, "Once we got through all that we launched the new North Tower project with remarkable speed."[29]

One board member had a special interest in assisting the institution's growth going forward. The $101 million philanthropic gift from Paula and Rusty Walter and the Walter Oil & Gas Corporation (the largest gift in the institution's history at the time of this writing) was not their first gift to the hospital. Joseph "Joe" C. Walter, Jr., Rusty's father, was a board member for three decades. During that time, he chaired the Finance Committee and received a heart transplant at Methodist as well. Notes Rusty Walter, "Years ago, my father got a new heart there that added ten more years to his life. When I had a stroke, they saved my life. Paula and I feel blessed to be able to give back and help these doctors and scientists move forward."[30] Previously, among other gifts, the J.C. Walter Jr. Transplant Center was named in 2010 with a gift from Carole Walter Looke and her brother Rusty Walter in honor of their father.

Notes Greg Nelson: "Rusty joined the board right after I did in 2003 and got involved in committee service including a term on the Research Institute board. I think over time he has come to really appreciate academics and research. That's where Paula and Rusty's money went. The building was built with hospital money, but the research and education are where they focused because that is really where the future is. They have put their money where they think it will do the most good for Houston Methodist and Houston."[31] The Walter gift directly supports an aggressive expansion of Houston Methodist's endowed chairs and other faculty, research, and teaching positions with a timely matching fund component designed to increase the number of endowed chairs to one hundred in recognition of the hospital's centennial anniversary.

At the dedication of the new Walter Tower on May 2, 2018, Dr. Boom reminded the audience, "When we announced plans for this building, we simply called it 'North Tower.' We knew we wanted to name it something special and add to the legacy of other community stalwarts like Alkek, Brown, Dunn, Fondren, Jones, Scurlock, and Smith."[32]

The new twenty-two-story Paula and Joseph C. "Rusty" Walter III Tower (Walter Tower) opened for patients in mid-August of 2018 with 366 patient beds, eighteen high-tech operating room suites for neurosurgery and cardiovascular surgery, two intensive care floors, six acute care floors, and a helipad. Houston Methodist's DeBakey Heart & Vascular Center, Neurological Institute, Cancer Center, and Bone Marrow Transplant Program all now call Walter Tower their home.

Throughout the building one finds innovations designed with patient outcomes in mind. For example, an intraoperative MRI suite allows surgeons the ability to scan patients and perform procedures in the same location without moving them to an imaging suite during procedures. Surgeons will have a more precise view of tumors, aneurysms, and ischemic strokes and can adjust their surgical plan as needed, saving the patient from multiple procedures; patient safety, outcomes, and satisfaction are carefully monitored.

More than technology and innovative design, this is a place well grounded in the faith-based roots of the hospital. Here you will find the C. James and Carole Walter Looke Sanctuary and the Looke Family Pavilion. The three-story atrium named in honor of the late Barbara and President George H.W. Bush features their portrait as a special tribute to the entire Bush family. Here in the Bush Atrium you will also see another familiar sight with welcoming arms. The 1963 mosaic mural, *Extending Arms of Christ*, has been relocated from above the Fannin Street entrance, making a statement that neither time nor hospital expansion will diminish the spiritual foundation of Houston Methodist. The restored mural is dedicated in the memory of Florence Eberhardt. Lois Davis, Eberhardt's daughter, and Carl Davis, Lois's husband, are dedicated supporters.

Enough cannot be said about the entire Bush family and their love of this community, Houston Methodist, and the nation. George H.W. Bush not only loved Houston's medical center and Houston Methodist, he served as an ex-officio member of the Texas Medical Center's board—a proud Houstonian invested in his city and its premier medical institutions. Both Barbara and George H.W. Bush were gracious and longtime patients at Methodist and their loss was felt worldwide. Married for seventy-three years, they died in 2018 only seven months apart.

When asked to write the foreword for this book, President Bush did not hesitate. His message is both a testament to what Houston Methodist means to the Bush family and what the Bush family means to Methodist. It is only fitting that the *Extending Arms of Christ* mural has found a safe and comforting home overlooking Walter Tower's Bush Atrium—providing a faith-based statement that all patients of all nationalities from all walks of life (including U.S. presidents) have a home at Houston Methodist.

Blending the Art and the Science

With all the technology of modern medicine exemplified by highly advanced care and research that define Houston Methodist at this one hundred-year mark, it's easy to lose sight that providing patient-centered health care requires, in addition to faith-based healing, a strong dose of the arts.

Sir William Osler, a timeless role model for the humanities in medicine, once insisted medicine is *both* an art and a science, "twin berries on one stem."[33] While he died the very year Dr. Oscar Norsworthy sold his hospital to the Methodist church in 1919, Osler's voice can be heard today throughout the Houston Methodist network of hospitals and care facilities and should not be forgotten in the new medical world of 6D imaging, 7 Tesla magnet MRIs, and robotic surgery.

Through Houston Methodist's Center for Performing Arts Medicine (CPAM), guest musicians and artists can be found integrating their art into patient care—adding an important spiritual and artistic dimension in support of healing. Music therapists at the bedside, employee art and photography proudly displayed on hospital walls systemwide (Healing Arts Program), guest lectures blending the arts and medicine (in auditoriums and televised), research documenting the value of the arts in healing and wellness—all are part of the Houston Methodist CPAM approach that has been recognized nationally. J. Todd Frazier, a musician and composer himself, directs the program and also serves in 2019 as president of the National Organization for Arts in Health.[34]

More than integrating the arts into healing, Houston Methodist physicians and care teams are healing the artists themselves by maintaining a 24/7 hotline to consult and provide care while promoting prevention and wellness strategies. It was in 1996 when Dr.

C. Richard Stasney conveyed to Methodist leadership the unique health challenges that performing artists face. His vision launched the CPAM program. The Houston Symphony, Houston Ballet, Houston Grand Opera, visiting ballet troupes, and opera stars worldwide all know Houston Methodist as a place committed to the arts and the artist.

That same spirit of community outreach makes Houston Methodist a destination for professional athletes as well, originating with the pioneering work in sports medicine of Dr. Joe W. King and his orthopedic department. In earlier days Houston baseball teams were known as the Buffs and Colt .45s. For three decades the Houston Astros have looked to Houston Methodist physicians for medical care on and off the field. That care has evolved into a sports medicine specialty recognized far and wide. From day one Houston Methodist sports medicine expertise has cared for the Houston Texans of the National Football League, not just care on the field but care guiding injury prevention as well as rehabilitation.

In recent decades the Houston Methodist name in sports arenas like Rice Stadium, Minute Maid Park, and NRG Stadium represents much more than a branding opportunity—it is a statement that Houston Methodist specialists have been behind the scenes helping amateur and elite professional athletes alike to stay at the top of their sport. Not to be overlooked, when the Houston Astros won the 2017 World Series one of the team's special championship rings was presented by team owner Jim Crane to Houston Methodist in appreciation of the institution at large—the hospital team that helped the baseball team achieve their highest goal. During the centennial year, Dr. David Lintner of Houston Methodist serves as team medical director for the Astros while also serving as a team orthopedist for the Houston Texans.

Coming Full Circle

Buildings and state-of-the-art technology are just that. The decade of the centennial year is really about the employees who are the heart and soul of all Houston Methodist was, is, and will be. After all, without every last employee across the entire Houston Methodist system, there would be no centennial to celebrate. While this book about the hospital's history is by design the story of leadership decisions, buildings, historic moments, and turning points—without question the story of Houston Methodist is at its core the story of hardworking and dedicated employees from the physicians, nurses, and allied health professionals at the bedside, to the researchers, educators, and support personnel who keep the lights on and the cafeteria food hot. Each adds his or her own personalized "I" into I CARE.

And don't forget the board and administrative leadership, the network of community Methodist hospitals and care centers (each hospital with a dedicated board), and an army of Houston Methodist volunteers. The outstanding work of the Blue Bird Circle and the Auxiliary is complemented by the Methodist Service Corps, those dedicated volunteers who have been found at information desks and busy surgical waiting rooms and family areas throughout Houston Methodist since 1947.

In 1963 one young woman got a call from her best friend, who just happened to be married to a nephew of Ella Fondren. Fondren had suggested her nephew's wife, Florine, go down to Methodist. "They need you and bring a friend." In this way more than half a century later Florine's friend, Betty Jean Ligon, is still sharing her time and kind smile. "I started out passing out menus and filling them out for patients before computers came along, so then I moved to the information desk. The last fifteen years I've been on staffing the information desk on Dunn 2. I see busy employees every day stop to ask a stranger how they can help and then reverse their direction to escort that individual to where they need to go. I CARE is for real. This is a marvelous organization and the service is unbelievable."[35]

In reality, each medical specialty, each department, each discipline (the excellence of Houston Methodist's more than five thousand dedicated nurses comes to mind) deserves a book of its own. Gone are the days when nurse training courses focused on topics like *Etiquette When Addressing a Doctor*. "Today's Houston Methodist nurse is part of a collaborative health care team that also assists in shaping national health care policy while directly impacting the quality, safety, and service outcomes for every patient encounter," notes Dr. Liisa Ortegon, senior vice president for operations and chief nursing executive. A registered nurse with a doctorate in business administration, Dr. Ortegon points out that five of the system's eight hospitals are recognized as Magnet hospitals—the highest and most prestigious distinction a health care organization can receive for nursing excellence. Only eight percent of U.S. hospitals receive this designation. The other three hospitals, she adds, are on a path to earn this highest distinction. Like all Methodist employees, nurses live the I CARE values, and the Houston Methodist Center for Nursing Research, Education, and Practice is a key resource to enable nursing professionals to develop and implement their innovative ideas and publish in academic publications.[36]

The book you hold is a mural in words representing every employee along with volunteers like Betty Jean Ligon who have all added their brushstrokes of many colors to this 100-year mural. As noted in the introduction, the current board is now busy sketching on the blank pages of time going forward for the next one hundred years. This mural also includes community—a generous community of individuals who have given gifts of dollars and time to make Houston Methodist what it is today. As the city has grown Houston Methodist has grown. In 1919 as Dr. Norsworthy sold his 30-bed hospital to the church, Houston had fewer than 150,000 citizens. One hundred years later Houston is measured in counties including communities from The Woodlands to Sugar Land with a population approaching seven million.[37]

Today patients come to Houston Methodist not just from Houston but from all over the world. What began with international patients primarily seeking heart care has grown into an international patient population seeking care across the entire spectrum of medical specialties. Through Houston Methodist's Global Health Care Services, international patient care, training, and consulting are highly organized and coordinated, providing medical care and training in more than ninety countries around the world.[38]

· · ·

"Hitch your wagon to Methodist" was the advice Dr. Dan Jackson received nearly seven decades ago when he arrived in Houston to raise a family and find a hospital. He was the last living physician to have worked at the old hospital on Rosalie—sharp as a tack until the end and forever proud of the hospital he joined so many years ago. If he were here today, he could tell you some stories about the old hospital with its ornery elevator that sometimes delivered more babies than the medical staff. He might even tell you little-known stories about the pecan tree outside that mischievous neighborhood children were known to climb for a bird's-eye view of health care to the surprise of patients and medical staff.

If only we could step back in time and walk those polished wooden corridors watching Josie Roberts round the corner inspecting every inch for space to add just one more bed, or see a young Dr. Michael DeBakey bolting up the stairs to the operating room where a newly installed air-conditioning unit awaited, just as he requested. So much has changed yet so little has changed. The very soul of the hospital—faith-based and patient-centered— remains just as they left it. A century later that little hospital the Methodists built is still the place to hitch your wagon—still a place that is going places.

Houston Methodist – Leading Medicine.

APPENDICES

APPENDIX 1
Houston Methodist Board of Directors

CHAIRS

John T. Scott	1922–1941
Raymond P. Elledge	1941–1948
Walter L. Goldston	1948–1951
Robert A. Shepherd, Sr.	1951–1954
O'Banion Williams	1954–1963
Curtis B. Delhomme	1963–1977
A. Frank Smith, Jr.	1977–1991
John F. Bookout	1991–2007
Judge Ewing Werlein, Jr.	2007–2017
Gregory V. Nelson	2017–Present

APPENDIX 1 *(continued)*
Houston Methodist Board of Directors

CURRENT DIRECTORS

Kelty R. Baker, M.D.	2017–Present
Carlton E. Baucum	2004–Present
John F. Bookout	1979–Present
John F. Bookout III (Advisory)	2019–Present
Marc L. Boom, M.D.	2012–Present
Emily A. Crosswell	1986–Present
Mary A. Daffin	1997–Present
Martha Smith DeBusk	2015–Present
Gary W. Edwards	2003–Present
Juliet S. Ellis, CFA	2014–Present
Mark A. Houser	2011–Present
Bishop Scott J. Jones	2016–Present
Rev. Kenneth R. Levingston	2008–Present
Vidal G. Martinez	1992–Present
Faisal N. Masud, M.D.	2018–Present
W. Benjamin Moreland	2015–Present
Robert K. Moses, Jr.	1979–Present
Gregory V. Nelson	2003–Present
Rev. Thomas J. Pace III, D.Min.	2006–Present
Joe Bob Perkins	2013–Present
Rev. Edmund W. Robb III, D.D.	2016–Present
Stuart L. Solomon, M.D. (Advisory)	2019–Present
Spencer A. Tillman	2015–Present
David M. Underwood, Jr.	2015–Present
Joseph C. "Rusty" Walter III	2006–Present
Elizabeth Blanton Wareing	2008–Present
Judge Ewing Werlein, Jr.	1990–Present
Rev. B. T. Williamson (Advisory)	2010–Present

LIFE MEMBERS

Ernest H. Cockrell	2010–Present
James C. Dishman	2003–Present
Charles W. Duncan, Jr.	2007–Present
Connie M. Dyer	2015–Present
Isaac H. Kempner III	2004–Present
Sandra Gayle Wright, RN, Ed.D.	2015–Present

FORMER DIRECTORS

C. Quentin Abernathy	1973–1985	Dr. Stewart Clendenin	1950–1955;
Morrie K. Abramson	2006–2016		1970–1976 †
T. E. Acker	1941–1972	Zachary T. Click	1953–1959
Dr. R. W. Adams	1919–1928	Ernest D. Cockrell, Jr.	1951–1972
Dr. Charles L. Allen*	1960–2002	Ernest H. Cockrell*	1976–2010
Dr. E. Leo Allen	1967–1970	Judge Robert L. Cole	1919–1948
Joe B. Allen, Jr.	1986–1999	Marvin K. Collie, Jr.	1959–1989
Duane N. Andrews, M.D.	1986–2000	Guy L. Comeaux, M.D.	1999–2005
Hiram P. Arnold, M.D.	1972	Governor John B. Connally	1977–1979;
J. C. Bailey	1919– †		1981–1993
Hines H. Baker	1943–1951	Bishop Kenneth W. Copeland	1968–1973
Lewis E. Ball	1952–1970	John M. Craddock	1961–1965
Claud B. Barrett*	1959–1983	Edward Lillo Crain	1929–1950
Conrad Bering, Sr.*	1954–1984	Howard A. Craver*	1946–1989
Lynn A. Bernard, M.D.	1975–1978	Bishop Finis A. Crutchfield, Jr.	1976–1984
Dr. Mouzan Biggs	1978–1981	Oliver Daniel	1947–1970
David C. Bintliff*	1969–1989	William Daniel	1946–1953
W. H. Blades	1946–1954	George W. Davis	1922–1923
Jack S. Blanton, Sr.*	1967–1988;	Rev. K. Wayne Day	1985–1995
	1991–2008	W. L. Dean	1926–1927
W. N. Blanton	1946–1967	E. Moore Decker, Jr.	1946–1983
Bishop W. Earl Bledsoe, M.D.	1996–2007	Curtis B. Delhomme	1953–1977
J. H. Bohmfalk	1922–1923	James C. Dishman*	1983–2003
B. Frank Bonner	1930–1944	Stuart M. Dobbs, M.D.	1994–2003
C. W. Boone	1926–1938	Robert P. Doherty, Jr.	1974–1985
Ted C. Bowen	1953–1982	Charles W. Duncan, Jr.*	1983–2007
Jett R. Brady, M.D. (Advisory)	2017	Connie M. Dyer*	1988–2015
Rev. James A. Brannen	1976–1978	J. D. Ehman	1953–1962
Morris Brownlee	1953–1959	Judge James A. Elkins*	1919–1972
Dawson C. Bryan, M.D.	1957–1968	James A. Elkins, III	2003–2010
Peter W. Butler	1997–2001	Raymond P. Elledge	1940–1949
Charles L. Bybee*	1953–1972	Rafael Espada, M.D.	2007
Dr. Neal D. Cannon	1950–1957 †	Victor Fainstein, M.D.	2009–2012
C. Eugene Carlton, Jr., M.D.	1987–1990	R. W. Fair	1937–1966
Samuel F. Carter	1919–1954	Rev. John E. Fellers, D.D.	1976–1984
Dunbar N. Chambers	1950–1956	E. R. Filley	1950–1953
William Lockhart Clayton	1919–1966	Louis A. Fisher*	1948–1993

* Life Member   † Unable to Verify

APPENDIX 1 *(continued)*
Houston Methodist Board of Directors

FORMER DIRECTORS *(Continued)*

Dr. Durwood Fleming	1953–1961 †	William H. Hinson	1984–1997
Ella F. Fondren*	1939–1982	C. A. Hodges	1919–1920
Walter W. Fondren, Sr.	1919–1939	Rev. D. H. Hotchkiss	1926–1931
Walter W. Fondren III	1963–1996	Bishop Janice Riggle Huie	2004–2016
Rev. Homer T. Fort, Sr.	1955–1961	Rev. James F. Jackson	1996–2002
Rev. James W. Foster	1997–2006	P. Lamar Jackson, M.D.	1981–1985
Dr. Alfred H. Freeman	1957–1970 †	Robert E. Jackson, M.D.,	
James A. Friedman, M.D.	1989–1992	MACP	2005–2008
Bishop Paul V. Galloway	1973–1976	Daniel R. Japhet, Sr.	1992–2002
Ronnie A. Gentry, M.D.	2014–2018	Raleigh W. Johnson, Jr.	1972–1996
Jerry L. Gibson	1973–1988	Richard J. V. Johnson	1981–1997
Bernice K. Giddings*	1982–2001	Howell B. Jones	1946–1953
Ronald G. Girotto	2001–2011	Jesse H. Jones	1930–1956
George W. Glass	1919–1922	John T. Jones	1957–1969
Rev. V. A. Godbey	1926–1928	Luther F. Kay	1973–1984
Walter L. Goldston*	1942–1957	A. H. Keen	1954–1964
Henry B. Goodman	1919– †	Lawrence W. Kellner	2007–2013
Rev. Richard W. Goodrich	2006–2010	Isaac H. Kempner III*	1971–2004
Ghent Graves, Jr., M.D.	1973–1976	Allan C. King*	1976–2003
Marvin L. Graves, M.D.*	1929–1953	Joseph H. Kurth	1941–1954
Charles C. Green, M.D.	1926–1947	Sam W. Law II, M.D.	1997–2002
John E. Green	1919–1923	Rev. Asbury R. Lenox, D.D.	1986–1994
S. Marcus Greer*	1956–1991	James R. Lesch	1980–2004
Claud B. Hamill	1941–1949	Linda Letbetter	1999–2000
Fred L. Hartman	1982–1991	Hugh Liedtke, Sr.	1968–1974
William Hattaway, M.D.	1962–1968	William C. Lindley	1946–1951
Eric J. Haufrect, M.D.	2011–2015	C. A. Lord	1919– †
Bishop Sam R. Hay	1922–1925	Rev. Elza L. Love	1968–1971
Bishop J. Woodrow Hearn	1992–2000	Bishop Paul E. Martin	1960–1968
Lee E. Hearn*	1952–1989	Elsie Martin-Simon	1989–1999
Ralph P. Heisch	1973–1990	Larry L. Mathis	1983–1997
Sarah C. Helms, CPA	1996–1999	Dr. Wayne McCleskey	1961–1967 †
Simon W. Henderson, Jr.	1980–1991	Leonard F. McCollum, Sr.	1952–1969
W. Sam Henly, M.D.	1985–1988	Leonard F. McCollum, Jr.	1966–1981
Robert W. Hervey	1968–1996	Louis H. McGrede	1973–1994

* Life Member   † Unable to Verify

FORMER DIRECTORS *(continued)*

John W. Mecom, Jr.	1966–1970	Judge Thomas H. Routt	1986–1990
Randall Meyer	1981–1989	J. Lyman Rundell*	1948–1969
Judge J. W. Mills	1940–1954	George Rupp, Ph.D.	1987–1993
W. E. Mitchell	1919–1925	W. Houston Schweitzer	1982–1997
A. D. Moore*	1950–1981	John T. Scott*	1919–1955
Rev. James W. Moore, D.D.	1985–2006	Eddy C. Scurlock*	1953–1988
M. G. Moore	1986–1990	Fred Self	1973–1975
Donald N. Morriss	1986–2002	Bishop J. Kenneth Shamblin	1961–1976 †
Robert A. Mosbacher, Jr.	1985–1987;	Frank W. Sharp*	1954–1972
	1991–2005	Robert A. Shepherd, Sr.*	1943–1981
Latimer Murfee*	1962–1983	Robert A. Shepherd, Jr.	1968–1981
Loyal L. Nelms	1940–1953	Dr. Albert P. Shirkey	1949–1950 †
Claud Newsom	1973–1979	Rev. Jack W. Shoultz	1973–1976
Bishop Alfred L. Norris	2000–2004	Bishop A. Frank Smith, Sr.	1938–1960
Oscar L. Norsworthy, M.D.	1923–1936	A. Frank Smith, Jr.	1954–1994
Bishop Ben Oliphint	1984–1992	Bess P. Smith*	1963–1964
Robert R. Onstead	1989–1994	Harry K. Smith*	1980–2002
Benjamin F. Orman, M.D.	1981–1987	Pliny C. Smith, M.D.	1992–2009
Edwin M. Ory, M.D.	1978–1981	Robert E. Smith	1949–1974
Captain W. R. Parker	1950–1962	Wm. Randolph Smith, Sr.	1970–2001
Judge Ed S. Phelps	1922–1936	C. Richard Stasney, M.D.	2013–2016
Mayor C. A. Neal Pickett	1940–1953	Micajah S. Stude	1965–1981
Judge Claude Pollard	1923–1927	Dwayne A. Suter, Ph.D.	1997–1999
Claude Pollard, Jr., M.D.	1949–1960	Henry J. N. Taub	1967–2004
Bishop W. Kenneth Pope	1949–1960 †	Dr. R. C. Terry	1956–1962
Dr. Paul Quillian	1943–1949 †	Sellers J. Thomas, Jr., M.D.	1977–1980
Dr. W. Berlen Randolph*	1971–1996 †	Pat R. Thompson	1950–1954
Michael J. Reardon, M.D.	2003–2006	Ann G. Trammell	1989–1996
Keith O. Reeves, M.D.	2009–2014	Thomas S. Trammell	1969–1980
J. W. Reynolds	1923–1941	W. Bryan Trammell, Jr.	1963–1985
R. G. Rice	1962–1985	Todd W. Trask, M.D.	2015–2018
Josie M. Roberts	1932–1953	Leroy Trice	1922–1923
Corbin J. Robertson, Jr.	1971–2003	Percy E. Turner	1949–1953
Joseph W. Robertson, M.D.	1971–1974	David M. Underwood, Sr.	1963–2015
James W. Rockwell	1937–1941	Bishop Walter L.	
Nat S. Rogers*	1971–1996	Underwood, D.D.	1977–1984 †
Wade R. Rosenberg, M.D.	2007–2010	Dee Walker	1946–1952

* Life Member   † Unable to Verify

APPENDIX 1 *(continued)*
Houston Methodist Board of Directors

FORMER DIRECTORS *(continued)*

Joseph C. Walter, Jr.	1976–1997	Dr. Charles W. Williams	1970–1986
W. K. Waltmon, DDS	1946–1971	O'Banion Williams*	1945–1983
D. Gibson "Gib" Walton	1997–2013	Isabel B. Wilson	1986–2001
Ernest L. Wehner	1979–1991	W. C. Windham, M.D.	1946–1970
Irvin C. Weisinger	1952–1956	William L. Winters, Jr., M.D.	1979–1982
Rev. Stephen P. Wende, D.Min.	2001–2016	Jean M. Worsham	1969–1979
Tony B. Wessendorff	1919– †	Sandra Gayle Wright, RN,	
James Marion West, Sr.	1919–1941	Ed.D.*	1991–2015
T. P. Wier	1940–1968		

APPENDIX 2
Houston Methodist Presidents and Superintendents

Sam R. Hay, Jr.	1923–1925	Superintendent
Rev. D. H. Hotchkiss	1926–1931	Superintendent
Josie M. Roberts	1932–1953	Superintendent
Ted C. Bowen	1953–1982	President
Larry L. Mathis	1983–1997	President and CEO
Peter W. Butler	1997–2001	President and CEO
Ronald G. Girotto	2001–2011	President and CEO
Marc L. Boom, M.D.	2012–Present	President and CEO

* Life Member   † Unable to Verify

APPENDIX 3
Presidents of the Medical Staff

Charles C. Green, M.D.	1924	Joe W. King, M.D.	1959–1960
E. H. Lancaster, M.D.	1925	Hatch W. Cummings, Jr., M.D.	1961–1962
I. E. Pritchett, M.D.	1926	John W. Overstreet, M.D.	1963–1964
J. L. Taylor, M.D.	1927	Robert S. MacIntyre, M.D.	1965–1966
M. D. Levy, M.D.	1928	E. Stanley Crawford, M.D.	1967–1968
C. M. Griswold, M.D.	1929	Presley H. Chalmers, M.D.	1969–1970
R. K. McHenry, M.D.	1930	Hiram P. Arnold, M.D.	1971–1972
Ghent Graves, M.D.	1931	Joseph W. Robertson, M.D.	1973–1974
H. L. D. Kirkham, M.D.	1932	Ghent Graves, Jr., M.D.	1975–1976
Joe B. Foster, M.D.	1933	Lynn A. Bernard, M.D.	1977–1978
R. F. Bonham, M.D.	1934	Sellers J. Thomas, Jr., M.D.	1979–1980
E. M. Arnold, M.D.	1935	William L. Winters, Jr., M.D.	1981–1982
John G. Schilling, M.D.	1936	P. Lamar Jackson, M.D.	1983–1984
R. H. Kilgore, M.D.	1937	Benjamin F. Orman, M.D.	1985–1986
Hatch W. Cummings, Jr., M.D.	1938	W. Sam Henly, M.D.	1987–1988
John Z. Gaston, M.D.	1939	C. Eugene Carlton, Jr., M.D.	1989–1990
J. Charles Dickson, M.D.	1940	James A. Friedman, M.D.	1991–1992
L. L. D. Tuttle Sr., M.D.	1941	W. Richard Cashion, Jr., M.D.	1993–1994
James A. Greenwood, Jr., M.D.	1942	D. Robert Wiemer, M.D.	1995–1996
Herbert L. Alexander, M.D.	1943	Pliny C. Smith, M.D.	1997–1998
A. N. Boyd, M.D.	1944	Stuart M. Dobbs, M.D.	1999–2000
George W. Waldron, M.D.	1945	Sam W. Law II, M.D.	2001–2002
L. L. Handly, M.D.	1946	Guy L. Comeaux, M.D.	2003–2004
John T. Stough, M.D.	1947	Michael J. Reardon, M.D.	2005–2006
Emile Zax, M.D.	1948	Robert E. Jackson, M.D.	2007–2008
Ralph C. Patrick, M.D.	1949	Wade R. Rosenberg, M.D.	2009–2010
Curtis H. Burge, M.D.	1950	Victor Fainstein, M.D.	2011–2012
Dolph L. Curb, M.D.	1951	Eric J. Haufrect, M.D.	2013–2014
John D. Jerabeck, M.D.	1952	C. Richard Stasney, M.D.	2015–2016
J. Charles Dickson, M.D.	1953–1955	Todd W. Trask, M.D.	2017–2018
Frank J. Ernst, M.D.	1955–1956	Kelty R. Baker, M.D.	2019–Present
James A. Greenwood, Jr., M.D.	1957–1958		

APPENDIX 4
Presidents of the Blue Bird Circle

Mrs. Calvin Garwood	1923–1924	Mrs. George T. Morse, Jr.	1958–1959
Mrs. E. L. Crain	1924–1925	Mrs. M. E. True	1959–1960
Mrs. Margaret Scott Bailey	1925–1926	Mrs. W. R. Edmondson	1959–1960
Mrs. Court Norton	1926–1927	Mrs. John G. Jones	1960–1961
Mrs. Margaret Scott Bailey	1927–1928	Mrs. Harrison O. Parsons, Jr.	1961–1962
Mrs. R. C. Kuldell	1928–1929	Mrs. J. Bates Thomas, Jr.	1962–1963
Mrs. Harold C. Bishop	1929–1930	Mrs. W. Neal Greer	1963–1964
Mrs. Marvin L. (Laura) Graves	1930–1931	Mrs. Clyde L. Coleman	1964–1965
Mrs. Fred L. Heyne	1931–1932	Mrs. Bernice Beard	1965–1966
Mrs. James E. Park, Jr.	1932–1933	Mrs. Harold T. Hulett	1966–1967
Mrs. P. F. Graves	1933–1934	Mrs. Thomas M. Van Bergen	1967–1968
Mrs. C. C. Cody, Jr.	1934–1935	Mrs. William C. Green, Sr.	1968–1969
Mrs. T. P. Wier	1935–1936	Mrs. Paul J. Taber	1969–1970
Mrs. George E. Woods	1936–1937	Mrs. P. Gordon Rouse	1970–1971
Mrs. Charles G. Heyne	1937–1938	Mrs. Gordon R. Waddell	1971–1972
Mrs. Malcolm J. Monroe	1938–1939	Mrs. Joe G. Fender	1972–1973
Mrs. T. E. Swigart	1939–1940	Mrs. Robert W. Hervey	1973–1974
Mrs. John T. Sprouse	1940–1941	Mrs. W. E. (Ruby) Dyche, Jr.	1974–1975
Mrs. R. Bruce Carter	1941–1942	Mrs. Frank T. Abraham	1975–1976
Mrs. Harry H. Ford	1942–1943	Mrs. L. A. Kucera	1976–1977
Mrs. Marvin L. (Laura) Graves	1943–1944	Mrs. R. C. L. (Marjorie)	
Mrs. J. C. Leonard	1944–1945	Robertson	1977–1978
Mrs. Harry L. Walker	1945–1946	Mrs. John C. (Virginia)	
Mrs. R. E. Smith	1946–1947	Kennedy	1978–1979
Mrs. A. E. Riedel	1947–1948	Mrs. Giles M. Townsend	1979–1980
Mrs. Ghent Graves, Sr.	1948–1949	Mrs. Robert L. Boone	1980–1981
Mrs. C. M. Hightower	1949–1950	Mrs. Alva Carlton, Jr.	1981–1982
Mrs. Charles L. Bybee	1950–1951	Mrs. R. Byron (Betty)	
Mrs. Hatch W. Cummings, Jr.	1951–1952	Robinson	1982–1983
Mrs. Lewis R. (Beulah) Kier	1952–1953	Mrs. Robert L. (Karen) Moore	1983–1984
Mrs. Jack V. Cooley	1953–1954	Mrs. Francis G. (Nell) Winters	1984–1985
Mrs. Roy C. Hohl	1954–1955	Mrs. Edgar A. (Gloria) Christy	1985–1986
Mrs. C. B. (Roberta)		Mrs. Walter D. (Evelyn)	
Delhomme	1955–1956	Murphy	1986–1987
Mrs. Clyde J. Verheyden	1956–1957	Mrs. H. Michael (Judy) Tyson	1987–1988
Mrs. Latimer Murfee	1957–1958	Mrs. James R. (Betty Ann)	
		Graves	1988–1989

Presidents of the Blue Bird Circle *(continued)*

Jule Collins Smith	1989–1990	Gayle Garbs Ramsey	2005–2006
Betty Bills Broyles-Pettey	1990–1991	Carole Stovall McGarry	2006–2007
Teeta Marks Udden	1991–1992	Kathy Brown Keckley	2007–2008
Pat Sammons Copeland	1992–1993	Martha Perdue Yates	2008–2009
Carolyn Baurenschmidt		Linda M. Wells	2009–2010
Purifoy	1993–1994	Pat Workman Lucas	2010–2011
Walta Jean Sturgis Smith	1994–1995	Mills McMahon Toomey	2011–2012
Kathy Hervey Dalton	1995–1996	Gina Hall Saour	2012–2013
Shari Collins Carroll	1996–1997	Maggie Wise Austin	2013–2014
Joan FitzGerald Curry	1997–1998	Patricia Edwards-Carroll	2014–2015
Bette Flossel Haynie	1998–1999	Mary Ann Hansen Macey	2015–2016
Lynn Russell Teague	1999–2000	Gwen Habermacher	
Ann Brittain Reed	2000–2001	Wilkinson	2016–2017
Marilynne Capps Gorman	2001–2002	Ellen Cook Stough	2017–2018
Annette Emery Moore	2002–2003	Mary Carolyn Malone	
Carol Linhardt Sharpe	2003–2004	Williams	2018–Present
Kathy Delaney Dissen	2004–2005		

APPENDIX 5

Presidents of the Houston Methodist Hospital Service Corps

Mrs. S. J. Patricia Rieger	1947–1949	Mrs. Hugh T. (Laura) Lilly	1982–1984
Mrs. Raymond P. (Minda)		Mrs. L. L. (Peggy) Hill	1984–1986
Elledge	1949–1950	Mrs. R. C. (Kathryn) Ziegler	1986–1988
Mrs. Winfred G. (Kathleen)		Mrs. R. A. (Martha) Vansickle	1988–1990
Ellis	1950–1952	Mrs. Laura Hale	1990–1992
Mrs. Sam R. (Gessner) Hay, Jr.	1952–1954	Mrs. Anne Lewis	1992–1994
Mrs. J. M. (Pauline) Richardson	1954–1956	Mrs. Margie Danvers	1994–1996
Mrs. Willard M. (Ruth) Johnson	1956–1958	Mrs. Betty Jean Ligon	1996–1998
Mrs. Z. V. (Marjorie) Donigan	1958–1960	Mrs. Dorothy McCaine	1998–2000
Mrs. C. A. (Roberta) Dwyer	1960–1962	Mrs. Mary Catherine Kleiderer	2000–2002
Mrs. Blake L. (Bernice) Speer	1962–1964	Ms. Patricia C. Deckert	2002–2004
Mrs. Floyd (Nan) Bullard	1964–1966	Mrs. Dorris Maynard	2004–2006
Mrs. J. P. (Mary Lou)		Mr. Richard G. Palmer	2006–2008
Rutherford	1966–1968	Mrs. Betty Jean Ligon	2008–2012
Ms. Patricia McCall	1968–1970	Mrs. Dorris Maynard	2012–2014
Mrs. Carlos T. (Marjie) Knight	1970–1972	Mrs. Judy Vaughn	2014–2016
Mrs. Floyd (Nan) Bullard	1972–1980	Mrs. Pat Nickell	2016–2018
Mrs. Jim M. (Vera) Ford	1980–1982	Mrs. Susan Brittain	2018–Present

APPENDIX 6
Presidents of the Houston Methodist Hospital Auxiliary

Mrs. Marvin L. (Laura) Graves, Founder	1928–1930
Mrs. B. F. (Cleo) Bonner	1930–1932
Mrs. William A. (Gussie) Cortes	1932–1934
Mrs. C. B. Grandbury	1934–1936
Mrs. W. Neal (Irene) Greer	1936–1938
Mrs. Margaret Scott Bailey	1938–1940
Mrs. A. F. (Elna) Settlemyre	1940–1942
Mrs. R. M. Farrar	1942–1944
Mrs. L. L. D. (Vita) Tuttle	1944–1948
Mrs. C. A. (Roberta) Dwyer	1948–1954
Mrs. Winfred G. (Kathleen) Ellis	1954–1958
Mrs. Hillard W. (Elma) Carey	1958–1962
Ms. Rae Peden	1962–1966
Mrs. William M. (Arlena) Dow	1966–1970
Mrs. William D. (Sarah) Dwyer	1970–1974
Mrs. Jim M. (Vera) Ford	1974–1978
Mrs. Henry (Jo) Rachford	1978–1980
Mrs. Leon B. (Lee) Sowell	1980–1982
Mrs. T. B. (Bettye) Drisdale, Sr.	1982–1986
Mrs. Harriet Sharp Bibo	1986–1988
Mrs. John M. (Dorothy) Sturdevant	1988–1990
Mrs. Dorothy Cutler	1990–1992
Mrs. Olga L. McMillan	1992–1994
Mrs. Emma Hurlock	1994–1997
Mrs. Bettye Drisdale	1997–1998
Mrs. Bette DeLay	1998–1999
Mrs. Betty DeBakey	1999–2000
Mrs. Sophie Mize	2000–2001
Mrs. Alvretta DeVillier	2001–2002
Mrs. Emma Hurlock	2002–2003
Mrs. Claire Whaley	2003–2004
Mrs. Donna Meador	2004–2005
Mrs. Sophie Mize	2005–2006
Mrs. Paula Koehn	2006–2007
Mrs. Penny Fenner	2007–2008

Presidents of the Houston Methodist Hospital Auxiliary *(continued)*

Mrs. Dee Flournoy	2008–2009
Mrs. Donna Meador	2009–2010
Mr. Vince Hefley	2010–2011
Mrs. Donna Meador	2011–2012
Mrs. Donna Jackson	2012–2013
Mrs. Jo Page	2013–2014
Mrs. Evelyn McGraw	2014–2015
Mrs. Donna Jackson	2015–2016
Mrs. Marilyn Speer	2016–2017
Mrs. Sarah Elolf	2017–2019
Mrs. Donna Meador	2019–Present

APPENDIX 7
John W. Overstreet, M.D. Award Recipients

John W. Overstreet, M.D.	1997	J. Bob Blacklock, M.D.	2011
Juan J. Olivero, Sr., M.D.	1998	Christopher M. Leveque, M.D.	2011
William L. Winters, Jr., M.D.	1999	Thomas P. Hedrick, M.D.	2012
Michael J. Reardon, M.D.	2000	Victor Fainstein, M.D.	2013
George P. Noon, M.D.	2001	Faisal N. Masud, M.D.	2014
Raymond H. Kaufman, M.D.	2002	Eric J. Haufrect, M.D.	2015
Robert G. Grossman, M.D.	2003	Albert E. Raizner, M.D.	2015
Bruce L. Ehni, M.D.	2004	Eugene L. Alford, M.D.	2016
Timothy B. Boone, M.D., Ph.D.	2005	Mary R. Schwartz, M.D.	2016
Stuart M. Dobbs, M.D.	2006	Richard A. Goldfarb, M.D.	2017
Alan L. Kaplan, M.D.	2007	C. Richard Stasney, M.D.	2017
Donald T. Donovan, M.D.	2008	Alberto O. Barroso, M.D.	2018
Parry J. Lauzon, Jr., M.D.	2009	Ranjit C. Chacko, M.D.	2019
John C. McKechnie, M.D.	2010	A. Osama Gaber, M.D.	2019

APPENDIX 8
Department Chairs and Centers of Excellence Directors

CURRENT CHAIRS AND DIRECTORS

Stanley H. Appel, M.D.

Barbara L. Bass, M.D.

Timothy B. Boone, M.D., Ph.D.

Jett R. Brady, M.D.

Gavin W. Britz, M.D.

E. Brian Butler, M.D.

Jenny C. Chang, M.D.

A. Osama Gaber, M.D.

Jaime Gateno, M.D., DDS

Mark W. Kline, M.D.

Andrew G. Lee, M.D.

Alan B. Lumsden, M.D.

Susan M. Miller, M.D.

Tristi W. Muir, M.D.

James M. Musser, M.D., Ph.D.

Joseph J. Naples, M.D.

Eamonn Martin Quigley, M.D.

Richard J. Robbins, M.D.

Mas Takashima, M.D.

Kevin E. Varner, M.D.

Benjamin L. Weinstein, M.D.

William A. Zoghbi, M.D.

FORMER CHAIRS AND DIRECTORS
BEGINNING IN 2004

Bobby R. Alford, M.D.

Donald A. Briscoe, M.D.

Donald T. Donovan, M.D.

Ralph D. Feigin, M.D.

Robert G. Grossman, M.D.

Alan L. Kaplan, M.D.

King C. Li, M.D.

Michael W. Lieberman, M.D., Ph.D.

Kenneth B. Mathis, M.D.

Reginald F. Munden, M.D.

Miguel A. Quiñones, M.D.

Stuart C. Yudofsky, M.D.

APPENDIX 9
One Hundred Notable Physicians from
Houston Methodist's First Century

Bobby R. Alford, M.D.

Eugene L. Alford, M.D.

Clarence P. Alfrey, Jr., M.D.

Stanley H. Appel, M.D.

Kelty R. Baker, M.D

David S. Baskin, M.D.

Barbara L. Bass, M.D.

Milton M. Boniuk, M.D.

Marc L. Boom, M.D.

Timothy B. Boone, M.D., Ph.D.

Malcolm K. Brenner, M.D.

Gavin W. Britz, M.D.

Curtis H. Burge, M.D.

E. Brian Butler, M.D.

C. Eugene Carlton, Jr., M.D.

Ranjit C. Chacko, M.D.

Presley H. Chalmers, M.D.

Jenny C. Chang, M.D.

Don W. Chapman, M.D.

E. Lillo Crain, Jr., M.D.

E. Stanley Crawford, M.D.

Hatch W. Cummings, Jr., M.D.

Stuart M. Dobbs, M.D. **

George J. Ehni, M.D.

Victor Fainstein, M.D. **

Jeffrey D. Friedman, M.D.

Adaani E. Frost, M.D.

A. Osama Gaber, M.D.

Ronald R. Galfione, M.D.

Jaime Gateno, M.D., DDS

Frank Gerow, M.D.

R. Mark Ghobrial, M.D.

Antonio M. Gotto, Jr., M.D., D.Phil.

Marvin L. Graves, M.D.

Charles C. Green, M.D.

James A. Greenwood, Jr., M.D.

Robert G. Grossman, M.D.

Dale J. Hamilton, M.D.

Richard L. Harper, M.D.

James E. Harrell, Sr., M.D.

Paul R. Harrington, M.D.

Helen E. Heslop, M.D.

Robert A. Hettig, M.D.

Jimmy F. Howell, M.D.

Daniel E. Jackson, M.D.

Robert E. Jackson, M.D.

Paul H. Jordan, Jr., M.D.

Alan L. Kaplan, M.D.

Raymond H. Kaufman, M.D.

Peter Kellaway, M.D.

Joe W. King, M.D.

Michael J. Klebuc, M.D.

Neal S. Kleiman, M.D.

Eugene C. Lai, M.D., Ph.D.

Gerald M. Lawrie, M.D.

Andrew G. Lee, M.D.

Michael W. Lieberman, M.D., Ph.D.

Alan B. Lumsden, M.D.

Edward C. Lynch, M.D.

Joseph C. Masdeu, M.D., Ph.D.

Faisal N. Masud, M.D.

Charles H. McCollum III, M.D.

John C. McKechnie, M.D.

Alice R. McPherson, M.D.

Brian J. Miles, M.D.

Susan M. Miller, M.D.

**Achieved recognition as a John W. Overstreet, M.D. Award recipient, a Notable
100 Physician, and president of the Medical Staff

APPENDIX 9 *(continued)*
One Hundred Notable Physicians from
Houston Methodist's First Century

Dina R. Mody, M.D.

James E. Muntz, M.D.

James M. Musser, M.D., Ph.D.

Joseph J. Naples, M.D.

George P. Noon, M.D.

Oscar L. Norsworthy, M.D.

Juan J. Olivero, Sr., M.D.

Edwin M. Ory, M.D.

John W. Overstreet, M.D.

Eamonn M. Quigley, M.D.

Miguel A. Quiñones, M.D.

Albert E. Raizner, M.D.

Michael J. Reardon, M.D. **

Patrick R. Reardon, M.D.

Lawrence Rice, M.D.

Antoinette C. Ripepi, M.D.

Richard J. Robbins, M.D.

John O. Roehm, Jr., M.D.

Wade R. Rosenberg, M.D.

Mary R. Schwartz, M.D.

William H. Spencer III, M.D.

Melvin M. Spira, M.D.

C. Richard Stasney, M.D. **

Wadi N. Suki, M.D.

Bin S. Teh, M.D.

Jack L. Titus, M.D.

L. L. D. Tuttle, Sr., M.D.

Kevin E. Varner, M.D.

Mario S. Verani, M.D.

Martin R. White, M.D.

William L. Winters, Jr., M.D. **

Martha A. Wood, M.D.

Stuart C. Yudofsky, M.D.

William A. Zoghbi, M.D.

**Achieved recognition as a John W. Overstreet, M.D. Award recipient, a Notable 100 Physician, and president of the Medical Staff

APPENDIX 10
Houston Methodist Hospital Foundation
Board of Directors

CHAIRS

John F. Bookout	1994–2015
John W. Johnson	2016–Present

CURRENT DIRECTORS

Dorothy M. Ables	2017–Present
John F. Bookout	1994–Present
Marc L. Boom, M.D.	2012–Present
Michael M. Cone	2008–Present
Susan H. Coulter	2018–Present
Emily A. Crosswell	2004–Present
Charles W. Duncan, Jr.	1997–Present
John S. "Steve" Dunn, Jr.	2010–Present
Marvy A. Finger	2010–Present
John W. Johnson	2011–Present
Raleigh W. Johnson, Jr.	1996–Present
Vidal G. Martinez	2007–Present
W. Benjamin Moreland	2017–Present
Robert K. Moses, Jr.	1994–Present
Gregory V. Nelson	2017–Present
David M. Underwood, Jr.	2016–Present
Joseph C. "Rusty" Walter III	2016–Present
James V. "Jim" Walzel	2007–Present
Elizabeth Blanton Wareing	2011–Present
Marcus "Marc" A. Watts	2017–Present
Judge Ewing Werlein, Jr.	2007–Present

APPENDIX 10 *(continued)*
Houston Methodist Hospital Foundation
Board of Directors

FORMER DIRECTORS

Morrie K. Abramson	2007–2016
Jack S. Blanton, Sr.	2005–2008
Peter W. Butler	1997–2001
Ernest H. Cockrell	1986–2006
Marvin K. Collie	1986–1989
Bishop Finis A. Crutchfield	1986– †
Robert P. Doherty, Jr.	1986– †
James A. Elkins III	2003–2010
Ronald G. Girotto	1994–2011
Daniel R. Japhet, Sr.	1996–1999
Richard J. V. Johnson	1996– †
Larry L. Mathis	1986–1997
Robert A. Mosbacher, Jr.	2003–2005
Corbin J. Robertson, Jr.	1986–2003
W. Houston Schweitzer	1997–2003
A. Frank Smith, Jr.	1986–1994
Wm. Randolph Smith, Sr.	1986–2001
Ann G. Trammell	1996–2003
Jack T. Trotter	2007–2008
David M. Underwood, Sr.	1994–2015
Joseph C. Walter, Jr.	1986–1997
Ernest L. Wehner	1986–1991

† Unable to Verify

APPENDIX 11
Houston Methodist Research Institute
Board of Directors

CHAIRS

Ernest H. Cockrell	2006–2010
Gregory V. Nelson	2010–2013
D. Gibson "Gib" Walton	2013
Joseph C. "Rusty" Walter III	2013–2015
Mark A. Houser	2015–2019
John F. Bookout III	2019–Present

CURRENT DIRECTORS

David C. Baggett, Jr.	2017–Present
John F. Bookout	2007–Present
John F. Bookout III	2013–Present
Marc L. Boom, M.D.	2012–Present
Timothy B. Boone, M.D., Ph.D.	2015–Present
Carrie L. Byington, M.D.	2017–Present
Joseph R. "Rod" Canion	2013–Present
David T. Chao	2018–Present
Stephen I. Chazen	2017–Present
Augustine M. K. Choi, M.D.	2016–Present
Ernest D. Cockrell II	2012–2017; 2019–Present
John P. Cooke, M.D., Ph.D.	2015–Present
Martha Smith DeBusk	2019–Present
Dan O. Dinges	2014–Present
Antonio M. Gotto, Jr., M.D., D.Phil.	2007–Present
Edward A. Jones	2019–Present
Evan H. Katz	2016–Present
Edwin "Ed" H. Knight, Jr.	2018–Present
Rev. Kenneth R. Levingston	2015–Present
Kevin J. Lilly	2017–Present
Steven S. Looke	2018–Present
Vidal G. Martinez	2015–Present
Gregory V. Nelson	2009–Present

APPENDIX 11 *(continued)*
Houston Methodist Research Institute
Board of Directors

CURRENT DIRECTORS *(continued)*

Mary Eliza Shaper	2018–Present
H. Dirk Sostman, M.D., FACS	2019–Present
Douglas E. Swanson, Jr.	2019–Present
Andrew C. von Eschenbach, M.D.	2014–Present
Joseph C. "Rusty" Walter III	2006–2015; 2017–Present
Martha S. Walton	2015–Present
Elizabeth Blanton Wareing	2014–Present
Judge Ewing Werlein, Jr.	2007–Present

FORMER DIRECTORS

Morrie K. Abramson	2007–2014
Edward R. Allen III, Ph.D., CFA	2007–2014
Steven D. Arnold	2013–2019
Carin M. Barth	2007–2013
Allen J. Becker	2008–2014
Jack S. Blanton, Jr.	2007–2012
Giorgio Borlenghi	2013–2019
Albert Y. Chao	2012–2018
Ernest H. Cockrell	2007–2011
M. Scott Cone	2007–2012
Mary A. Daffin	2007–2015
Charles W. Duncan III	2007–2012
Mauro Ferrari, Ph.D.	2010–2019
Joe B. Foster	2014–2017
Ronald G. Girotto	2006–2011
Laurie H. Glimcher, M.D.	2012–2016
Mark A. Houser	2013–2019
Catherine S. Jodeit	2013–2019
Renu Khator, Ph.D.	2008–2014
John P. Kotts	2008–2014
Leo E. Linbeck III	2008–2014
James M. Musser, M.D., Ph.D.	2006–2012
L. E. Simmons	2007–2013
C. Richard Stasney, M.D.	2007–2015
Stuart W. Stedman	2013–2017
David M. Underwood, Jr.	2007–2012
D. Gibson "Gib" Walton	2011–2013

APPENDIX 12
Houston Methodist Global Health Care Services
Board of Directors

CHAIRS

Ronald G. Girotto	2007–2011
Marc L. Boom, M.D.	2012–Present

CURRENT DIRECTORS

John F. Bookout	2007–Present
Marc L. Boom, M.D.	2012–Present
Cathy L. Easter	2010–Present
Gary W. Edwards	2007–Present
Vidal G. Martinez	2007–Present
Robert K. Moses, Jr.	2007–Present
Gregory V. Nelson	2007–Present

FORMER DIRECTORS

Ronald G. Girotto	2007–2011
Lynn M. Schroth, Dr.P.H.	2007–2009
Judge Ewing Werlein, Jr.	2007–2016

APPENDIX 13
Hospital CEOs 2019

Houston Methodist Baytown Hospital	David P. Bernard
Houston Methodist Clear Lake Hospital	Daniel B. Newman
Houston Methodist Hospital Texas Medical Center	Roberta L. Schwartz, Ph.D.
Houston Methodist Sugar Land Hospital	Christopher D. Siebenaler
Houston Methodist West Hospital	Wayne M. Voss
Houston Methodist Willowbrook Hospital	Keith Barber
Houston Methodist The Woodlands Hospital	Debra F. Sukin, Ph.D., MPH
Houston Methodist Continuing Care Hospital	Wayne M. Voss

APPENDIX 14
Houston Methodist Baytown Hospital
Board of Trustees

CHAIRS

Lawrence J. Reilly	1983–2012
Richard A. Peebles	2012–Present

CURRENT TRUSTEES

Pete C. Alfaro	1997–Present
Wayne L. Baldwin	2006–Present
David P. Bernard	2015–Present
Marc L. Boom, M.D.	2012–Present
Dennis Brown, Ph.D.	2012–Present
R. D. Burnside III	2008–Present
Mary Hartman Brown Cody	2008–Present
Mark E. Franklin, M.D.	2019–Present
Rev. John N. Newsome	2016–Present
Richard A. Peebles	1986–Present
Gilbert Santana	2008–Present
Gary T. Schmidt	2013–Present
Christopher D. Siebenaler	2018–Present

FORMER TRUSTEES

S. Jeffery Ackerman, M.D.	2004–2008
Becky L. Clayton	1992–2016
Dan Coombs	2006–2008
Richard W. Demmler, M.D.	2011
Paul J. Edwards	1992–2008
Martha M. Ellis, Ph.D.	2003–2009
Donna A. Gares	2003–2015
Ronald G. Girotto	2002–2011
Christopher D. Hays, M.D.	2008
Ludie Hernandez-Buck, M.D.	1999–2018
Rev. Thomas Hill	2003–2005
Buddy Irby	1999–2017

FORMER TRUSTEES *(continued)*

APPENDIX 16
Houston Methodist Sugar Land Hospital
Board of Trustees

CHAIR

William F. Schwer	1998–Present

CURRENT TRUSTEES

Marc L. Boom, M.D.	2012–Present
Elizabeth P. Butler	2019–Present
Suehing W. Y. Chiang	2004–Present
Anthony Francis	2019–Present
Gene E. Huebner, M.D.	1999–Present
Jeffrey A. Jackson, M.D.	2006–Present
Lonnie E. Meadows	2007–Present
Rev. W. Martin Nicholas	2008–Present
Scott Rivenes, M.D.	2019–Present
William F. Schwer	1998–Present
Christopher D. Siebenaler	2007–Present
Sutapa Sur	2009–Present

FORMER TRUSTEES

Gary W. Flores, M.D.	2013–2018
Ronald G. Girotto	2001–2011
James F. Heitzenrater	2004–2007
Rev. Morris F. Matthis	2006–2011
Rev. Thomas J. Pace III, D.Min.	2004–2006
Mary A. Simpson	2000–2007
Larry F. Willman	2009–2016

APPENDIX 17
Houston Methodist West Hospital
Board of Trustees

CHAIRS

Ronald G. Girotto	2010–2012
Marc L. Boom, M.D.	2012–2014
Vidal H. Ramirez	2014–Present

CURRENT TRUSTEES

Marc L. Boom, M.D.	2012–Present
William A. Callegari	2015–Present
Ramon M. Cantu	2011–Present
Don Chaney	2019–Present
Irfan Iftikhar, M.D.	2019–Present
Stuart I. Levin	2013–Present
Rahul B. Mehta	2013–Present
Vidal H. Ramirez	2013–Present
Rev. John Robbins, D.Min.	2019–Present
Wayne M. Voss	2011–Present
Manish K. Wani, M.D.	2017–Present

FORMER TRUSTEES

Ronald G. Girotto	2010–2012
Hector J. Herrera, M.D.	2013–2017
Ann F. Hodge	2015–2018
Todd Holt, M.D.	2015–2019
Rev. James E. Leggett	2011–2013
George Mammen, M.D.	2011–2015
Clive Shkedy, M.D.	2010–2015
Rev. Charles B. Simmons, D.Min.	2013–2019
Robert C. Vanzant, M.D.	2010–2019

APPENDIX 18
Houston Methodist Willowbrook Hospital
Board of Trustees

CHAIRS

Steven H. Hamblin	2001–2011
Jack C. Searcy, Jr.	2011–2015
Rev. James W. Foster	2015
Rev. Reginald Lillie	2015–Present

CURRENT TRUSTEES

Khawaja Azimuddin, M.D.	2019–Present
Mukarram Baig, M.D.	2017–Present
Keith D. Barber	2015–Present
Marc L. Boom, M.D.	2012–Present
J. David Cabello	2003–Present
Linda B. Humphries	2007–Present
Audre F. Levy, Ph.D.	2010–Present
Rev. Reginald Lillie	2008–Present
Lee Robison	2014–Present
Barbara J. Schlattman	2014–Present
Debra F. Sukin, Ph.D., MPH	2015–Present
Pastor Ken Werlein	2006–Present

FORMER TRUSTEES

Hazel L. Awalt, M.D.	2011–2014
Michael A. Barnard, M.D.	2004–2006
Susan S. Brown, M.D.	2000–2005
Andrew S. Cochrane	2002–2008
Thomas L. Dumler, M.D.	2000–2003
Rev. James W. Foster	2007–2015
Ronald G. Girotto	2001–2011
Steven H. Hamblin	2001–2011
Muhammad W. Hanif, M.D.	2009–2012
Benjamin D. Harvey, M.D.	2015–2018
Kourosh F. Jafarnia, M.D.	2007–2010

APPENDIX 20

Official Health Care Provider Partners

Houston Texans
Houston Astros
Houston Livestock Show and Rodeo™
Rice University Athletics
Houston Ballet
Houston Symphony
Houston Grand Opera

University and Health Partners

Weill Cornell Medicine
Texas A&M Health Science Center
Baylor College of Medicine
Rice University
Texas Children's Hospital
Texas Medical Center
University of Houston
University of St. Thomas

Community Clinic Partners

Access Health
Christ Clinic
El Centro de Corazon
Healthcare for the Homeless – Houston
HOPE Clinic
Houston Area Women's Center
Interfaith Community Clinic
Legacy Community Health
Northwest Assistance Ministries
The Rose
San Jose Clinic
Spring Branch Community Health
TOMAGWA Health Care Ministries
Vecino Health Centers

APPENDIX 21
Philanthropic Recognition

With enormous thanks to our benefactors, Houston Methodist would not be the premier clinical care, research, and education center it is today without philanthropic support.

1919–October 14, 2019

Named Buildings

Official Building Name	Opening Year
Fondren and Brown Cardiovascular and Orthopedic Research Center – Fondren Building named in honor of Ella F. and Walter W. Fondren – Brown Building named in honor of Herman Brown	1968
Neurosensory Center – Alice and David C. Bintliff Blue Bird Building – Mary Gibbs and Jesse H. Jones Patient Tower – Stella Wolters and Willard Lorraine Russell Building	1977
Alkek Tower named in honor of Margaret and Albert Alkek	1978
Scurlock Tower named in honor of Elizabeth and Eddy C. Scurlock	1980
Dunn Tower named in honor of John S. Dunn	1989
Smith Tower named in honor of Bess and Bishop A. Frank Smith	1989
Walter Tower named in honor of Paula and Joseph C. "Rusty" Walter III	2018

Endowed Positions

Endowed Positions are appointed to distinguished faculty, physicians, and researchers for a period of years. They provide stable, long-term financial resources necessary to accelerate research and lead medicine. In 2017, as a part of their $101 million gift, Paula and Joseph C. "Rusty" Walter III issued the **Centennial Chair Challenge** (**C³**) to match non-estate or partial-estate commitments of $1 million or more with $500,000 to create 50 new Centennial endowed chairs. Holders of Centennial Chairs make up the Walter College of Centennial Chairs.

Overall Chair Number	C³ Chair Number	Donor Impact	Donor Recognition Name	Year
1	—	John S. Dunn Chair in Orthopedic Surgery	John S. Dunn Foundation	1989
2	—	John S. Dunn Chair in Clinical Cardiovascular Research and Education	John S. Dunn Foundation	1991
3	—	John S. Dunn Chair in General Internal Medicine	John S. Dunn Foundation	1996
4	—	Ernest Cockrell, Jr. Presidential Distinguished Chair in the Houston Methodist Research Institute	The Cockrell Foundation	2004
5	—	Fondren Presidential Distinguished Chair in the Houston Methodist Research Institute	The Fondren Foundation	2004
6	—	John F., Jr. and Carolyn Bookout Presidential Distinguished Chair in the Department of Surgery	Carolyn and John F. Bookout	2005
7	—	Charles and Anne Duncan Presidential Distinguished Chair in the Department of Medicine	Mr. and Mrs. Charles W. Duncan, Jr.	2005
8	—	John S. Dunn Presidential Distinguished Chair in Biomedical Engineering	John S. Dunn Foundation	2005

Overall Chair Number	C³ Chair Number	Donor Impact	Donor Recognition Name	Year
9	–	Robert W. Hervey Chair for Parkinson's Research and Treatment	Mrs. Doris Delhomme Hervey	2005
10	–	Peggy and Gary Edwards Distinguished Chair in ALS Research	Peggy and Gary Edwards	2005
11	–	M.D. Anderson Foundation Distinguished Chair in Molecular Imaging	M.D. Anderson Foundation	2006
12	–	Robert G. Grossman Chair in Neurosurgery	Carolyn Payne, in honor of Leon Payne, Jr.	2007
13	–	Joseph C. "Rusty" Walter III and Carole Walter Looke Presidential Distinguished Chair in Cardiovascular Disease Research	Walter Oil & Gas; Paula and Joseph C. "Rusty" Walter III; C. James and Carole Walter Looke	2007
14	–	C. Richard Stasney, M.D. Distinguished Chair in Performing Arts Medicine	Dr. Bobby R. and Mrs. Othelia D. Alford; Mr. Thomas D. and Mrs. Janice H. Barrow; Mrs. Ginger and Mr. Jack S. Blanton, Sr.; Mr. and Mrs. Albert Y. Chao; Ting Tsung and Wei Fong Chao Foundation; Mrs. Nanette B. and Mr. Jerry E. Finger; The Alkek and Williams Foundation	2008
15	–	Jack S. Blanton Presidential Distinguished Chair for the Study of Neurological Disease	Scurlock Foundation	2008
16	–	Michael E. DeBakey Distinguished Chair in Cardiac Surgery	Carolyn and Bob Allison	2008
17	–	W. Bryan Trammell Jr. Family Distinguished Chair in Allergy and Immunology	Ann G. Trammell	2009

Overall Chair Number	C³ Chair Number	Donor Impact	Donor Recognition Name	Year
18	–	Alan L. Kaplan, M.D. Chair in Obstetrics and Gynecology	Anonymous; Mrs. Rolaine and Mr. Morrie K. Abramson; Mr. and Mrs. Marvy A. Finger; Dr. and Mrs. Alan L. Kaplan; Mr. and Mrs. Kenneth C. Margolis; The Oshman Foundation; The Paradies, Haber, and Shoob Families; Phillips 66; Patients, Family, Friends, and Colleagues of Dr. Alan L. Kaplan	2010
19	–	J.C. Walter Jr. Presidential Distinguished Chair in the J.C. Walter Jr. Transplant Center at Houston Methodist	Walter Oil & Gas through the generosity of Joseph C. "Rusty" Walter III and Carole Walter Looke	2011
20	–	Walter W. Fondren III Presidential Distinguished Chair for the Medical Director of the Houston Methodist DeBakey Heart & Vascular Center	The Fondren Foundation	2011
21	–	John F., Jr. and Carolyn Bookout Chair in Surgical Innovation and Technology	Carolyn and John Bookout	2011
22	–	John F., Jr. and Carolyn Bookout Distinguished Professor in Surgical Quality and Outcomes Science	Carolyn and John Bookout	2011
23	–	Harriet and Joe B. Foster Distinguished Chair in Neurosciences	Harriet and Joe Foster	2012
24	–	Daniel E. Lehane, M.D. Distinguished Chair in Cancer Excellence	Judy L. and Glenn R. Smith	2012
25	–	Lynn and Oscar Wyatt, Jr. Chair in Cardiology in honor of Mohammed Attar, M.D.	Lynn and Oscar Wyatt, Jr.	2012

Overall Chair Number	C³ Chair Number	Donor Impact	Donor Recognition Name	Year
26	–	Dottie and Jimmy C. Adair Distinguished Chair in Hematology	Dottie and Jimmy C. Adair	2012
27	–	David M. Underwood Chair of Medicine in Digestive Disorders	Mrs. Lynda K. and Mr. David M. Underwood	2013
28	–	David M. Underwood Chair of Surgery in Digestive Disorders	Mrs. Lynda K. and Mr. David M. Underwood	2013
29	–	David M. Underwood Distinguished Professor of Medicine in Digestive Disorders	Mrs. Lynda K. and Mr. David M. Underwood	2013
30	–	David M. Underwood Distinguished Professor of Surgery in Digestive Disorders	Mrs. Lynda K. and Mr. David M. Underwood	2013
31	–	Kenneth R. Peak Presidential Distinguished Chair	Donna and Kenneth R. Peak	2013
32	–	Graham Family Distinguished Chair for Neurological Sciences	Robert H. and Laurel "Annie" Graham	2013
33	–	The Elkins Family Distinguished Chair in Cardiac Health in honor of Dr. William A. Zoghbi	The Elkins Foundation	2013
34	–	Emily Herrmann Chair in Cancer Research	Walter Oil & Gas; Paula and Joseph C. "Rusty" Walter III; C. James and Carole Walter Looke	2013
35	–	Lenny C. Katz Chair in Health Outcomes and Quality in honor of Stuart M. Dobbs, M.D.	Lenny C. Katz	2013
36	–	Fondren Distinguished Professor in Inflammatory Bowel Disease	The Fondren Foundation	2013
37	–	Elaine and Marvy A. Finger Distinguished Chair for Translational Research in Metabolic Disorders	Marvy Finger Family Foundation and Elaine and Marvy A. Finger	2014

Overall Chair Number	C³ Chair Number	Donor Impact	Donor Recognition Name	Year
38	–	Jimmy F. Howell, M.D. Chair in the Houston Methodist DeBakey Heart & Vascular Center	Joseph C. "Rusty" Walter III and Carole Walter Looke; Mrs. Barbara D. Mackey in honor of Jimmy F. Howell, M.D.; The Cullen Foundation	2014
39	–	John S. "Steve" Dunn, Jr. Distinguished Professorship in Brain Tumor Research	John S. Dunn Foundation	2014
40	–	Dagmar Dunn Pickens Gipe Distinguished Professorship in Brain Tumor Research	John S. Dunn Foundation	2014
41	–	Elizabeth Blanton Wareing Chair in the Eddy Scurlock Stroke Center	Scurlock Foundation	2014
42	–	John F. III and Ann H. Bookout Distinguished Chair for Research Excellence	John F. III and Ann H. Bookout	2014
43	–	Allison Family Distinguished Chair in Cardiovascular Research	The Carolyn J. and Robert J. Allison, Jr. Family Foundation	2014
44	–	Jim and Joan Harrell Chair in Radiation Oncology or NeuroRadiology	Dr. James E. Harrell, Sr. and Mrs. Joan Harrell	2015
45	–	Stanley H. Appel Chair in Translational Neuroscience	Joan Wilson Appel	2015

Overall Chair Number	C³ Chair Number	Donor Impact	Donor Recognition Name	Year
46	–	Beverly B. and Daniel C. Arnold Distinguished Chair in Cardiology in honor of William L. Winters, Jr., M.D.	Shadywood Foundation; Beverly and Daniel Arnold; Steven D. Arnold; Alice A. and Randy Helms; Susan A. and Tom Martin; Alice and David C. Bintliff Foundation; Marjorie and Raleigh Johnson; Anonymous; Mr. and Mrs. Frank E. Driscoll; Richard Rubin on behalf of Hawkeye Capital; Taub Foundation; Mr. and Mrs. Thomas C. Thompson; Rusty and Paula Walter/C. James and Carole Walter Looke; Mary and Bill Winters; Marilyn and Chris Winters/Christopher W. Winters/Andrew S. Winters/ Scott Winters	2016
47	–	John S. "Steve" Dunn, Jr. and Dagmar Dunn Pickens Gipe Chair in Brain Tumor Research	John S. Dunn Foundation	2016
48	–	The Sumner Family Chair in Neuromuscular Research	Sharon and William Sumner Family	2016
49	–	The Wyatt Foundation Distinguished Professorship in Neurosurgery	The Wyatt Foundation	2016
50	–	Marlee A. and Dr. Gary M. Schwarz Distinguished Professorship	Marlee A. and Dr. Gary M. Schwarz	2016
51	–	David B. Rosenfield, M.D. Chair in Speech and Language in Neurology	Hoffberger Family; M.R. Bauer Foundation; Drew Ranier; Stanley H. Appel Department of Neurology and Friends	2016

Overall Chair Number	C³ Chair Number	Donor Impact	Donor Recognition Name	Year
52	–	Kathy and Jack Reichenthal Distinguished Chair in Neurosurgery in honor of Robert G. Grossman, M.D.	Kathy Hathorn Reichenthal	2017
53	1	Candy and Tom Knudson Distinguished Centennial Chair in Neurosurgery in honor of Gavin W. Britz, M.D.	Candy and Tom Knudson	2017
54	–	Sherrie and Alan Conover Chair for Excellence in Liver Transplantation in honor of R. Mark Ghobrial, M.D., Ph.D.	Sherrie and Alan Conover	2017
55	2	Dr. Ronny W. and Ruth Ann Barner Centennial Chair in Spiritual Care	Anonymous	2017
56	–	Alice R. McPherson, M.D. Chair in Ophthalmology	Dr. Alice R. McPherson	2017
57	3	J.C. "Rusty" Walter III Centennial Chair in the Houston Methodist DeBakey Heart & Vascular Center	Elizabeth C. Walter	2017
58	4	Lois and Carl Davis Centennial Chair in Multiple Sclerosis	Lois E. and Carl A. Davis	2017
59	5	Lois and Carl Davis Centennial Chair I in the Houston Methodist DeBakey Heart & Vascular Center	Lois E. and Carl A. Davis	2017
60	6	Lois and Carl Davis Centennial Chair II in the Houston Methodist DeBakey Heart & Vascular Center	Lois E. and Carl A. Davis	2017
61	7	Winters Family Distinguished Centennial Chair in Cardiovascular Education in honor of Christopher, William and Scott Winters	Dr. and Mrs. William L. Winters, Jr.	2017

Overall Chair Number	C³ Chair Number	Donor Impact	Donor Recognition Name	Year
62	–	Emily Herrmann Chair in Immunology Research	Walter Oil & Gas; Paula and Joseph C. "Rusty" Walter III; C. James and Carole Walter Looke	2017
63	8	Elizabeth Blanton and Peter S. Wareing Centennial Chair in Gastrointestinal Health	Mr. and Mrs. Peter S. Wareing	2017
64	9	Crowning Achievement Centennial Chair in Nursing Excellence	Anonymous	2017
65	10	John F. III and Ann H. Bookout Clinical Academic Scholar in the Research Institute	John F. III and Ann H. Bookout	2017
66	11	Ann and Billy Harrison Centennial Chair in Alzheimer's Research	Ann and Billy Harrison	2017
67	12	Henrietta and Terence Hall Distinguished Centennial Chair in Orthopedic Surgery	Henrietta and Terence Hall	2017
68	13	Cathy and Ed Frank Centennial Chair in Plastic and Reconstructive Surgery	Cathy and Ed Frank	2017
69	14	Deborah C. and Clifton B. Phillips Centennial Chair for Clinical Research in Transplant Medicine	Deborah C. and Clifton B. Phillips	2017
70	15	C. James and Carole Walter Looke Presidential Distinguished Centennial Chair in Behavioral Health	C. James and Carole Walter Looke	2018
71	16	The Coneway Family Centennial Chair in Quality and Outcomes	The Coneway Family Foundation	2018

Overall Chair Number	C³ Chair Number	Donor Impact	Donor Recognition Name	Year
72	17	Occidental Petroleum Centennial Chair in Quality and Outcomes Research	Occidental	2018
73	18	Ella Fondren and Josie Roberts Presidential Distinguished Centennial Chair	Anonymous	2018
74	19	Max and Lillie Frosch Centennial Chair in Transplant Research	Anonymous	2018
75	20	Ralph S. O'Connor Centennial Chair in the Houston Methodist Cancer Center	Ralph S. O'Connor	2018
76	21	Carol Cockrell Curran Distinguished Centennial Chair in Hematologic Oncology	The Cockrell Foundation	2018
77	22	Mary A. and M. Samuel Daffin, Sr. Centennial Chair in Anesthesia and Critical Care	Mary and Sam Daffin; Anonymous	2018
78	23	Beverly B. and Daniel C. Arnold Distinguished Centennial Chair in the Department of Cardiology in Honor of William L. Winters, Jr., M.D.	Shadywood Foundation; Steven D. Arnold; Susan A. and Tom Martin; Alice A. and Randy Helms; Beverly B. and Daniel C. Arnold	2018
79	24	The Elkins Family Distinguished Centennial Chair in Neurodegenerative Diseases	The Elkins Foundation	2018
80	25	The Elkins Family Distinguished Centennial Chair in Cardiac Health	The Elkins Foundation	2018
81	26	Charles and Anne Duncan Centennial Chair in Nephrology	The Duncan Fund	2018
82	27	Charles and Anne Duncan Centennial Chair in Endocrinology	The Duncan Fund	2018

Overall Chair Number	C³ Chair Number	Donor Impact	Donor Recognition Name	Year
83	28	John S. Dunn Foundation Distinguished Centennial Chair in Behavioral Health	John S. Dunn Foundation	2018
84	29	The Allison Family Centennial Chair in Cardiovascular Innovation I	Carolyn J. and Robert J. Allison, Jr. Family Foundation	2018
85	30	The Allison Family Centennial Chair in Cardiovascular Innovation II	Carolyn J. and Robert J. Allison, Jr. Family Foundation	2018
86	31	The John M. O'Quinn Centennial Chair in Concussion Research and Care	The John M. O'Quinn Foundation	2018
87	32	Carole Walter Looke Centennial Chair in Cardiovascular Intensive Care	Elizabeth C. Walter	2018
88	33	Nina and Michael Zilkha Centennial Chair in Gastrointestinal Health in honor of Dr. Eamonn Quigley in the Lynda K. and David M. Underwood Center for Digestive Disorders	Nina and Michael Zilkha	2018
89	34	Barbara Lee Bass Centennial Chair for Surgical Education	K.C. and Randa Weiner Family Fund; Tevia W. and Chris McLaren Family	2019
90	35	The Fondren Centennial Chair in Immunology	The Fondren Foundation	2019
91	36	The Fondren Centennial Chair in Gastrointestinal Microbiome	The Fondren Foundation	2019
92	37	The Fondren Distinguished Centennial Chair in Inflammation I	The Fondren Foundation	2019
93	38	The Fondren Distinguished Centennial Chair in Inflammation II	The Fondren Foundation	2019

Overall Chair Number	C³ Chair Number	Donor Impact	Donor Recognition Name	Year
94	39	Nicole Mary Follansbee Centennial Chair in the J.C. Walter Jr. Transplant Center	Kenneth Grant Follansbee, Sr. and Janet Monty Follansbee	2019
95	40	Ann Kimball and John W. Johnson Centennial Chair for Cellular Therapeutics I	Ann and John W. Johnson	2019
96	41	Ann Kimball and John W. Johnson Centennial Chair for Cellular Therapeutics II	Ann and John W. Johnson	2019
97	42	Blake and Roswell "Sandy" F. Vaughan III Centennial Chair in honor of Dr. Ashrith Guha	Blake and Roswell "Sandy" F. Vaughan III	2019
98	–	Diane Harkins Modesett Chair in the Houston Methodist Cancer Center	Diane and David Modesett	2019
99	43	Craig C. Brown and Suzanne H. Smith Centennial Chair in Medical Education at Houston Methodist	Craig C. Brown and Suzanne H. Smith	2019
100	44	William A. Zoghbi, M.D. Centennial Chair in Cardiovascular Health	The Family of William and Huda Zoghbi	2019
101	45	Lois and Carl Davis Centennial Chair in Cancer Research	Lois E. and Carl A. Davis	2019
102	46	Frank J. and Jean Raymond Centennial Chair in Medical Education at Houston Methodist	Frank J. and Jean Raymond Foundation	2019
103	47	Jim and Joan Harrell Centennial Chair in Radiation Oncology	Joan M. Harrell, in memory of Dr. James E. Harrell, Sr.	2019
104	48	Centennial Chair in Urologic Oncology	The Estate of Elsie Landram Layton	2019
105	49	Sanford I. Weill and Antonio M. Gotto, Jr., M.D. Centennial Chair in Translational Biomedical Sciences Education	Joan and Sanford I. Weill and the Weill Family Foundation	2019

Jerold B. Katz Academy of Translational Research Investigators
(As of September 2019, two of eight Katz Investigators have been appointed)

Nestor F. Esnaola, M.D., MPH, MBA, FACS	2017
Khurram Nasir, M.D., MPH, MSc	2018

Impact of Other Leadership Gifts

Listed alphabetically by donor, this list primarily includes leadership gifts committed since 2004, when the Houston Methodist Hospital Foundation began its first campaign. Many of these generous donors have also supported other programs and initiatives in addition to the leadership commitments listed below.

Donor Impact	Donor Recognition Name
Margaret Alkek Williams Center for Performing Arts Medicine Endowment for Arts Integration at Houston Methodist	Margaret Alkek Williams and the Albert and Margaret Alkek Foundation
The Allison Family Academy of Cardiovascular Innovators	The Carolyn J. and Robert J. Allison, Jr. Family Foundation
ALS Research	Anonymous
Cardiovascular Training	Anonymous
Crowning Achievement Awards for Excellence in Nursing	Anonymous
Mark J. Hausknecht, M.D. Cardiac Intensive Care Unit	Anonymous
Myotonic Dystrophy Research and Clinical Care	Anonymous
Neuroinflammation in ALS: Novel Therapeutic Pathways	Anonymous
Quality and Outcomes	Anonymous
Translational Research Endowed Chair Matching Fund in the Research Institute	Anonymous

Donor Impact	Donor Recognition Name
The Woodlands Community Care Endowment in honor of Dr. Fredric Lyone Hochman	Anonymous
Bioenergetics Research; Translational Research Initiative	The Honorable Hushang Ansary and Mrs. Shahla Ansary
Stanley H. Appel Department of Neurology	Joan Wilson Appel
Janice H. Barrow Endowment for Artist Treatment, Research and Injury Prevention	Janice H. Barrow
The Dr. Bobby R. Alford Fund, Dr. Robert G. Grossman Fund, Dr. Dan B. Jones Fund, and Dr. Antonio M. Gotto, Jr. Fund	Perry R. and Nancy Lee Bass
Everett and Randee Bernal Neurosurgery Family Lounge	Everett and Randee Bernal
Jack S. Blanton, Sr. Eye Institute	Jack S. Blanton, Sr.
Blue Bird Circle Auditorium	The Blue Bird Circle in memory of Bishop and Mrs. A. Frank Smith
Craig C. Brown and Suzanne H. Smith Engineering Medicine "EnMed" Capstone Innovator Awards Program	Craig C. Brown and Suzanne H. Smith
Brown Foundation Outstanding Nursing Award; The Regenerative Medicine Program; Alzheimer's Disease Diagnosis, Treatment and Research; Research Institute	The Brown Foundation, Inc.
Barbara and President George H.W. Bush Atrium	Bush Family and friends of Houston Methodist and the Bush Family
Cardiology Research Funding	Mr. Charles Eugene "Gene" Campbell and Mrs. Judy C. Campbell
Chao Center for Bioinformatics Research and Imaging for Neurosciences (BRAIN)	Ting Tsung and Wei Fong Chao Foundation
Virginia and Ernest Cockrell Jr. Center for Advanced Therapeutics	The Cockrell Foundation
Sherrie and Alan Conover Center for Liver Disease and Transplantation	Sherrie and Alan Conover

Donor Impact	Donor Recognition Name
Endowment for Specialty Care for the Medically Underserved; Houston Methodist Community Scholars Program	The Cullen Foundation
Regenerative Medicine Program; Transplant Center	The Cullen Trust for Health Care
Extending Arms of Christ Mosaic in Memory of Florence Eberhardt to support Multiple Sclerosis Care and Research; Walter Eberhardt Cardiac Catheterization Labs	Lois E. and Carl A. Davis
Houston Methodist DeBakey Heart & Vascular Center; Michael E. DeBakey, M.D. Institute for Cardiovascular Education and Training (DICET)	DeBakey Medical Foundation
Vic and Eleanor DiFranco Research Award Endowment in the Houston Methodist Research Institute	Vic and Eleanor DiFranco
The William Doré Family Fund for Heart Initiatives	The Doré Family Foundation
Charles and Anne Duncan Scholars Program in the Houston Methodist Department of Medicine	Anne S. and Charles W. Duncan, Jr. and The Duncan Fund
Dagmar Dow Dunn Innovator Award in Medical Product Discovery and Development in Memory of Dagmar Dow Dunn and Charles Milby Dow	Eva Lynn and John S. "Steve" Dunn, Jr.
Eva Lynn and John S. Dunn, Jr. Center for Research & Education in Reconstructive and Plastic Surgery; John S. Dunn Plaza at Houston Methodist Baytown Hospital	John S. Dunn Foundation
Constance M. and Byron F. Dyer Fellows; Jeffrey Lane Dyer Pancreatic Cancer Research Endowment	Constance M. and Byron F. Dyer
Peggy and Gary Edwards ALS Laboratory in Memory of Jeannette M. (Sonja) Edwards; Peggy and Gary Edwards Fund for Neurodegenerative Disease Research and Education in memory of Paul Henry Edwards	Peggy and Gary Edwards

Donor Impact	Donor Recognition Name
Chronic Organ Rejection Research	The William Stamps Farish Fund
Fondren Inflammation Collaborative; Food and Health Alliance; Immunology Center; Sue Fondren Trammell Pavilion; Sue Fondren Trammell Family Lounge	The Fondren Foundation
Cell Based Therapy Program in Neurodegenerative Disease	Harriet and Joe Foster
Translational Research Initiative	Freeport LNG Development, L.P.
Cancer Research	Golfers Against Cancer Houston
Men's Comprehensive Health Initiative; Transplant Program; Bereavement; Stroke Education; Nursing Excellence	The Hamill Foundation
Nantz National Alzheimer Center; Emily Herrmann Chair in Cancer Research; Chronic Traumatic Encephalopathy (CTE) Research; Schizophrenia Research	Ann and Billy Harrison
Cardiovascular Regenerative Research	The Hearst Foundations
Houston Methodist/Texas A&M Research and Education Collaborative (EnMed); Translational Research Initiative	Lou and Mark Houser
Department of Surgery/Houston Methodist Institute for Technology, Innovation & Education (MITIE^{SM})	Houston Endowment
Patient Care Equipment	The Houston Methodist Auxiliary
Concussion Center Outreach Education Fund; Sports Medicine Fellowship Fund	Houston Texans Foundation
ALS Research	Hunting and Fishing for ALS Research Inc.
Transplant Patient Care Funds	JLH Foundation, Inc.
Ann Kimball and John W. Johnson Center for Cellular Therapeutics at Houston Methodist	Ann and John W. Johnson

Donor Impact	Donor Recognition Name
Sheri Kaye and Alard Kaplan Kidney Transplant Research Fund; Sheri Kaye and Alard Kaplan Cardiac Recovery Training Program; Sheri Kaye and Alard Kaplan Fund for Nursing Education	Sheri Kaye and Alard Kaplan
Jerold B. Katz Academy of Translational Research	Jerold B. Katz Foundation
Lenny C. Katz Endocrinology Program	Lenny C. Katz Foundation & Jerold B. Katz Foundation
Department of Surgery/Houston Methodist Institute for Technology, Innovation & Education (MITIE^{SM})	Barbara Monroe Kirsch
Cardiovascular Inflammation Research; Transplant Rejection Prevention	Robert J. Kleberg, Jr. and Helen C. Kleberg Foundation
Cancer Research	Susan G. Komen© Houston Affiliate
George and Angelina Kostas Research Center for Cardiovascular Nanomedicine	George J. and Angelina P. Kostas Charitable Foundation
Michael C. Linn Family Foundation Conference Room; Michael C. Linn Family Foundation Consultation Room; Alzheimer's Research	Michael C. Linn Family Foundation
C. James and Carole Walter Looke Family Pavilion – "Looke 21"; C. James and Carole Walter Looke Sanctuary for Faith, Hope and Healing; C. James and Carole Walter Looke Matching Challenge in the Cancer Center; C. James and Carole Walter Looke Matching Challenge in the J.C. Walter Jr. Transplant Center	C. James and Carole Walter Looke
Houston Alzheimer's Study; Immunomodulatory Cell Therapy Research Program in Neurodegenerative Disease	Donald L. and Sally S. Lucas
Marling Childbirth Center at Houston Methodist The Woodlands Hospital	Kim and Robert Marling
Cancer Patient Support	Estate of Morris D. Matthews

Donor Impact	Donor Recognition Name
Alzheimer's Disease Research	Debbie and Jack Moore
The Latimer and Kathryn Murfee Endowed Fund for Clinical Scholars in Alzheimer's Disease	Kathryn Murfee Endowment
Eileen Murphree McMillin Blood Center	Murphree family and friends
MDA Care Center & MDA/ALS Care Center at Houston Methodist Neurological Institute	Muscular Dystrophy Association
Nantz National Alzheimer Center	Nantz Family Foundation; friends of the Nantz Family and Houston Methodist
Cancer Immunotherapy Research	Ron Neal and Mary Neal, M.D.
Cardiology and Urology Research	Notsew Orm Sands Foundation
Occidental Petroleum Innovation Hall; Occidental Petroleum Scholars	Occidental
Translational Research Initiative	Kalli O'Malley and Terry Giles
Kenneth R. Peak Brain and Pituitary Tumor Treatment and Research Center	Donna and Kenneth R. Peak
Houston Alzheimer's Study Matching Challenge Program	Jeanne and Joe Bob Perkins
Betty Adams Crain Garden	The Stockholders of R. Lacy, Inc. (Mrs. Ann Lacy and Mr. Bluford Walter Crain, Jr.; Mrs. Ann Lacy Crain II; Mr. and Mrs. Bluford Walter Crain III; Mr. and Mrs. Rogers Lacy Crain; E.L. Crain, Jr., M.D.)
Frank J. and Jean Raymond Engineering Medicine "EnMed" Capstone Innovator Awards Program	Frank J. and Jean Raymond Foundation
Sid Richardson Institute for Preventive Medicine	Sid W. Richardson Foundation of Fort Worth
Neuroimaging ALS Research	The Leandro P. Rizzuto Foundation
Eddy Scurlock Stroke Center	Scurlock Foundation

Donor Impact	Donor Recognition Name
Mary Hubbell Sides Fund for the Houston Methodist Neurological Institute	Estate of Howard Sides
Novel Therapy for Diabetes through Nanomedicine	Vivian L. Smith Foundation
Patrick J. Studdert Fund for Clinical Translation in the Center For Bioenergetics	Patrick J. Studdert
East Texas Heart & Vascular Initiative; East Texas Stroke Initiative	T.L.L. Temple Foundation
Lynda K. and David M. Underwood Center for Digestive Disorders	Lynda K. and David M. Underwood
Carole Walter Looke Cardiovascular Intensive Care Family Lounge; J.C. "Rusty" Walter III Cardiac Intensive Care Family Lounge	Elizabeth C. Walter
Walter College of Centennial Chairs; Walter Neurological Restoration Initiative; Walter Fund for Innovation	Paula and Joseph C. "Rusty" Walter III
Emily Herrmann Cancer Research Laboratory	Walter Oil & Gas; Paula and Joseph C. "Rusty" Walter III; C. James and Carole Walter Looke; Emily Herrmann famil and friends
J.C. Walter Jr. Transplant Center	Walter Oil & Gas through the generosity of Joseph C. "Rusty" Walter III and Carole Walter Looke
Kent Walters Endowment for Excellence in Neurosurgery	Kent Walters
The Grace Fund	Bonnie and David Weekley
Louisa Elizabeth Carothers Wiess Memorial Chapel	Harry C. and Olga Wiess
Woodforest National Bank Sky Plaza at Houston Methodist The Woodlands Hospital	Woodforest National Bank

Every attempt has been made to identify leadership gifts committed during our first 100 years. Please email donor@houstonmethodist.org if you are aware of leadership or other important gifts that are not reflected on this list. We would be very grateful for your assistance.

APPENDIX 22
President's Leadership Council

SENIOR CABINET

Steven D. Stephens, Chair

Gregory V. Nelson, Past Chair

Robert J. Allison, Jr.

Eva C. Bisso

Kelli L. Blanton

Marc L. Boom, M.D.

Stephen I. Chazen

David A. Cockrell

Clayton Erikson

Daniel M. Gilbane

George Kelly

David D. Kinder

John P. Kotts

William Gentry Lee, Jr.

Michael C. Linn

Rahul B. Mehta

Cynthia Pickett-Stevenson

Veronica Selinko-Curran, M.D.

Douglas E. Swanson, Jr.

David M. Underwood, Jr.

MEMBERS AT-LARGE

Arch H. Aplin III

Bruce R. Bilger

Isabel G. David

Jack Dinerstein

Nancy S. Dinerstein

Carolyn W. Dorros

Celia J. Dupré

Jenny Elkins

W. Lawrence Elliott

Thomas L. Elsenbrook

Jeffrey H. Foutch

Linda C. Gill

Steven J. Kean

Michael J. Plank

Cullen R. Spitzer

Alan L. Stein

Scott Wegmann

Paul Yetter

APPENDIX 22 *(continued)*
President's Leadership Council

ADVOCACY COMMITTEE

George M. Masterson, Chair
David A. Cockrell, Past Chair
Gina B. Andrews
Jonathan Baksht
Eddy S. Blanton
Kelli L. Blanton
Muffin Clark
Claudia Contreras
David R. Dominy
Jeffrey E. Margolis
David McKeithan
Mary Ann McKeithan

Denise D. Monteleone
Joel L. Moore
Rick Moore
Cabrina F. Owsley
Rick Perez
Suzanne H. Smith
Marcy E. Taub
Franco Valobra
Karen D. Walker
Dancie Perugini Ware
Kelley Young

PATIENT EXPERIENCE COMMITTEE

Ward Sheffield, Chair
David M. Underwood, Jr.,
    Past Chair
Matthew K. Baird
George M. Britton, Jr.
R. D. Burnside III
Gerardo A. Chapa
Muffin Clark
M. Scott Cone
Denis A. DeBakey
William J. Doré, Jr.
Ann H. Elvin
Marc P. Gordon

Laura Laux Higgins
Vicki A. Hollub
David D. Kinder
Jeffrey E. Margolis
Dale L. Martin
Grant Martinez
Andrew D. McCullough, Jr.
Rahul B. Mehta
Rick Moore
Frank D. Perez
Melanie C. Rothwell
Scott E. Schwinger
Duncan K. Underwood

CAMPAIGN STEERING COMMITTEE

Elizabeth Blanton Wareing,
  Co-Chair
Joseph C "Rusty" Walter III,
  Co-Chair
Dorothy M. Ables
E. William Barnett
Daphne Bernicker
Marc L. Boom, M.D.
Lloyd "Lucky" Burke
Stephen I. Chazen
Claudia Contreras
Paula Criel
Gary W. Edwards
Rob Fondren
Ed Frank
James G. Frankel

Richard Harper, M.D.
Mark A. Houser
John W. Johnson
Evan H. Katz
Thomas C. Knudson
W. Benjamin Moreland
Gregory V. Nelson
Cynthia Pickett-Stevenson
Suzanne H. Smith
H. Dirk Sostman, M.D., FACS
Douglas E. Swanson, Jr.
David M. Underwood, Jr.
Duncan K. Underwood
W. Temple Webber III
Kelley Young

FACULTY/PHYSICIAN CAMPAIGN COMMITTEE

Richard Harper, M.D., Co-Chair
H. Dirk Sostman, M.D., FACS,
  Co-Chair
Jett R. Brady, M.D.
Ron Gentry, M.D.

Robert Jackson, M.D.
Gerald Lawrie, M.D.
Brian Miles, M.D.
Todd Trask, M.D.

HOUSTON METHODIST CANCER CENTER COUNCIL

Daphne Bernicker, Chair
Dorothy M. Ables, Vice Chair
Jud Bailey
Carin M. Barth
Vicki L. Baucum
Eric H. Bernicker, M.D.
E. Brian Butler, M.D.
Jenny Chang, M.D.
Scott A. Davis
Ann H. Elvin
Heather Firestone
Alan L. Kaplan, M.D.
Cissie Rauch-Kaplan

John W. Lodge III
Christine Lukens
Dale L. Martin
Peggy D. Martin
Maryanne W. McCormack
David A. Modesett
Diane Modesett
Rick Moore
Glenn R. Smith
Betty A. Sommer
Bin S. Teh, M.D.
Christine L. Underwood
Stephen T. Wong, Ph.D., PE

APPENDIX 22 *(continued)*
President's Leadership Council

HOUSTON METHODIST CENTER FOR PERFORMING ARTS MEDICINE ADVISORY BOARD

Robert E. Jackson, M.D., Chair
C. Richard Stasney, M.D.,
　Founder, Past Chair
E. William Barnett
Janice H. Barrow
Ginger Blanton
Anthony K. Brandt, Ph.D.
Sharon Bryan
Albert Y. Chao
James W. Crownover
Françoise A. Djerejian
Deborah K. Duncan
Gina Eandi, RN
Victor Fainstein, M.D.
Jeremy Finkelstein, M.D.
J. Todd Frazier
Robert Freeman, Ph.D.
Elizabeth L. Ghrist
Suzanne M. Glasscock
Carole J. Hackett, BSN, Ed.M.
Richard Harper, M.D.
Eric J. Haufrect, M.D.
Patricia P. Hubbard
Christof Karmonik, Ph.D.
Thomas A. Krouskop, Ph.D., PE

Michael W. Lieberman, M.D., Ph.D.
Sharon Ley Lietzow
Judy E. Margolis
Gabby Martinez
Vidal G. Martinez
Hoyt T. "Toby" Mattox
Edwards U. McReynolds, M.D.
Rev. Charles R. Millikan, D.Min.
James M. Musser, M.D., Ph.D.
Judy Nyquist
Nicholas A. Phillips
Patricia Rauch
Keith O. Reeves, M.D.
L. E. Simmons
Jerome B. Simon
Lois F. Stark
Apurva A. Thekdi, M.D.
Ron Tintner, M.D.
Laura Jennings Turner
Kevin E. Varner, M.D.
Richard E. Wainerdi, Ph.D., PE
Margaret Alkek Williams
Aline D. Wilson
Stephen T. Wong, Ph.D., PE
Robert A. Yekovich, DMA

HOUSTON METHODIST DEBAKEY HEART & VASCULAR CENTER COUNCIL

Connie M. Dyer, Co-Chair
Cynthia Pickett-Stevenson,
　Co-Chair
Robert J. Allison, Jr.
Seth M. Barrett
J. Denny Bartell

Marc L. Boom, M.D.
Kenneth E. Breaux
John R. Butler, Jr.
P. Embry Canterbury
Carl M. Carter III
Gerardo A. Chapa

HOUSTON METHODIST DEBAKEY HEART &
VASCULAR CENTER COUNCIL *(continued)*

Mary A. Daffin
Denis A. DeBakey
Joann P. DiGennaro
William J. Doré, Jr.
William J. Doré, Sr.
Nan Duhon
Jean Durdin
Danielle Ellis
Eva K. Farha
William E. Gipson, Sr.
Marc P. Gordon
David B. Greenberg
Miguel Hernandez
Wendy Hines

Fadila B. Kibsgaard
William E. King
William E. Kline, Ph.D.
Cynthia G. Kostas
Huntley Anderson Kubitza
Carole Walter Looke
John M. McCormack
Mason L. Mote
Taylor Norris
Frank D. Perez
Douglas R. Quinn
Tony Vallone
Elizabeth C. Walter

HOUSTON METHODIST NEUROLOGICAL INSTITUTE
NATIONAL COUNCIL

Gary W. Edwards, Co-Chair
William E. Chiles, Co-Chair
David M. Underwood, Sr.,
    Past Chair
James P. Bailey, Jr.
James R. Bath
Everett E. Bernal
Randee K. Bernal
Eddy S. Blanton
Ginger Blanton
John F. Bookout
Allen Brivic
J. David Cabello
Mary Kay Cimo
Kathleen Crist
Frank Gay
Paula Gay
Kate H. Gibson

Robert H. Graham
Sylvia Harris
Titus H. Harris III
Billy Harrison
Gregory Hintz
Mary F. Johnston
Elise Joseph
Thomas C. Knudson
Gregory A. Kozmetsky
Jack B. Moore
Meg Murray
James W. Oden
Cabrina F. Owsley
Leon M. Payne, Emeritus
Arthur A. Seeligson III
Donna S. Stahlhut
Roxane R. Strickling
Henry J. N. "Kitch" Taub II

APPENDIX 22 *(continued)*
President's Leadership Council

HOUSTON METHODIST NEUROLOGICAL INSTITUTE
NATIONAL COUNCIL *(continued)*

Anne G. Thobae

Andrew C. von Eschenbach, M.D.

Dancie Perugini Ware

Elizabeth Blanton Wareing

W. Temple Webber III

Steven B. Wyatt

HOUSTON METHODIST BEHAVIORAL HEALTH (PSYCHIATRY)
TASK FORCE

David B. Lumpkins, Chair

Frank Amsler

Kelly Hackett

Gayle Kennedy

Joseph S. Looke

Kristi P. Lumpkins

Caroline Negley

HOUSTON METHODIST JACK S. BLANTON EYE INSTITUTE
TASK FORCE

Andrew G. Lee, M.D., Chair

Hilary A. Beaver, M.D.

Jack S. Blanton, Jr.

Leslie D. Blanton

David M. Brown, M.D.

Petros Carvounis, M.D.

Jorie Jackson

Frances M. Jones, DDS

Herbert Lyman

Jean Lyman

Alice R. McPherson, M.D.

Kevin Merkley, M.D.

Aaron Miller, M.D.

Rick Raanes

Vanessa Raanes

Sandy Rosenberg

Florence Rutherford

Michael G. Rutherford

C. Richard Stasney, M.D.

Charles Wykoff, M.D.

HOUSTON METHODIST BRAIN & BONE
COLLABORATIVE

Jon D. Deutser, Co-Chair

Cynthia R. Levin Moulton,
   Co-Chair

J. D. "Bucky" Allshouse

Lauren G. Anderson

Eric Brueggeman

Clint Cannon

Jennifer Davenport

Jace Duke

Heather Firestone

John Granato

Debbie Hance

Joshua D. Harris, M.D.

Vijay Jotwani, M.D.

Terry Lohrenz, Ph.D.

Mark Loveland

HOUSTON METHODIST BRAIN & BONE
COLLABORATIVE *(continued)*

Larry Margolis

Patrick McCulloch, M.D.

Hannah McNair

Keith Morris

Randy Nelson

Jason B. Ostrom

Kenneth Podell, Ph.D.

Margaret Dolbear Reppert

James C. Rootes

Todd E. Siff, M.D.

Alan L. Smith

S. Shawn Stephens

Ennio Tasciotti, Ph.D.

Donald Trull

Kevin E. Varner, M.D.

Daryl W. Wade

Barry D. Warner

HOUSTON METHODIST LYNDA K. AND DAVID M. UNDERWOOD CENTER
FOR DIGESTIVE DISORDERS TASK FORCE

Rob Fondren, Co-Chair

Duncan K. Underwood,
    Co-Chair

James J. Braniff III

Shari Fish

Jay Golding

Pedro L. Durán Gomez

Marcy Margolis

James C. Pappas

C. Loren Vandiver

Brock Wagner

Karen Wagner

Marie Wise

William Wise

Michael Zilkha

Nina Zilkha

HOUSTON METHODIST IMMUNOLOGY CENTER
TASK FORCE

Lloyd "Lucky" Burke, Co-Chair

James G. Frankel, Co-Chair

Laura T. Baird

Sandy L. Burke

Louis B. Cushman

Stevan L. Dinerstein, M.D.

Annie Criner Eifler

Carol Frankel

Jennie Getten

Michael J. Graff

Rhonda Graff

Sippi K. Khurana, M.D.

Carolyn C. Light

David W. Light III

Moez Mangalji

Sultana Mangalji

Aimee B. McCrory

Donald Poarch

Angela E. "Nikki" Richnow

Mary Eliza Shaper

Ann G. Trammell

David M. Underwood, Jr.

APPENDIX 22 *(continued)*
President's Leadership Council

HOUSTON METHODIST SHERRIE AND ALAN CONOVER CENTER FOR LIVER DISEASE & TRANSPLANTATION TASK FORCE

Paula D. Criel, Chair

Deborah Keener Brown

Alan Conover

Sherrie Conover

Kandice Fogle

Kathy Ghobrial

Elizabeth A. Hoff

Tami Houston

Edward A. Jones

Burt H. Keenan

Lawrence W. Kellner

Linda G. Lykos

Walter McFadden

Eugene A. O'Donnell

Elizabeth Rotan

Mary Seefluth

Patricia Sloan

Samuel Sloan

HOUSTON METHODIST NURSING COUNCIL

Emily A. Crosswell, Chair

Ginger Blanton

Carla Dawson

Marcy Duncan

Lynda K. Underwood

HOUSTON METHODIST SURGICAL INNOVATIONS TASK FORCE

Bridget B. Wade, Co-Chair

Jack Moriniere, Co-Chair

Marcos Basso

Henry Bragg, Sr.

Michael Ellington

Douglas Getten

Dana Myers, M.D.

Jon P. Spiers, M.D.

James E. Taussig

Randa Weiner

John B. Young, Jr.

Anat Zeidman

HOUSTON METHODIST J.C. WALTER JR. TRANSPLANT CENTER TASK FORCE

W. Gregory Looser, Chair

Jeff Smisek, Past Chair

Vicki L. Baucum

John Dawson, Jr.

Martha Smith DeBusk

Myrna J. Deckert

Janet M. Follansbee

Kenneth G. Follansbee, Sr.

Anita W. Garten

David B. Garten

Vicki H. Hitzhusen

George P. Joseph

Gayle G. Kennedy

Huntley Anderson Kubitza

HOUSTON METHODIST J.C. WALTER JR. TRANSPLANT CENTER
TASK FORCE *(continued)*

J. Colter Lewis

Steven S. Looke

Michael M. Metz

Deborah C. Phillips

Ahmed A. Rabie

Rev. Edmund W. Robb III, D.D.

Nora Smati

Terrell Eastman Sprague

Wilma Carter "Helen" Streaker

Steven M. Thorpe

Ellis L. Tudzin

Christine L. Underwood

Martha S. Walton

HOUSTON METHODIST UROLOGY CENTER
TASK FORCE

John M. Bonner III

Cathy Derrick

Robert Derrick

Karen Feld

Larry Feld

Carolyn Putterman

Leland Putterman

Steven Selsberg

Patricia Selsberg

APPENDIX 23
2019 Centennial Events

MAJOR CELEBRATIONS

Employee Centennial Celebration
Sesame Street Live! Family Show
Rock Concert featuring Imagine Dragons
Family Activities
April 6, 2019
NRG Stadium

Centennial Documentary Premiere
Houston Methodist: The Hospital with a Soul
Celebrating 100 Years of Leading Medicine
June 11, 2019
IPIC Theatre Houston

Rendezvous of the Century
Houston Methodist's Centennial Gala
Honorary Chairs: The Family of President and Mrs. George H.W. Bush
Chairs: Ann and John F. Bookout III
November 14, 2019
Minute Maid Park

APPENDIX 23 *(Continued)*
2019 Centennial Events

LECTURE SERIES

Centennial Lecture Recognizing Marquee Honorees
Ella and Walter Fondren and Family
Unveiling of the Centennial Wall of History
February 25, 2019
Keynote: Bryant Boutwell, Dr.P.H.
Barbara and President George H.W. Bush Atrium
Paula and Joseph C. "Rusty" Walter III Tower

Physicians Lecture & Dinner Recognizing Marquee Honoree
Michael E. DeBakey, M.D.
April 25, 2019
Lecture Keynote: Craig A. Miller, M.D.
John F. Bookout Auditorium
Houston Methodist Research Institute
Dinner Keynote: Bryant Boutwell, Dr.P.H.
Barbara and President George H.W. Bush Atrium
Paula and Joseph C. "Rusty" Walter III Tower

Partners Lecture Recognizing Marquee Honoree
Houston Astros
May 21, 2019
Keynote: Jeff Luhnow, President, Baseball Operations, Houston Astros
John F. Bookout Auditorium
Houston Methodist Research Institute

Leadership Lecture Recognizing Marquee Honoree
John F. Bookout
September 17, 2019
Keynote: John F. Bookout
John F. Bookout Auditorium
Houston Methodist Research Institute

LECTURE SERIES *(Continued)*

Philanthropy Lecture Recognizing Marquee Honorees
Paula and Joseph C. "Rusty" Walter III
October 21, 2019
Keynote: David Weekley
Barbara and President George H.W. Bush Atrium
Paula and Joseph C. "Rusty" Walter III Tower

Faith Lecture Recognizing Marquee Honorees
Bess and Bishop A. Frank Smith
December 9, 2019
Keynote: Bishop Scott J. Jones
John F. Bookout Auditorium
Houston Methodist Research Institute

By means of a wide breadth of archival material and current sources, every attempt was made to ensure the accuracy of information throughout the Appendices. We apologize for any errors or omissions. Please email donor@houstonmethodist.org with updates and corrections.

NOTATIONS

Abbreviations

HMA-PEC — Houston Methodist Archives, Professional Education Center, Methodist Hospital Main Building, Texas Medical Center, Houston.

JPM-HC — John P. McGovern Historical Collections and Research Center, Texas Medical Center Library, Houston.

INTRODUCTION

1. Daniel Jackson interview by Dr. William L. Winters, Jr., April 18, 2011, in Dr. William L. Winters, Jr., and Betsy Parish, *Reflections: Houston Methodist Hospital* (Houston: Elisha Freeman Publishing, 2016), 218.

2. Ibid.

3. Ruth Abeles, interview by the author, January 19, 2018.

ONE – PREQUEL

1. Emmanuel Domenech, *Texas and Mexico: A Personal Narrative of Six Years' Sojourn in Those Regions* (London: Longman, Brown, Green, Longmans, and Roberts, 1858), 24.

2. Garvin Berry and Betty Chapman, "The Allen Brothers: Bold Entrepreneurial Venture Launched City of Houston," in *2-Minute Histories of Houston* (Houston: Houston Business Journal,1996), 7.

3. A. C. Allen, "The Town of Houston," *Telegraph and Texas Register* 1, no. 97 (August 30, 1834): 1.

4. Marguerite Johnson, *Houston The Unknown City: 1836–1946* (College Station: Texas A&M University Press, 2011), 45.

5. James Q. Dealey, "The Spanish Source of the Mexican Constitution of 1824." *Quarterly of the Texas State Historical Association*, no. 3 (January 1900).

6. First Methodist Church of Houston, "Historic Snapshots of First Methodist Houston," accessed October 29, 2018, http://www.fmhouston.com/history/.

7. Norman W. Spellmann, "Methodist Church," *Handbook of Texas Online*, accessed October 29, 2018, https://tshaonline.org/handbook/online/articles/imm01.

8. Olin W. Nail, *History of Texas Methodism 1900–1960* (Austin: Capital Printing Co., 1961), 29.

9. Emmanuel Domenech, *Texas and Mexico: A Personal Narrative*, 24.

10. Ibid., 25.

11. Pat Ireland Nixon, *A History of the Texas Medical Association 1853–1953* (Austin: University of Texas Press, 1953), 8.

12. Andrew Forest Muir and Sylvia Stallings Morris, *William Marsh Rice and His Institute: A Biographical Study* (Houston: Rice University Press, 1972), 25.

TWO – BEGINNINGS

1. "Founder of Hospital Here Dies Suddenly: Dr. O. L. Norsworthy Succumbs to Heart Attack While on Honeymoon; Established Hospital," *Houston Chronicle*, January 6, 1935.

2. "The Ambulance Corps to Graduate," *The Times-Picayune*, March 29, 1895, 3. This article features ten recent Tulane graduates from the ambulance corps, including Dr. Oscar Norsworthy, and states they are "graduates who have finished the required course of study and who have had special advantages and proven worthy of trust."

3. F. E. Daniel, M.D., and S. E. Hudson, *Texas Journal of Medicine and Surgery* Vol XI (July 1895 to June 1896). The editor notes, "This is a pretty good showing of Texas students, considering Texas has a high grade [sic] school of her own, and charges a nominal fee."

4. "Founder of Hospital Here Dies Suddenly."

5. Rosemary Stevens, *American Medicine and the Public Interest: A History of Specialization* (Berkeley: University of California Press, 1998).

6. Peter Harry Brown and Pat H. Broeske, *Howard Hughes: The Untold Story* (Cambridge, MA: Da Capo Press, 1996), 6.

7. Marguerite Johnson, *Houston The Unknown City: 1836–1946* (College Station: Texas A&M University Press, 2011), 78.

8. William Henry Kellar, *Enduring Legacy* (College Station: Texas A&M University Press, 2014), 14.

9. Ibid., 14.

10. Sandra Cook, "125 Years of Compassionate Care," *Downtown Houston*, accessed October 29, 2018, https://www.downtownhouston.org/news/article/125-years-compassionate-care/. This article by Houston's Downtown District was published June 1, 2012.

11. Ted Francis and Carole McFarland, *The Memorial Hospital System: The First Seventy-Five Years* (Houston: Larksdale Press, 1982), 18.

12. Kellar, *Enduring Legacy*, 16.

13. O. Howard "Bud" Frazier, personal conversation with the author, March 2, 2017.

14. W. Alexander Smith, *Family Tree Book Genealogical and Biographical: Listing the Relatives of General William Alexander Smith and of W. Thomas Smith*. Published by author, 1922. https://archive.org/details/familytreebookge00byusmit/page/n3. Entry 950 provides a biographical sketch of Sarah Sandford Gibbs Norsworthy and her husband, Dr. Oscar L. Norsworthy.

15. Pat Ireland Nixon, *A History of the Texas Medical Association 1853–1953* (Austin: University of Texas Press, 1953), 282–283.

16. Johnson, *Houston The Unknown City: 1836–1946*, 147.

17. "Norsworthy Hospital," Advertisement in the *Bulletin of the Harris County Medical Society*, (undated) 1924, 3.

18. Johnson, *Houston The Unknown City: 1836–1946*, 147.

19. Alan Dronsfield and Pete Ellis, "Radium-A Key Element in Early Cancer Treatment," *Education in Chemistry* (March 2011): 57.

20. Ibid., 58.

21. Bryant Boutwell, "Fred Elliott and the UTHealth School of Dentistry," *'Bout Time: 4-Minute Histories of the Texas Medical Center* (Houston: University of Texas Printing Division, 2017), 37. This collection of short histories was first published as a blog found online at https://www.uth.edu/blog/bout-time/.

22. Johnson, *Houston The Unknown City: 1836–1946*, 148.

23. Jeffrey D. Dunn, "Bellaire, TX," *Handbook of Texas Online*, accessed October 29, 2018, https://tshaonline.org/handbook/online/articles/heb05.

24. Smith, *Family Tree Book Genealogical and Biographical Listing: the Relatives of General William Alexander Smith and of W. Thomas Smith*.

25. This information was gathered through the life story of Dr. Oscar L. Norsworthy posted in Ancestry.com with access granted by permission from the site author. Dr. Norsworthy's father passed away in Kirbyville, Texas in 1872 at the age of twenty-eight. His sister died at the age of four the following year in Jasper, Texas.

26. Louis F. Aulbach, Linda C. Gorski, and Robbie Morin, *Camp Logan: Houston, Texas 1917–1919* (Houston, 2014), 52.

27. Gina Kolata, *Flu: The Story of the Great Influenza Pandemic of 1918 and the Search for the Virus that Caused It* (New York: Farrar, Staus and Girous, 2011), Kindle Edition, 14.

28. Norman Spellmann, "Methodist Church," *Handbook of Texas Online*, 3.

29. John H. Wigger, *Taking Heaven by Storm: Methodism and the Rise of Popular Christianity in America* (New York: Oxford University Press, 1998), 175.

30. Patricia Pando, "A Brief History of the Fourth Ward." *Houston History* 8, no. 2, (undated): 39.

31. Ibid.

32. David T. Morgan, "John Wesley's Sojourn in Georgia Revisited," *The Georgia Historical Quarterly* 64, no. 3 (Fall, 1980): 253.

33. Marilyn McAdams Sibley, *The Methodist Hospital of Houston: Serving the World* (Austin: Texas State Historical Association, 1989), 10.

34. N. Don Macon, *Monroe Dunaway Anderson, His Legacy: A History of the Texas Medical Center, 50th Anniversary Edition* (Houston: Texas Medical Center, 1994), 65.

35. Harold M. Hyman, *Craftsmanship & Character: A History of the Vinson & Elkins Law Firm of Houston*, 1917–1997 (Athens: University of Georgia Press, 1998), 32.

36. Sibley, *The Methodist Hospital of Houston*, 16.

37. Carolina Gonzales, "The Haunted Jefferson Davis Hospital," *Houston Chronicle*, October 27, 2015.

38. Sibley, *The Methodist Hospital of Houston*, 17.

39. H. B. Smith, *Journal of the Eighty-Third Annual Session of the Texas Conference*, Methodist Episcopal Church, South, held in Marshall, Texas, November 22–27, 1922, 40. To reach the stated goal, the conference report notes, "it is [sic] been unanimously agreed upon to bring on a hospital campaign for the early part of the Conference year … to raise the sum of the obligation of this conference. Also it is desired to have a campaign in the city of Houston, including all the people, as we are to open the institution to all, Jew and Gentile, Catholic and Protestant."

40. Sibley, *The Methodist Hospital of Houston*, 19.

41. Harris Hillburn, L.L.P., "History of our Building," accessed October 30, 2018, http://www.hhstxlaw.com/index-1.html. This Houston-based law firm at the time of the Houston Methodist centennial occupies the old Sarah Francelia Bell building on Rosalie. Their website provides a current photo of the restored building and offers a brief history of the home, noting, "No exterior changes to the home have been made since its construction, although all original windows were removed and had to be replaced … a wood deck and ramp has been installed at the back of the building for ADA purposes. The interior, which had been completely gutted by previous owners and vandals, has been reconstructed as offices."

42. Rev. Charles Claude Selecman also served as the third president of Southern Methodist University (SMU) 1923–1938. His papers are in the SMU University Archives, DeGolyer Library. In 1951 he was elected to the Methodist Hall of Fame in philanthropy. He died March 27, 1958, age eighty-three.

43. Sibley, *The Methodist Hospital of Houston*, 43.

44. Transcript, Josie M. Roberts, interview by James B. Speer, Houston, Texas, March 1975, Series 15, Drawer 21-101, 3. HMA-PEC.

45. Ibid., 7.

46. D. H. Hotchkiss to Board of Trustees, Methodist Hospital, April 29, 1929, in *Quarterly and Annual Audits 1929–1930 Methodist Hospital*, prepared by R.E. St. John & Co., October, 1930, HMA-PEC.

47. Transcript, Josie Roberts interview by James B. Speer, March 1975, 3. HMA-PEC.

48. Frank Smith, personal conversation with the author, March 8, 2018. On this day the author made a presentation on Houston history for the Kiwanis Club of Houston. While the author was signing books, an elder gentleman escorted by his son approached with a friendly smile to tell the story of his good friend, the late A. Frank Smith. "Bishop Smith was a wonderful friend who I'll never forget." This serendipitous meeting seemed destined for inclusion in these stories.

49. Olin W. Nail, *The History of Texas Methodism 1900–1960* (Austin: Capital Printing Co., 1961), 372.

50. "New Methodist Hospital Open for Inspection: Beautiful Furnishings and Modern Equipment Prompted Favorable Comment from Visitors," *Houston Post*, April 14, 1924.

51. As the city's health officer, Dr. Charles Green was featured weekly in local newspaper birth announcements. For example, the *Houston Post*, March 29, 1914, notes, "Thirty births were officially reported last week to the office of Dr. C. C. Green, City Health Officer." Dr. Marvin L. Graves was featured in the *Houston Post* on January 30, 1935, in an article by Dr. Chauncey D. Leake, "Pioneer Medical Men Required to be First Rate in Many Jobs."

52. J. Charles Dickson, "Methodist Hospital History: Special Reference to the Executive Committee of the Staff," HMA-PEC, undated. This typed document is ten pages and provides Dr. Dickson's personal recollections of the early years of Methodist Hospital. Summarizing the board's support of the young doctors, he adds, "Because of this approach, the Executive Committee and Staff were made to feel they were a part of the hospital and had a say in how the Hospital was run. In time this made a very loyal dedicated staff, which backed the Hospital in good times and bad times."

53. "Local Hospitals Get High Ratings: Again on Approved List of American College of Surgeons," *Galveston Daily News*, October 21, 1924.

54. Advertisement, *Houston Post*, September 7, 1951. This ad promoted the sale of Methodist Hospital "… with 200-ft. frontage on San Jacinto, now being widened and repaved, a 125-ft frontage on Anita, and 100-ft. frontage on Rosalie. Property consists of one five-story concrete building, one 3½-story brick veneer building, one two-story fame building, and one one-story frame building. Frame buildings may be converted into either office or residence buildings. The five-story concrete building may be converted into an office or apartment building or living quarters. Delivery of property can be made by November 1st."

55. Sibley, *The Methodist Hospital of Houston*, 37.

56. Amanda Guest, email message to Houston Methodist employees, February 9, 2018. The message notes, "Over the years, the Auxiliary has donated more than $6 million in funds to Houston Methodist."

57. Advertisement, *Houston Post*, November 14, 1924. This ad for Methodist's nursing school notes, "The first unit of this building is now completely equipped. 5 Operating Rooms and an Emergency Operating Room, X-Ray Laboratory, Pathological Laboratory, Phototherapy Laboratory, Radium Department. Separate Children and Maternity Building."

58. Sibley, *The Methodist Hospital of Houston*, 37.

THREE – GROWING PAINS

1. "Dr. Greenwood's Sanitarium: For Nervous Diseases, Alcohol and Drug Addictions, Selected Cases of Mental Diseases and Pellagra," Advertisement in the *Bulletin of the Harris County Medical Society*, (undated) 1924: 8.

2. James "Jim" Greenwood, email to Tom Knudson, June 22, 2019. Jim Greenwood, Dr. James Greenwood, Jr.'s oldest son, served on Houston City Council for twelve years (1981–1993) and was an associate/partner at Vinson & Elkins for twenty years (1961–1980). This email was shared with the author. He also notes, "When I was running for office, I frequently encountered Houstonians who asked if I was Dr. Greenwood's son. I was proud to tell them I was and heard countless stories about his kindness in caring for their family members, always taking time to listen to them."

3. Transcript, Josie Roberts interview by James B. Speer, March 1975, 22. HMA-PEC.

4. William K. Brown, interview by Dr. William Winters, Jr., April 4, 2007 in Dr. William L. Winters, Jr., and Betsy Parish, *Reflections: Houston Methodist Hospital* (Houston: Elisha Freeman Publishing, 2016), 32.

5. John W. Overstreet, interview by Dr. William Winters, Jr., June 17, 2004, *Reflections*, 352.

6. Marilyn McAdams Sibley, *The Methodist Hospital of Houston: Serving the World* (Austin: Texas State Historical Association, 1989), 56.

7. Ibid., 32.

8. Bruce Popka, "Nurse Recalls 1929, "The Old Days," *TMC News*, July 1982.

9. Ibid.

10. Sibley, *The Methodist Hospital of Houston*, 30.

11. "Baby Parties at Hospitals on Saturday: Special Events Arranged in Connection with Annual Red Cross Founding," *Houston Chronicle*, May 10, 1928. The article begins, "Mr. Average Baby, hitherto acclaimed only in his own household, Saturday will come into his own in Houston, when all city hospitals celebrate National Hospital day with baby parties on the lawns in front of the institutions."

12. Ted Bowen, "Address to be Given by Mr. Ted Bowen to the Women's Auxiliary to the Methodist Hospital at its 40th Anniversary Meeting," HMA-PEC, February 15, 1968, 4. Bowen adds, "There was an old elevator in that building that was enclosed in a steel cage complete with hand-operated gates. This elevator was controlled by a pull rope and when it ran, it had a peculiar habit of stopping between floors causing fuses to blow and circuit breakers to kick out. It ran with a somewhat jerky motion."

13. Sibley, *The Methodist Hospital of Houston*, 42.

14. D. H. Hotchkiss to Board of Trustees, Methodist Hospital, October 27, 1930, in *Quarterly and Annual Audits 1929–1930 Methodist Hospital*, October, 1930.

15. Ibid.

16. D. H. Hotchkiss to Board of Trustees, Methodist Hospital, January 22, 1930, in *Quarterly and Annual Audits 1929–1930 Methodist Hospital*, October, 1930.

17. St. John, Smith & Co. to D. H. Hotchkiss (for distribution to Methodist Hospital Board of Trustees), April 15, 1930, in *Quarterly and Annual Audits 1929–1930 Methodist Hospital*, October, 1930. Another recommendation provided by the auditors included, "Our investigation clearly reflects that the maximum possible income can barely cope with the minimum amount of expense. While the Institution is not organized for profit, its revenues and expenses should be so arranged as to meet each other. We suggest that some consideration be given to the matter of raising room rates, which, in our opinion, could stand an approximate increase of 10%."

18. John Nova Lomax, "Houston 101: Will Hogg, Houston's Forgotten, Eccentric and Downright Badass Philanthropist," *Houston Press*, May 28, 2012.

19. Ray Miller, *Ray Miller's Houston* (Austin: Capital Printing, 1982), 159.

20. N. Don Macon, *Monroe Dunaway Anderson, His Legacy: A History of the Texas Medical Center, 50th Anniversary Edition* (Houston: Texas Medical Center, 1994), 40.

21. Ibid., 71.

22. Ibid., 67.

23. Ibid., 84.

24. "75 Years of Vision – The Lasting Gift of Southwestern Medical Foundation: Part 1: 1939–1979," *Southwestern Medical Perspectives*, spring 2014, 9.

25. Abraham Flexner and Daniel Berkeley Updike, "Medical Education in the United States and Canada: A Report to the Carnegie Foundation for the Advancement of Teaching," [publisher not identified], 1910.

26. "75 Years of Vision – Part 1, 1939–1979," 28. When interest in vaudeville dwindled in the 1930s, Hoblitzelle built "motion picture" theaters with air-conditioning and the latest technical advances in sound. His theaters with eloquent décor seated thousands and made him a fortune. The Hoblitzelle Foundation donated $125,000 to purchase the sixty-two acres on Harry Hines Boulevard. The land was given as a memorial tribute to Hoblitzelle's late wife, Esther, who had died of cancer in 1943 at age forty-eight.

27. Ibid., 19.

28. Dr. Walter H. Moursund, *A History of Baylor University College of Medicine 1900–1953* (Houston: Gulf Printing Company, 1956), 111.

29. N. Don Macon, *South from Flower Mountain: A Conversation with William B. Bates* (Houston: Texas Medical Center, 1975), 63.

30. Advertisement, "Cure Through Research. Vote for the Texas Medical Center Today," *Houston Post*, December 13, 1943. This was a full-page ad that appeared in Houston's morning newspaper.

31. Robert S. McElvaine, *The Great Depression: America 1929–1941* (New York: Random House, 1993), Kindle edition.

32. Transcript, Josie Roberts interview by James B. Speer, March 1975, 8. HMA-PEC.

33. J. Charles Dickson, "Methodist Hospital History: Special Reference to the Executive Committee of the Staff," HMA-PEC.

34. St. John, Smith & Co. to D. H. Hotchkiss (for distribution to Methodist Hospital Board of Trustees), April 15, 1930, in *Quarterly and Annual Audits 1929–1930 Methodist Hospital*. The audit report for April 15 included an analysis of job duties for all employees along with suggested letters to improve collections.

35. Dr. William L. Winters, Jr. and Betsy Parish, *Houston Hearts: A History of Cardiovascular Surgery and Medicine and The Methodist DeBakey Heart & Vascular Center Houston Methodist Hospital* (Houston: Elisha Freeman Publishing, 2014), 20.

36. "Work is to Start This Week on Children's Unit at Methodist Hospital," *Houston Chronicle*, March 30, 1934. The article also notes, "The building will be of one-story frame construction, 64 feet by 34 feet, and is designed to accommodate 32 beds, although in emergencies approximately 30 per cent more patients can be accommodated."

37. Sibley, *The Methodist Hospital of Houston*, 84.

38. "Dr. Norsworthy Leaves Fund for Aid of Hospital," *Houston Chronicle*, undated, 1935. The article also notes, "Dr. Norsworthy specified that the Methodist is to receive the money providing it attains the highest rating of the American Hospital Association and has 200 beds within five years after his death, or 300 beds 10 years after his death. The hospital now has 75 beds."

39. Sibley, *The Methodist Hospital of Houston*, 62.

40. Ibid.

41. Transcript, Josie Roberts interview by James B. Speer, March 1975, HMA-PEC, 8.

42. Mary Jane Schier, "Life of Service: Ella Fondren's 6th Sense for Oil Brought in Gusher of Philanthropy," *Houston Post*, May 27, 1980.

43. Sibley, *The Methodist Hospital of Houston*, 63.

FOUR – The Greatest Good

1. William Henry Kellar, *Enduring Legacy* (College Station: Texas A&M University Press, 2014), 88.

2. Ibid., 89.

3. Ibid., 93.

4. J. Charles Dickson, "Methodist Hospital History: Special Reference to the Executive Committee of the Staff," HMA-PEC, undated.

5. "Our Hospital Superintendent," *Methodist Hospital News Bulletin*, April 1945.

6. Elmer Bertelsen, "Mrs. Josie Roberts Quits Hospital Post," *Houston Chronicle*, December 30, 1952.

7. N. Don Macon, *Mr. John H. Freeman and Friends: A Story of the Texas Medical Center and How it Began* (Houston: Texas Medical Center, 1973), 48.

8. Ibid., 47.

9. Dr. Walter H. Moursund, *A History of Baylor University College of Medicine 1900–1953* (Houston: Gulf Printing Company, 1956), 119.

10. Ibid., 120.

11. "Hospital Jobs Threshed out at Forum: Administrators Discuss the Problem of Handling Increasing Numbers of Maternity Cases in Texas," *Houston Chronicle*, February 22, 1942.

12. "Need for More Student Nurses to be Stressed," *Houston Chronicle*, October 3, 1943. The article notes, "The need for more student nurses, so that demands of civilians and the armed forces may be filled, will be emphasized by Maj. Julia C. Stimson, director of the United States Army Nurses Corps, at a joint commencement exercises for 102 graduates of four Houston schools of nursing at 8 p.m. Wednesday in the Music Hall."

13. Macon, *Mr. John H. Freeman and Friends*, 48.

14. Kellar, *Enduring Legacy*, 84.

15. "Cullen Gift Provides New Methodist Plant: Hospital Given $1,000,000; It's a Dream Come True, Says Bishop Smith," *Houston Chronicle*, March 4, 1945.

16. Art Leatherwood, "Fondren Foundation," *Handbook of Texas Online*, accessed October 31, 2018, https://tshaonline.org/handbook/online/articles/vrf01.

17. Josie Roberts, interview by James B. Speer, Jr., March 1975, in Dr. William L. Winters, Jr., and Betsy Parish, *Reflections: Houston Methodist Hospital* (Houston: Elisha Freeman Publishing, 2016), 410.

18. Transcript, Josie Roberts interview by James B. Speer, March 1975, HMA-PEC, 13.

19. Marilyn McAdams Sibley, *The Methodist Hospital of Houston: Serving the World* (Austin: Texas State Historical Association, 1989), 78.

20. *Hospital and Health Survey of Harris County for the Texas Medical Center, Inc.*, James A. Hamilton and Associates, Minneapolis Minnesota, 1949. JPM-HC, Texas Medical Center Library, Houston, Texas.

21. Sibley, *The Methodist Hospital of Houston*, 78.

22. Ibid., 86.

23. June Clendenin Bowen interview by Dr. William Winters, Jr., February 12, 2004, *Reflections*, 21.

24. Ibid.

25. Sibley, *The Methodist Hospital of Houston*, 88.

26. Ibid.

27. "Methodist Hospital Each Day of the Year," *The Christian Evangel: Golden Cross and Methodist Hospital Edition*, November 1949. The article also notes, "A typical day … includes 118 patients served, 8 operations performed, 32 x-ray examinations and treatments, 195 laboratory examinations, 150 pharmacy items ordered, 24 patient records, 4 blood transfusions, 2 births, 820 meals served (using 2,000 pounds raw food) and 16 new patients admitted."

FIVE – New Hospital, New Partners

1. Warner Roberts, "Heart of a Hero," *Texas Magazine*, September 2008, 28.

2. David K. C. Cooper, *Open Heart: The Radical Surgeons Who Revolutionized Medicine* (New York: Kaplan Publishing, 2010), xi.

3. Ibid., 370.

4. William T. Butler, *Arming for Battle Against Disease Through Education, Research, and Patient Care at Baylor College of Medicine* (Houston: Baylor College of Medicine, 2011), Vol. 1, 38. Dr. DeBakey accepted the appointment on July 14, 1948, to become effective October 1, 1948. He notes in his acceptance that he looked "forward with much pleasure and enthusiasm to the opportunity of joining your faculty soon and of participating in its development as one of the nation's great medical centers."

5. Cooper, *Open Heart*, 368.

6. Dr. George P. Noon interview by Dr. William Winters, Jr., July 23, 2008, in Dr. William L. Winters, Jr., and Betsy Parish, *Reflections: Houston Methodist Hospital* (Houston: Elisha Freeman Publishing, 2016), 313.

7. Ruth SoRelle, "Surgeon, Educator, Medical Statesman," *The Journal*, The Methodist Hospital System 37 (Winter 1998): 4.

8. Dr. Denton A. Cooley interview by Dr. William Winters, Jr., July 11, 2007, *Reflections*, 60.

9. Dr. Walter H. Moursund, *A History of Baylor University College of Medicine 1900–1953* (Houston: Gulf Printing Company, 1956), 170.

10. Marilyn McAdams Sibley, *The Methodist Hospital of Houston: Serving the World* (Austin: Texas State Historical Association, 1989), 112.

11. Transcript, Dr. Michael E. DeBakey, HMA-PEC, undated. A single typed page of a transcript was found marked "DeBakey" and page "19." While the full transcript has not been located, it offers important insights as Dr. DeBakey reflects on the hospital's patient care. He adds, "And the final thing I would say which I think is extremely important, in terms of this hospital, and maybe is reflective of the administration and of Mr. Bowen, is the compassion and concern and kindness which is generally involved in the patient's care."

12. Unauthored document, "Residents and Interns," May, 29, 1975, HMA-PEC. This one-page document summarizes residency and intern information provided by Rose Tracey of the American Medical Association (AMA) who notes, "[The] AMA first started approving interns in 1914 and residents after World War II. The AMA has records of interns and residents by name only—not by date." It also notes Dr. Hatch W. Cummings, Jr. "provided [the] following information from memory: Methodist first had interns in 1929 and residents in 1947."

13. Transcript. Josie Roberts interview by James B. Speer, March 1975, HMA-PEC, 11. Regarding the two unnamed hospitals, the full quote reads: "We were the only hospital then … we were approved for internship. We were the only place here in Houston. There was St. Joe's and Memorial. I shouldn't call names, but anyway, they were twice as large as we were but you see, they were not interested because an educational program costs you money."

14. Dr. Antonio Gotto, Jr., personal conversation with the author, November 11, 2018.

15. Amy Storrow, *The Doctors' Doctors: Baylor College of Medicine Department of Pathology 1943–2003* (Huntsville: Texas Review Press, 2004), 245.

16. Sibley, *The Methodist Hospital of Houston*, 108.

17. Recollections document, J. Charles Dickson, "Methodist Hospital History: Special Reference to the Executive Committee of the Staff," HMA-PEC, undated.

18. Sibley, *The Methodist Hospital of Houston*, 118.

19. Ibid.

20. William Henry Kellar, *Enduring Legacy* (College Station: Texas A&M University Press, 2014), 133. The author notes, "The weather that day was bad. … A special ramp had been constructed so that his car could be pulled up next to the platform. After the ceremony, friends and well-wishers offered greetings to an exhausted Bertner." Two months later Dr. Bertner died. He was sixty-one.

21. "Neighbor of Note," *Houston Chronicle*, May 24, 1957. This article notes McGinty received the first traveling fellowship ever awarded by Rice University. His year of architectural study included Italy, France, Spain, and England.

22. Elmer Bertelsen, "Methodist Hospital Has Modern Gadgets," *Houston Chronicle*, November 5, 1951. The *Houston Chronicle* ran a full section titled "The Magnificent New Methodist Hospital," with photos and tributes to the newest Texas Medical Center addition in their November 11, 1951, edition. The *Houston Post* likewise ran a full section with photos in their edition of the same date titled, "Great Dream Realized: Josie Roberts Achieves Goal." The opening was also featured in *The New York Times* on November 11, 1951. "$4,500,000 Hospital Opened in Houston: Texas Methodist Conference Dedicates Structure Having Latest in Equipment."

23. Sibley, *The Methodist Hospital of Houston*, 133.

24. Ibid., 132.

25. Ibid.

26. Undated document, "The New Methodist Hospital (As it Was)," HMA-PEC. This internal document notes the new hospital opened for operation in the Texas Medical Center November 15, 1951. "The old Hospital at 3020 San Jacinto was closed the same day and all patients transferred to the new building. By 6 P.M. on the day of opening all available beds on the general Medical and Surgical floors were filled to capacity."

27. Sibley, *The Methodist Hospital of Houston*, 133.

28. Bertelsen, "Methodist Hospital Has Modern Gadgets." Among the modern features highlighted in this article was "an intercommunication system that allows nurses to talk to patients from their service desk in the corridor. There's a gadget on which a nurse can write an order, press a button that transforms the message to a similar gadget in the supply room, the cashier's office or other distant office."

29. Ibid.

30. "The Modern Hospital of the Month: The New Methodist Hospital," *Modern Hospital* 79, no. 5 (November, 1952): 53–58. The article includes photos throughout the new hospital along with floor design drawings.

31. Event program for the dedication of Wiess Memorial Chapel, Methodist Hospital, November 10, 1951. Mrs. William Wiess was born Louisa Elizabeth Carothers on March 27, 1856, and died July 7, 1936. Her son, Harry C. Wiess, died August 26, 1948, soon after the gift of the chapel was conceived.

32. William S. Fields, *To and Through the Texas Medical Center* (Austin: Eakin Press, 1995), 134.

33. Moursund, *A History of Baylor University College of Medicine 1900–1953*, 185. He adds, "This clinic provided facilities for a material enlargement of the original 'seizure clinic' and includes facilities for research, care and teaching in the field of all nervous diseases of children."

34. Fields, *To and Through the Texas Medical Center*, 135.

35. Ibid.

36. Sibley, *The Methodist Hospital of Houston*, 133.

37. Ibid.

38. *Modern Hospital*, "The New Methodist Hospital," 56. The article notes, "This joint facility of the power plant and laundry of the three hospitals will be operated by a manager of the facilities who will be responsible to the administrator of each hospital. All services will be billed to the hospitals on a cost basis."

39. Dr. Michael E. DeBakey interview by Dr. William Winters, Jr., December 20, 2007, *Reflections*, 74.

40. Fields, *To and Through the Texas Medical Center*, 132.

41. Sibley, *The Methodist Hospital of Houston*, 142.

42. Dennis R. Wenger, *Dogged Persistence-Harrington, Post-Polio Scoliosis, and the Origin of Spine Instrumentation*, (Traverse City, MI: Chandler Lake Books, 2015).

43. "In Memorandum: E. Stanley Crawford, M.D. 1922-1992," *J. Vascular Surgery*, no. 17 (1993):18.

44. Butler, *Arming for Battle Against Disease*, 280.

45. Sibley, *The Methodist Hospital of Houston*, 136.

46. Transcript. Josie Roberts interview by James B. Speer, March 1975, HMA-PEC, 11.

SIX – Hospital with a Soul

1. Atul Gawande, *Being Mortal* (New York: Henry Holt and Co., 2014), Kindle edition, 192.

2. "An Evaluation of Problems, Responsibilities, Opportunities of Religious Activities and Recommendations for the Formation of an Institute of Religion in the Texas Medical Center," 1956, JPM-HC, IC 020, Series 1, Box 4, Folder 89: Institute of Religion. Members of the committee: Dawson C. Bryan (Chairman), Ella Fondren, Julia Bertner, Earl Hankamer, Dr. Elmer W. Henson, Dr. Charles L. King, Rev. Virgil E. Lowder, Otis Massey, Howard Tellepsen.

3. World Health Organization Constitution, accessed November 6, 2018, https://www.who.int/about/mission/en/. The Constitution was adopted by the International Health Conference held in New York, June 19–July 22, 1946.

4. Marilyn McAdams Sibley, *The Methodist Hospital of Houston: Serving the World* (Austin: Texas State Historical Association, 1989), 155.

5. Good Samaritan Foundation, "Our History," accessed November 6, 2018, http://www.gsftx.org/about-us/.

6. Melissa L. King, email to author, April 27, 2018.

7. Rev. Charles R. Millikan, interview by the author, January 25, 2018.

8. William T. Butler, *Arming for Battle Against Disease Through Education, Research, and Patient Care at Baylor College of Medicine* (Houston: Baylor College of Medicine, 2011), Vol. 1, 281.

9. Methodist Hospital statistics, January 1, 1952–October 30, 1976, JPM-HC, IC 020, Series 7, Box 9, Folder 171: Statistics, Twenty-Five Years of Hospital Patient and Financial operation, 1951–1976, Patient Services 1952–1976.

10. Frederick C. Elliott, *The Birth of the Texas Medical Center: A Personal Account* (College Station: Texas A&M University Press, 2004), 31.

11. O'Banion Williams, Jr. to Frederick C. Elliott, August 3, 1956, JPM-HC, IC 020, Series 1, Box 2, Folder 129: Physical Plant Expansion, Main Building, West Wing. Williams also notes, "Our development has been very costly but we have succeeded in stabilizing our financial problems along with our continuous program expansion. Our budget for the year of 1956 is over four (4) million dollars," 2.

12. Ibid., 3.

13. Minutes, "The Methodist Hospital Doctor's Planning Committee of the Medical Staff," October 29, 1956. JPM-HC, IC 020, Series 1, Box 2, Folder 129: Physical Plant Expansion, Main Building, West Wing.

14. Louis Blackburn, "Ground-Breaking Tomorrow: 36-Year-Old Methodist Hospital Will Be One of the South's Largest," *Houston Press*, May 31, 1960.

15. Hospital brochure copy, "The Methodist Hospital: Hospital Expansion," prepared by the Administration Office, stamped "Approved: December 10, 1958," HMA-PEC. This document provides an overview of the following: Surgical Wing; Main Hospital Expansion; Ground Floor; First Floor; Second Floor; Third Floor – Obstetrics and Gynecology; Fourth Floor – Neurosurgery, Neurology, and Vascular Surgery; Fifth Floor – Ear, Nose and Throat, Eye and Orthopedic; Sixth Floor – General Surgery and Surgical Specialties; Seventh Floor North – Psychiatry.

16. Brochure, "The Mosaic Mural, 'The Extending Arms of Christ,'" HMA-PEC. This two-fold brochure was designed to be mailed. When opened it shows a color photo of the entire mural across all four panels with copy describing in detail Bruce Hayes's design. "The mural suggests that his [Christ's] arms reach out through past and future years to embrace, support and strengthen those who dedicate their lives to helping others."

17. Rampini Ceramics, accessed November 6, 2018, http://www.rampiniceramics. com/about/staff.php. Giuseppe Rampini was born in Gubbio, Italy, in 1923 and apprenticed at an early age to learn all the various processes connected to the production of beautiful ceramics. After his first work experiences in Gubbio he became director in two important glass factories in Florence.

18. "Toward an Artificial Heart," *Time* magazine cover story, May 28, 1965. "The Texas Tornado" nickname was picked up by media across the country and stuck. For example, when the National Library of Medicine honored Dr. DeBakey in 2017, they titled their program with it, https://infocus.nlm.nih.gov/2017/05/09/ the-texas-tornado-nlm-commemorates-heart-surgeon-debakey/.

19. Patricia Ann Temple, RN, interview by Dr. William Winters, Jr., November 29, 2006, in Dr. William L. Winters, Jr., and Betsy Parish, *Reflections: Houston Methodist Hospital* (Houston: Elisha Freeman Publishing, 2016), 491.

20. Marilyn McAdams Sibley, *The Methodist Hospital of Houston: Serving the World* (Austin: Texas State Historical Association, 1989), 5.

21. Manus J. O'Donnell, interview by Betsy Parish, August 19, 2009, *Reflections*, 325.

22. Dr. Juan Jose Olivero, interview by Dr. William Winters, Jr., February 13, 2012, *Reflections*, 334.

23. Dr. Michael DeBakey, interview by Dr. William Winters, Jr., February 13, 2012, *Reflections*, 74.

24. Dr. William L. Winters, Jr., "Houston Hearts: A History of Cardiovascular Surgery and Medicine at Houston Methodist DeBakey Heart & Vascular Center," *Methodist DeBakey Cardiovascular Journal*, XI (3s), 2015, 10. This supplement was published as well as presented by Dr. Winters at the seventh Michael E. DeBakey Lecture on January 19, 2015. Dr. Winters also suggests that when Dr. Cooley heard of the plans for the Fondren and Brown Cardiovascular and Orthopedic Research Centers he "preferred to have this type of facility closer to Texas Children's and St. Luke's hospitals … [and] decided to create a specialized cardiovascular facility of his own. So was chartered the Texas Heart Institute on August 3, 1962."

25. Sibley, *The Methodist Hospital of Houston*, 172.

26. Gillian Kruse, "An MD Anderson time capsule," June 25, 2015, accessed November 7, 2018, https://www.mdanderson.org/publications/cancerwise/2015/06/an-md-anderson-time-capsule.html. "When the ashtray was produced in the 1950s, we didn't know that smoking caused cancer. The dish stands in the display case as a stark reminder of how much has changed over time."

27. Dr. Daniel Jackson, interview by Mouth Watering Media, February 3, 2017. Dr. Jackson adds, "So, I went through every committee in the hospital and everybody said get rid of those machines except one doctor. I said, 'Arthur, why don't you want that machine removed from the hospital premises?' He blew smoke in my face and said, 'I don't believe smoking causes cancer.'"

28. Terry O'Reilly, "Summer Series – The Most Interesting Adman in the World: The Story of Albert Lasker," CBC Radio One, Aired August 31, 2018, accessed November 7, 2018, https://www.cbc.ca/radio/undertheinfluence/summer-series-the-most-interesting-adman-in-the-world-the-story-of-albert-lasker-1.4120833. CBC Radio One is the English-language news and information radio network of the publicly owned Canadian Broadcasting Corporation.

29. Butler, *Arming for Battle Against Disease,* Vol. 1, 201.

30. Ibid., 198.

31. Ibid., 204.

32. Ruth SoRelle, "Surgeon, Educator, Medical Statesman," *The Journal,* The Methodist Hospital System 37 (Winter 1998), 5.

33. Dr. Marc L. Boom, Memorandum to Houston Methodist, "1,000th Heart Transplant," January 2, 2018. Dr. Boom adds, "In addition I would like to thank and congratulate Drs. Bhimaraj, Bruckner, Estep, Guha, Hussain, MacGillivray, Noon, Park, Ren, Suarez, Torre-Amione, Trachtenbert and our anesthesiologists, endocrinologists, gastroenterologists, hospitalists, infections disease physicians, and all of the other specialists who care for our transplant patients before and after their transplants."

34. Dr. Michael DeBakey, interview by Dr. William Winters, Jr., December 20, 2007, *Reflections,* 74.

35. Ibid.

36. David K. C. Cooper, *Open Heart: The Radical Surgeons Who Revolutionized Medicine* (New York: Kaplan Publishing, 2010), 364.

37. Dr. Lawrence K. Altman, "The Feud," *The New York Times,* November 27, 2007.

38. Ibid.

39. Cooper, *Open Heart,* 365.

SEVEN – Five Buildings and a Flood

1. Ted Bowen, "Address to be Given by Mr. Ted Bowen to the Women's Auxiliary to the Methodist Hospital at its 40th Anniversary Meeting," February 15, 1968, 14.

2. Rachel Carson, *Silent Spring* (New York: Houghton Mifflin Co., 1962).

3. Dr. Michael E. DeBakey, "Current Status of the Baylor University College of Medicine," September 1, 1968, HMA-PEC (DeBakey Files), 11. This double-spaced, 12-page document was prepared as a "Critique" providing historical perspective and reasoning behind the school's 1969 separation from Baylor University ending with "The crisis is grave, and the need for resolution immediate."

4. Ibid., 5.

5. Marilyn McAdams Sibley, *The Methodist Hospital of Houston: Serving the World* (Austin: Texas State Historical Association, 1989), 183.

6. Ibid., 176.

7. Ted Bowen, "The Methodist Hospital, Houston, Texas: Its Past, Present, and Future," Presentation to the medical staff of The Methodist Hospital, November 16, 1965, HMA-PEC, 5.

8. Edward C. Lynch, interview by Dr. William Winters, Jr., March 5, 2008, in Dr. William L. Winters, Jr., and Betsy Parish, *Reflections: Houston Methodist Hospital* (Houston: Elisha Freeman Publishing, 2016), 242.

9. William Henry Kellar, *Kelsey-Seybold Clinic: A Legacy of Excellence in Health Care* (Houston: KS Management Services, 1999), 77.

10. Ibid, 78.

11. Dr. William L. Winters, Jr. and Betsy Parish, *Houston Hearts: A History of Cardiovascular Surgery and Medicine and The Methodist DeBakey Heart & Vascular Center Houston Methodist Hospital* (Houston: Elisha Freeman Publishing, 2014), 248.

12. Alice R. McPherson, interview by Dr. William Winters, Jr., June 6, 2011, *Reflections*, 273.

13. McGill University, "Wilder Penfield (1891–1976), accessed November 7, 2018, https://www.mcgill.ca/about/history/penfield. As a Rhodes Scholar at Oxford University, Penfield trained (1914–1916) with Sir William Osler who undoubtably influenced his holistic view.

14. William S. Fields, *To and Through the Texas Medical Center* (Austin: Eakin Press, 1995), 142.

15. Ibid.

16. Sibley, *The Methodist Hospital of Houston*, 184.

17. Ronald G. Girotto, interview by the author, February 28, 2018.

18. J. R. Gonzales, "At Home at Bill Williams' Chicken House," Bayou City History, *Houston Chronicle*, June 8, 2010. The author notes the Chicken House opened in 1936.

19. Sibley, *The Methodist Hospital of Houston*, 187.

20. Ibid.

21. Dr. John C. McKechnie, interview by Dr. William Winters, Jr., January 25, 2006, *Reflections*, 270. Dr. McKechnie recalled, "and my understanding was that there were not even lids on the commodes in some of the bathrooms back then."

22. Sibley, *The Methodist Hospital of Houston*, 189.

23. Ibid., 191.

24. Garvin Berry and Betty Chapman, "Houston Floods: Excess Water Turned Political Tide for Judge Roy Hofheinz," in *2-Minute Histories of Houston* (Houston: Houston Business Journal,1996), 87.

25. Amy Storrow, *The Doctors' Doctors: Baylor College of Medicine Department of Pathology 1943–2003* (Huntsville: Texas Review Press, 2004), *The Doctors' Doctors*, 208.

26. Personal memoirs, Michael V. Williamson, "It's the Way it Was: Part Two—The Methodist Years," unpublished manuscript, undated, HMA-PEC, 17. This 31-page document is drawn from the author's three decades as a Houston Methodist administrator, February 4, 1964–November 30, 1997.

27. Ibid., 19.

EIGHT – Changing of the Guard

1. Dr. Kenneth M. Ludmerer, *Time to Heal: American Education from the Turn of the Century to the Era of Managed Care* (New York: Oxford University Press, 1999), 102.

2. White paper, Ted Bowen and Jim Henderson, "A Position Paper on Hospital Costs," distributed to hospital leadership and stakeholders, July 25, 1977. In his cover memo Mr. Bowen suggested, "If you agree with the viewpoints we have expressed in the paper, please share them with your Congressmen and anyone else who might have influence on the proposed legislation."

3. Dr. Raymond D. Pruitt to Ted Bowen, September 8, 1977, JPM-HC, MS 113, Series 2: Correspondence.

4. Mary Jane Schier, "Bowen Retires as President of Methodist Hospital," *Houston Post*, October 20, 1982.

5. Dr. William Winters, Jr., to Methodist Hospital Medical Staff, October 20, 1982.

6. Schier, "Bowen Retires as President of Methodist Hospital."

7. Table, "The Methodist Hospital: Comparison of Median Charges for Private and 2-bed Rooms with 7 Local Hospitals, Revised 26 January 1973, HMA-PEC." This document shows that among seven area hospitals in the 1970s, Methodist had the lowest rates for both private ($42) and 2-bed rooms ($36.50). Rates ranged from $42–$52.50 (private) and $36.50–$45 (2-bed).

8. Marilyn McAdams Sibley, *The Methodist Hospital of Houston: Serving the World* (Austin: Texas State Historical Association, 1989), 201.

9. Resolution in memoriam, Ella F. Fondren, excerpted from the minutes of the meeting of the Board of Directors, The Methodist Hospital, May 25, 1982. This resolution was signed by Wm. Randolph Smith, board secretary on June 14, 1982.

10. Schier, "Bowen Retires as President of Methodist Hospital."

11. Ibid.

12. Larry L. Mathis, *The Mathis Maxims: Lessons in Leadership* (Houston: Leadership Press, 2001), 42.

13. Ibid., 48.

14. Ibid., 34.

15. Ibid., 50.

16. Ibid., 51.

17. Ibid.

18. Ronald Girotto, interview by the author, February 28, 2018.

19. Mathis, *The Mathis Maxims*, 52.

20. Ibid., 54.

21. Ibid., 55.

22. Sibley, *The Methodist Hospital of Houston*, 191.

23. Ibid, 192.

24. Ronald Girotto, interview by the author, February 28, 2018.

25. Ibid.

26. Larry Mathis, interview by the author, February 14, 2018.

27. Sibley, *The Methodist Hospital of Houston*, 211.

28. Bryant Boutwell, *I'm Dr. Red Duke* (College Station: Texas A&M University Press, 2018), 153. The author's chapter on Life Flight tells the story in Steve Dunn's words of how Life Flight came to be and the essential role both Steve Dunn and his father, John Dunn, played in its creation.

29. Edward Lillo Crain, Jr. (1917–2003) worked in private practice for fifty years in Houston and was active in teaching and patient care at both Baylor and Methodist Hospital. He was consistently listed in the Best Doctors in America (internal medicine) and is remembered as a dedicated and talented physician beloved by all. His gift of the Crain Garden and Fountain in Methodist's Dunn Tower is enjoyed by patients, family, and hospital guests daily and honors his late wife, Betty, and mother.

30. *Arts Angle: The Newsletter for the Center for Performing Arts Medicine at Houston Methodist*, "CPAM by the Numbers," Fall 2018, accessed November 8, 2018, https://bit.ly/2CAeRfC. In 2017 Houston Methodist was the only Texas institution and only hospital to be named a BCA top ten—best businesses partnering with the arts in America. BCA is a division of Americans for the Arts, founded by David Rockefeller.

31. Sharon Thornton, "The Smith Family," *The Journal*, The Methodist Hospital System, undated, 28.

32. Ibid.

33. David Moore, *David Moore's World of Fungi: Where Mycology Starts*, "The Discovery of Cyclosporine," accessed November 8, 2018, http://www.davidmoore.org.uk/Sec04_01.htm. The fungus Tolypocladium inflatum was isolated from two soil samples, the first from Wisconsin and the second from the mountain plateau Hardangervidda in Norway. Sandoz employees had collected both samples.

34. Houston Methodist, "A Brief List of Firsts," accessed November 11, 2018, https://www.houstonmethodistcareers.org/our-history.html.

35. Gül Dabak and Ömer Senbaklavaci, "History of Lung Transplantation," *Turkish Thoracic Journal* 17, no. 2 (April, 2016), accessed November 11, 2018, https://www.ncbi.nlm.nih.gov/pmc/articles/PMC5792120/.

36. Dr. Antonio M. Gotto, Jr., interview by Dr. William Winters, Jr., October 31, 2011, in Dr. William L. Winters, Jr., and Betsy Parish, *Reflections: Houston Methodist Hospital* (Houston: Elisha Freeman Publishing, 2016), 161.

37. Sibley, *The Methodist Hospital of Houston*, 214.

38. Christine Postolos, "The Methodist Hospital Timeline: Methodist Looks Back Over 75 Years," *The Journal*, The Methodist Hospital System, December 1994, 17.

39. Pete Brewton, "State Begins Probe of Methodist Hospital," *Houston Post*, January 10, 1986.

NINE – Weathering the Storm

1. D. H. Hotchkiss to Board of Trustees, Methodist Hospital, October 22, 1929, in *Quarterly and Annual Audits 1929–1930 Methodist Hospital*, October 22, 1930.

2. Houston Methodist, "Community Benefits Activities," *MindBodySoul: Strengthening the Community*, Third Edition, Community Development, 2018. Updated by Ryane K. Jackson, email correspondence with the author, July 12, 2018.

3. Richard Vara, "Methodists Applaud Defense of Hospital: Delegates Given Report, *Houston Post*, May 28, 1986.

4. Mary Lenz, "Methodist Says Mattox Lawsuit Effort to Remedy Medicaid Woes," *Houston Post*, November 28, 1990.

5. Ibid.

6. Ibid.

7. Debra Beachy, "A Healthy Balance Sheet: Methodist Leads Non-profit Hospitals in Profit Margins," *Houston Chronicle*, January 19, 1993.

8. Ken Herman, "Judge Sides with Methodist Hospital," *Houston Post*, February 20, 1993.

9. D. J. Wilson, "Methodist Hospital Suit Could Have National Impact," *Houston Post*, December 15, 1990.

10. Houston Methodist, "Community Benefits Activities," *MindBodySoul: Strengthening the Community*, Third Edition, 2018. For the year 2017 Houston Methodist reported $805 million in total community benefits representing 24.7 percent of net patient revenues. Combining charity care and community benefits they reported $1.04 billion or 32 percent of net patient revenues. They define charity care as "free or discounted health and health-related services to people who cannot afford to pay. It does not include bad debt. Community benefits are programs and services designed to improve health in communities and increase access to health care."

11. Dr. Kenneth M. Ludmerer, *Time to Heal: American Education from the Turn of the Century to the Era of Managed Care* (New York: Oxford University Press, 1999), 356.

12. Ibid., 353.

13. Ibid., 351.

14. Ibid., 352.

15. Ibid., 264.

16. Ibid., 354.

17. Robert Mechanic, Kevin Coleman, and Allen Dobson, "Teaching Hospital Costs: Implications for Academic Missions in a Competitive Market," *JAMA* 280, no. 11 (September 16, 1998): 1015.

18. Larry L. Mathis, *The Mathis Maxims: Lessons in Leadership* (Houston: Leadership Press, 2001), 59.

19. J. Daniel Beckham, "Leadership and Complexity," accessed November 9, 2018, http://webcache.googleusercontent.com/search?q=cache:oBAv_SPzRM8J:www.beckhamco.com/index_files/070_leadershipandcomplexity.doc+&cd=1&hl=en&ct=clnk&gl=us.

20. Mathis, *The Mathis Maxims*, 59.

21. L. Burns, J. Cacciamani, J. Clement, and W. Aquino, "The Fall of the House of AHERF: the Allegheny Bankruptcy," *Health Affairs* 19, no. 1, (January–February 2000).

22. William T. Butler, *Arming for Battle Against Disease Through Education, Research, and Patient Care at Baylor College of Medicine*, Vol. IV, 1317.

23. Judge Ewing Werlein, Jr., interview by the author, December 18, 2018.

24. Bill Mintz, "Methodist's CEO Stepping Down: Mathis to Head Hospital Until Successor Found," *Houston Chronicle*, September 26, 1996. Summarizing Mathis's legacy, the reporter noted Mathis had completed a $197 million expansion (including Smith and Dunn towers), built a long-lasting executive team, and served as chairman of the Texas Hospital Association, American Hospital Association, and the American College of Healthcare Executives. During his tenure the institution was recognized as one of the nation's best 100 companies to work for in addition to expanding international affiliations and building $2 billion in investments. Two decades after his retirement he was inducted into the Health Care Hall of Fame.

25. Ibid.

26. "Health Care Hall of Fame 2016," *Modern Healthcare*, accessed November 9, 2018, https://www.modernhealthcare.com/section/halloffame-2016.

27. Butler, *Arming for Battle Against Disease*, Vol. IV, 1329.

28. "Spotlights: Marc L. Boom, M.D.," *TMC Pulse*, Texas Medical Center, April 2016, accessed November 11, 2018, http://www.tmc.edu/news/2016/04/marc-l-boom-m-d-2/.

29. Dr. Marc Boom, interview by the author, January 10, 2017.

30. Kyle L. Grazier, "Interview with Peter Butler, President and CEO, Methodist Health Care System," *Journal of Healthcare Management* 46, no. 4 (July-Aug 2001): 214.

31. Ibid.

32. Ludmerer, *Time to Heal*, 364.

33. Ronald Girotto, interview by Betsy Parish, August 1, 2012, in Dr. William L. Winters, Jr., and Betsy Parish, *Reflections: Houston Methodist Hospital* (Houston: Elisha Freeman Publishing, 2016), 147–148.

34. Balanced Budget Act of 1997 Enacted August 5, 1997, accessed November 9, 2018, https://en.wikipedia.org/wiki/Balanced_Budget_Act_of_1997.

35. Susan Kreimer, "Methodist Hospital, CEO Part Ways Out of the Blue," *Houston Chronicle*, September 29, 2001.

36. Lynn M. Schroth, interview by the author, February 13, 2018.

37. Lynn M. Schroth, interview by Betsy Parish, August 9, 2012, *Reflections*, 445.

38. Lynn M. Schroth, interview by the author, February 13, 2018.

39. Unpublished 2012 Houston Methodist manuscript, Write Stuff Enterprises, LLC, HMA-PEC, 45.

40. Dr. Albert E. Raizner, interview by Dr. William Winters, Jr., February 29, 2012, *Reflections*, 396.

41. Ed Tyrrell, interview by the author, January 1, 2018.

42. Ibid.

43. Dr. Marc Boom, interview by the author, January 10, 2017.

44. Ibid.

TEN – Steering a New Course

1. Encyclopedia Britannica, "Y2K Bug," accessed November 9, 2018, https://www.britannica.com/technology/Y2K-bug. The Y2K problem was not limited to computers running conventional software. From elevators to medical equipment, many devices with computer chips were believed to be at risk.

2. William T. Butler, *Arming for Battle Against Disease Through Education, Research, and Patient Care at Baylor College of Medicine*, Vol. IV, 1331.

3. Ibid.

4. Stacy R. Stewart, "Tropical Cyclone Report: Tropical Storm Allison 5–17 June 2001," Published November 28, 2001, National Hurricane Center, accessed November 9, 2018, https://www.nhc.noaa.gov/data/tcr/AL012001_Allison.pdf.

5. Ibid. The author notes that of the $5 billion in damage, approximately $4.8 billion was in the Houston metropolitan area with $2.04 billion of Houston's losses being public facilities, "especially the Texas Medical Center."

6. Dr. Marc Boom, interview by the author, January 10, 2017.

7. Roberta Schwartz, interview by Marco Ricci, May 22, 2018. Ricci is a director, producer, and general manager of the New York office for Mouth Watering Media (MWM Partners, LLC). He conducted interviews for the Houston Methodist centennial video project and provided the author access to MWM transcripts or attendance at interview sessions to maximize efficiencies during the research phase of both the video and book projects.

8. Amy Storrow, *The Doctors' Doctors: Baylor College of Medicine Department of Pathology 1943–2003* (Huntsville: Texas Review Press, 2004), *The Doctors' Doctors*, 220.

9. Ed Tyrrell, interview by the author, January 18, 2018.

10. Butler, *Arming for Battle Against Disease*, Vol. IV, 1373.

11. Ibid., 1378.

12. Denny Angelle, personal conversation with the author, September 26, 2018.

13. In 2019 Dr. Gustavo Ayala is the Distinguished Chair in Pathology and Laboratory Medicine at Houston's McGovern Medical School and notes he is a good friend but not related to Dr. Alberto Ayala, Houston Methodist professor of pathology and genomic medicine. Dr. Alberto Ayala joined Methodist in 2004 following a distinguished thirty-three-year career at MD Anderson Cancer Center.

14. Storrow, *The Doctors' Doctors*, 212.

15. John Bookout, interview by Marco Ricci, September 26, 2018.

16. Susan Kreimer, "Methodist Hospital, CEO Part Ways Out of the Blue." *Houston Chronicle*, September 29, 2001.

17. John Bookout, personal conversation with the author, March 6, 2019.

18. Ronald Girotto, interview by the author, February 28, 2018.

19. Unpublished 2012 Houston Methodist manuscript, HMA-PEC, 41.

20. Judge Ewing Werlein, Jr., interview by the author, December 18, 2018

21. Matthew Gilbert, "True Believers at Methodist Hospital," *Workforce*, February 1, 2005.

22. Ibid.

23. Judy Girotto, email message to the author, March 23, 2018.

24. Ronald Girotto, interview by Dr. William Winters, Jr., October 31, 2011, in Dr. William L. Winters, Jr., and Betsy Parish, *Reflections: Houston Methodist Hospital* (Houston: Elisha Freeman Publishing, 2016), 140.

25. Ibid.

26. During the hospital's centennial year, Houston Methodist is ranked #1 in Texas and holds best hospital rankings in eight adult specialties. *U.S. News & World Report* analysis of hospitals includes data from nearly five thousand centers across multiple medical specialties, procedures, and medical conditions, including neurology, orthopedics, psychiatry, and more. Scores are based on a variety of patient outcomes and care-related factors, such as patient safety and nurse staffing. *U.S. News* ranks hospitals in sixteen adult specialties and ten pediatric specialties. See https://health.usnews.com/best-hospitals/area/tx/houston-methodist-hospital-6741960 (accessed November 9, 2018).

27. Carole Hackett, interview by the author, December 19, 2017.

28. John Bookout, interview by Marco Ricci, September 21, 2018.

29. Ronald Girotto, interview by Betsy Parish, August 1, 2012, *Reflections*, 140.

30. Butler, *Arming for Battle Against Disease*, Vol. IV, 1317.

31. Ronald Girotto, interview by Betsy Parish, August 1, 2012, *Reflections*, 149.

32. Ronald Girotto, interview by Dr. William Winters, Jr., October 31, 2011, *Reflections*, 142.

33. John A. Kastor, *Governance of Teaching Hospitals: Turmoil at Penn and Hopkins* (Baltimore: The Johns Hopkins University Press, 2004).

34. Butler, *Arming for Battle Against Disease*, Vol. IV, 1332.

35. Ibid.

36. Unpublished 2012 Houston Methodist manuscript, HMA-PEC, 49.

37. Ronald Girotto, interview by Betsy Parish, August 1, 2012, *Reflections*, 150.

38. Ronald Girotto, interview by Dr. William Winters, Jr., October 31, 2011, *Reflections*, 142.

39. Butler, *Arming for Battle Against Disease*, Vol. V, 1434.

40. Ibid., 1435.

41. Ibid., 1443.

42. Ibid., 1435.

43. Leigh Hopper, "A Rumbling in the Medical Center: Baylor's Proposal of One-Stop Location for Care Rattles Methodist," *Houston Chronicle*, July 26, 2003.

44. Ronald Girotto to Peter G. Traber, September 25, 2003, HMA-PEC. Girotto's letter ends, "We want to work together to strengthen both of our institutions and to reestablish a relationship that will accomplish our goals. Baylor College of Medicine is our preferred partner. We look forward to hearing from you by October 15. Sincerely, R.G. Girotto (signed)."

45. Ronald G. Girotto to Methodist Physicians, August 27, 2003, HMA-PEC.

46. Butler, *Arming for Battle Against Disease*, Vol. V, 1441.

47. Ibid., 1448.

48. Ibid., 1452.

49. Ibid., 1455.

50. John Bookout to Corbin "Corby" J. Robertson, Jr., April 13, 2004.

51. Ronald Girotto, interview by Betsy Parish, August 1, 2012, *Reflections*, 151.

52. Butler, *Arming for Battle Against Disease*, Vol. V, 1465.

53. Ronald Girotto, interview by Dr. William Winters, Jr., October 31, 2011, *Reflections*, 142.

54. Darrin Schlegel and Todd Ackerman, "Baylor Splits with Methodist, Picks St. Luke's," *Houston Chronicle*, April 22, 2004.

55. John Bookout, personal conversation with the author, August 21, 2018.

56. Lone Star Flight Museum, "John F. Bookout, Jr.," accessed January 31, 2019, https://www.lonestarflight.org/john-f-bookout-jr.

57. John Bookout, personal correspondence and World War II clippings shared with the author, March 28, 2019. Interesting to note, in November 1981 Bookout received a letter of appreciation from a Dutch citizen who was a recipient of the lifesaving food dropped over his home. Recalling that most rewarding mission of the war, "After using our skills and B17s for awesome destruction that we never felt good about, but felt was necessary to restore peace to the world … it [the food drop] was a payment of gratitude to those that had suffered so much to defeat totalitarianism and at great risk had saved so many American lives."

58. John Bookout, interview by Marco Ricci, August 21, 2018.

59. Ibid.

60. Ronald Girotto, interview by Betsy Parish, August 1, 2012, *Reflections*, 150.

61. Ibid.

62. Daniel Sullivan, Rodrick Faccio, Michael L. Levy and Robert G. Grossman, "The Assassination of President John F. Kennedy: A Neuroforensic Analysis—Part 1: A Neurosurgeon's Previously Undocumented Eyewitness Account of the Events of November 22, 1963," *Neurosurgery* 53 (2003): 1019–1027.

63. Dr. Robert G. Grossman, interview by Dr. William Winters, Jr., June 18, 2012, *Reflections*, 185.

64. John Bookout, interview by Marco Ricci, August 21, 2018. Bookout recalled in this interview that Dr. Grossman's advice went something like this: "Well, I have always been associated with an academic teaching and research. That's my life. Most of my colleagues over here, that's their life. I would not be interested in being associated with Methodist if it's a community hospital or if it doesn't have a highly regarded and rated medical school."

65. Dr. Antonio Gotto, Jr., interview by Marco Ricci, June 20, 2018.

66. Antonio M. Gotto, Jr. and Jennifer Moon, *Weill Cornell Medicine: A History of Cornell's Medical School* (Ithaca, NY: Cornell University Press, 2016), 29. Weill Cornell's medical school is today formally known as the Joan & Sanford I. Weill Medical College of Cornell University. Weill Cornell Medicine is used when referring to both the biomedical research unit and the medical school of Cornell University. The medical school is at 1300 York Avenue on the Upper East Side of Manhattan along with the Weill Cornell Graduate School of Medical Sciences.

67. Ibid., 205.

68. Ibid.

69. John Bookout, personal conversation with the author, March 6, 2019.

70. Unpublished 2012 Houston Methodist manuscript, HMA-PEC, 92–93.

71. Press release, "Weill Cornell Medical College and NewYork-Presbyterian Hospital in New York City Announce Affiliation with The Methodist Hospital in Houston," June 23, 2004. The release notes Methodist "is one of the nation's largest private, non-profit hospitals with 1,269 beds." The Joan & Sanford I. Weill Medical College of Cornell University, founded in 1898, "has long ranked among the leading medical schools in the U.S." NewYork-Presbyterian Hospital, based in New York City, "is the largest not-for-profit, non-sectarian hospital in the country, with 2,369 beds. The Hospital has academic affiliations with two of the country's leading medical colleges: Joan & Sanford I. Weill Medical College of Cornell University and Columbia University College of Physicians and Surgeons."

72. H. Dirk Sostman, Laura L. Forese, Marc L. Boom, Lynn Schroth, et al., "Building a Transcontinental Affiliation: A New Model for Academic Health Centers," *Academic Medicine* 80, no. 11 (November, 2005): 1046–52.

73. Ibid., 1046.

74. Unpublished 2012 Houston Methodist manuscript, HMA-PEC, 85.

75. Ibid., 87–88.

76. Ronald Girotto, interview by Betsy Parish, August 1, 2012, *Reflections*, 151.

77. "Methodist VP Honored with Courage to Lead Award," *Methodist DeBakey Cardiovascular Journal* 8, no. 3 (July-September, 2012).

78. Jenna Colley, "Christus St. Joseph Hospital Transferring Residents to Methodist Hospital," *Houston Business Journal*, July 20, 2005.

79. Ronald Girotto, interview by Betsy Parish, August 1, 2012, *Reflections*, 151.

80. Dr. Marc Boom, personal conversation with the author, January 1, 2019.

81. Unpublished 2012 Houston Methodist manuscript, HMA-PEC, 87.

82. "Houston Methodist Specialty Physician Group (MHSPG)," accessed January 31, 2019, https://www.houstonmethodist.org/spg/. At the time of this writing the MHSPG comprised 634 physicians with another 119 in rotation in Houston Methodist's Primary Care Group.

83. Unpublished 2012 Houston Methodist manuscript, HMA-PEC, 89-90.

84. Butler, *Arming for Battle Against Disease*, Vol. V, 1470.

85. Dr. Marc Boom, interview by the author, January 10, 2017.

86. Unpublished 2012 Houston Methodist manuscript, HMA-PEC, 98.

87. Ibid.

88. Lynn Schroth, interview by the author, February 13, 2018.

89. Ronald Girotto, interview by Betsy Parish, August 1, 2012, *Reflections*, 151.

90. Barbara Bass, interview by Marco Ricci, May 25, 2018.

91. Mary Daffin, interview by the author, January 22, 2019. Board member Mary Daffin attended Dr. Lumsden's presentation and told the author it was a memorable line that captured the very spirit of Houston Methodist and its rapid transformation as an academic medical center.

92. Dr. Marc Boom, personal conversation with the author, January 1, 2019.

93. Steve Bailey, "Houston 1, Boston 0," *The Boston Globe*, June 13, 2007. Bailey noted in his column, "Wong can't throw a slider, or hit one, either. But until recently he was one of the top scientists, working in one of the hottest fields of research, at Harvard Medical School and Brigham and Women's Hospital in Boston. Now Wong is one of the top scientists, working in one of the hottest fields of research, in Houston."

94. Dr. Marc Boom, personal conversation with the author, January 1, 2019.

95. Alliance of Independent Academic Medical Centers, "About the Alliance of Independent Academic Medical Centers," accessed January 20, 1919, https://aiamc.org/.

96. Butler, *Arming for Battle Against Disease*, Vol. V, 1484.

97. "Baylor Fails in Bid to Stop Methodist," *Houston Chronicle*, June 16, 2005.

98. Richard E. Wainerdi, phone conversation with the author, December 3, 2018.

99. Greg Abbott, Attorney General of Texas correspondence to CEOs and legal counsel of Baylor College of Medicine and Methodist Hospital, July 27, 2005. Selected sections of this letter are reproduced in William Butler's history of Baylor College of Medicine, Vol. V, 1485.

100. Office of the Attorney General (OAG), "Charitable Trusts," accessed January 31, 2019, https://www.texasattorneygeneral.gov/divisions/financial-litigation/charitable-trusts.

101. Butler, *Arming for Battle Against Disease*, Vol. V, 1489.

102. Mary Daffin, interview by the author, January 22, 2019.

103. Richard E. Wainerdi, phone conversation with the author, January 26, 2018.

104. Judge Ewing Werlein, Jr., interview by the author, December 18, 2018

105. Ibid.

106. Mary Daffin, interview by the author, January 22, 2019.

107. Judge Ewing Werlein, Jr., interview by Marco Ricci, August 21, 2018.

108. Houston Methodist Hospital Foundation presentation by Susan H. Coulter to the Policy Committee, February 12, 2019.

109. Ibid.

110. "Nantz Friends," Houston Methodist, accessed July 12, 2019, https://www.houstonmethodist.org/giving/ways-to-give/giving-societies/nantz-friends/. Jim Nantz, born in Charlotte, North Carolina, is a graduate of the University of Houston. His father, Jim Nantz, Jr., moved the family to Houston in 1977. Jim Nantz, Jr. was diagnosed with Alzheimer's in 1995 and died June 28, 2008, at age seventy-nine. His father's courageous battle with the disease inspired Jim Nantz to write his book, *Always By My Side*. This website includes a video featuring Jim and his wife, Courtney, along with Drs. Appel and Masdeu.

111. Butler, *Arming for Battle Against Disease*, Vol. V, 1490.

112. Judge Ewing Werlein, Jr., interview by the author, December 18, 2018.

113. The Texas Annual Conference is the largest annual conference in the church's south-central jurisdiction and the third largest in the United Methodist denomination. Headquartered in Houston, the conference is divided into nine districts, which are the United Methodist equivalent of a Roman Catholic diocese. The presiding bishop in 2019 is Bishop Scott J. Jones. The 1996 restructuring of the hospital's board, recalls John Bookout, owes a debt of gratitude to Bishop Woodrow Hearn. Hearn's vision and dedication, backed by his knowledge of both hospital and church, proved essential for restructuring the hospital's board in ways that made a significant difference in the years ahead.

114. Judge Ewing Werlein, Jr., interview by Marco Ricci, August 21, 2018.

115. Mary Daffin, interview by the author, January 22, 2019. Daffin explains that every center of excellence at Houston Methodist (cancer, heart, transplantation, digestive disorders, neurological, and orthopedics and sports medicine) has a council comprising board members and invited community members who serve as ambassadors—advocates linking community with the faculty and finding additional resources for identified needs or program opportunities.

116. Ibid.

117. Butler, *Arming for Battle Against Disease*, Vol. V, 1513.

118. Ibid., 1516.

119. Todd Ackerman, "Saddled with Debt, Baylor Medical School Tries to Rebound," *Houston Chronicle*, March 2, 2010.

120. Todd Ackerman, "Baylor Breaks Ground on its First Hospital," *Houston Chronicle*, May 24, 2007.

121. Todd Ackerman, "Baylor Medical School Spreads Blame as it Axes Chief," *Houston Chronicle*, November 19, 2008.

122. Butler, *Arming for Battle Against Disease*, Vol. V, 1543.

123. Judge Ewing Werlein, Jr., interview by the author, December 18, 2018. Another precondition directed by Rice was that Baylor place itself on a path to financial stability.

124. Jack Stripling, "No Med School Merger for Rice," *Inside Higher Ed*, January 13, 2010, accessed February 1, 2019, https://www.insidehighered.com/news/2010/01/13/no-med-school-merger-rice.

125. Katherine Mangan, "Rice U. and Baylor College of Medicine Break Off Merger Talks," *The Chronicle of Higher Education*, January 12, 2010.

126. Stripling, *Inside Higher Ed*.

127. Dr. Marc Boom, email to the author, May 8, 2019.

128. Ibid.

129. Ibid.

130. Dr. Marc Boom, email to author, May 8, 2019.

131. Ibid.

132. Ibid.

133. Ibid.

134. "CHI Baylor St. Luke's Hospital at McNair Campus," accessed May 24, 2019, https://esarch.com/portfolio/chi-baylor-st-lukes-hospital-at-mcnair-campus/.

135. Dr. George P. Noon, interview by Dr. William Winters, Jr., July 23, 2008, *Reflections*, 316.

136. Ibid.

137. Dr. Michael DeBakey's gravesite: Arlington National Cemetery, Arlington, Virginia, Section 34, Site 399-A.

138. Executive Committee Report Minutes, January 23, 2002, Methodist Health Care System Board of Directors, Methodist Health Care System, Houston. A copy of these minutes was provided to the author by John Bookout. During this meeting Nicole Rubin discussed the challenge that the hospital's name (The Methodist Hospital System) posed at the time, noting "There are more than 60 'Methodist Hospitals' in the United States. And two-thirds of these hospitals are located in the Southeast." Changing to Houston Methodist solved this issue and branded the identity of the hospital's network of care facilities with the nation's fourth-largest city in important and recognizable ways.

139. "America's Best Hospitals: the 2009-10 Honor Roll," *U.S. News & World Report*, accessed February 1, 2019, https://health.usnews.com/health-news/best-hospitals/articles/2009/07/15/americas-best-hospitals-the-2009-2010-honor-roll.

ELEVEN – Celebrating the Centennial

1. *U.S. News & World Report*, "Regional Hospital Rankings 2018–19," accessed November 12, 2018, https://health.usnews.com/best-hospitals/area/tx. In addition to being ranked first in Texas, "Houston Methodist Hospital in Houston, TX is nationally ranked in 8 adult specialties, high performing in 2 adult specialties & 9 procedures/conditions." The hospital ranked second in Texas is UT Southwestern Medical Center in Dallas.

2. "Methodist Capital Construction Program: 2005–2011," Sidney "Sid" Sanders, Construction/Facilities Design and Real Estate Management, The Methodist Hospital, HMA-PEC, undated, 2005.

3. Judge Ewing Werlein, Jr., interview by Marco Ricci, August 21, 2018.

4. Dr. Marc Boom, interview by the author, January 10, 2017.

5. "Spotlights: Marc L. Boom, M.D.," *TMC Pulse*, April 2016.

6. Ernie Cockrell, interview by the author, January 21, 2019.

7. Ronald Girotto, interview by the author, February 28, 2018.

8. Ernie Cockrell, interview by the author, January 21, 2019.

9. Ibid.

10. For a simplified explanation of the complex field of nanotechnology, see the National Institutes of Health (NIH) publication, *Nanotechnology at the National Institutes of Health*, https://www.nih.gov/sites/default/files/research-training/nanotechnology-brochure.pdf, (accessed February 20, 2019). Dr. Ferrari's academic credentials include leadership in founding the field of nanomedicine at the National Cancer Institute (part of NIH) with expertise in nano/microtechnology, including applications for drug delivery, cell transplantation, implantable bioreactors, and other innovative therapeutic modalities.

11. Greg Nelson, interview by Marco Ricci, September 18, 2018.

12. Dr. Mauro Ferrari, interview by Marco Ricci, May 24, 2018.

13. Ibid.

14. Brochure, Houston Methodist Research Institute, "cGMP Core," April, 2016. The publication notes, "Most academic institutions and small biotechnology companies outsource GMP manufacturing to contract manufacturing organizations, which can be very costly and time consuming. The cGMP Core at Houston Methodist is designed to provide not only the infrastructure and equipment for cGMP manufacturing and release, but also the expertise to guide and implement GMP manufacturing protocols for investigators."

15. Dr. Barbara Bass, interview by Marco Ricci, May 25, 2018.

16. Ibid.

17. Ibid.

18. Ibid.

19. Ibid.

20. Eileen McGrath, telephone conversation with the author, February 4, 2019. Epic Systems Corporation, founded in 1979, is headquartered in Verona, Wisconsin. Epic software supports functions related to patient care, including registration and scheduling; clinical systems for doctors, nurses, emergency personnel, and other care providers; systems for lab technologists, pharmacists, and radiologists; and billing systems for insurers. EpicCare Link is Houston Methodist's secure, online tool for connecting private and referring physicians and associated clinical staffs to Houston Methodist resources and patient information in one electronic health record providing view-only access to patients' health records. In November 2018 Houston Methodist, in collaboration with the Houston Health Department and Epic, became the first hospital system in eight U.S. pilot sites to successfully test and launch an approach to electronic case reporting that can automatically send case reports directly from a hospital to public health agencies—supporting rapid reporting for disease surveillance and detection.

21. Greg Nelson, interview by Marco Ricci, September 18, 2018

22. Robert A. Phillips, Roberta L. Schwartz, William F. McKeon, and Marc L. Boom, "Lessons in Leadership: How the World's Largest Medical Center Braced for Hurricane Harvey, *New England Journal of Medicine*, Catalyst Lessons in Leadership Series, October 25, 2017, accessed November 12, 2018, https://catalyst.nejm.org/lessons-leadership-texas-medical-center-hurricane-harvey/.

23. ABC 13 News, KTRK-Houston, "Harvey Destroyed More Than 15,500 Homes in Texas," aired September 25, 2017, accessed November 12, 2018, https://abc13.com/harvey-destroyed-more-than-15500-homes-in-texas/2454379/.22.

24. Kaelyn Bujnoch, "Hurricane Harvey Couldn't Close the Doors at Houston Methodist Sugar Land Hospital," Houston Methodist press release, September 26, 2017.

25. Amber Elliott, *Houston Chronicle*, August 20, 2018. This was a photo feature including Dr. Park and her story—part of a retrospect series looking back a year after Hurricane Harvey. https://www.chron.com/news/houston-weather/hurricaneharvey/heroes/. Accessed February 1, 2019.

26. Dr. Marc Boom, interview by the author, January 10, 2018.

27. *Report to the Community*, "Together, We Heal: Recovering from Hurricane Harvey," Houston Methodist Hospital Foundation, May 22, 2018. Dr. Boom notes in his cover letter accompanying this report, "I am honored and so pleased to report to you that a total of $8.4 million was contributed to the Houston Methodist Employee Relief Fund, and 5,400 employees—nearly 24 percent of our workforce—benefited."

28. Ibid.

29. Judge Ewing Werlein, Jr., interview by the author, December 18, 2018.

30. Press Release, "Houston Methodist Opens New State-of-the-Art Patient Tower in Texas Medical Center," Houston Methodist Office of Communications and External Relations, August 7, 2018.

31. Greg Nelson, interview by Marco Ricci, September 18, 2018.

32. Dedication remarks delivered by Dr. Marc Boom during ceremonies recognizing the opening of Walter Tower, Houston Methodist, August 7, 2018. Dr. Boom's remarks conclude, "Paula's and Rusty's official portrait now hangs in the lobby at the main entrance to Walter Tower. Everyone who comes in the grand entrance will be able to see this lovely portrait and understand the story of the incredible couple who helped make so much progress possible."

33. Sir William Osler, *The Old Humanities and the New Science* (New York: Houghton Mifflin Co., 1920). This book provides a reprint of Osler's presidential address to the Classical Association delivered May 16, 1919, in Oxford, England. Olser's full quote is, "Twin berries on one stem, grievous damage has been done to both in regarding the Humanities and Science in other light than complemental."

34. Houston Methodist, "Center for Performing Arts Medicine (CPAM)," accessed November 12, 2018, https://www.houstonmethodist.org/performing-arts/.

35. Betty Jean Ligon, interview by the author, November 30, 2018. Lignon noted Ella Fondren's nephew was Allen Cochrum, whose wife, Florine Lenz Cochrum, was a close friend.

36. Liisa Ortegon, email to author, July 11, 2019.

37. Greater Houston Partnership, "Houston Metropolitan Statistical Area Profile," accessed November 12, 2018, https://www.houston.org/newgen/02_Geography/02C%20W001%20Houston%20Area%20Profile.pdf. This document notes, "The Houston MSA is the fifth most populous in the U.S. and spans an area larger than five states [and] covers 9,444 square miles. If Houston were a country, its economy would rank 24th in the world."

38. Houston Methodist, "International Patients," accessed November 12, 2019, https://www.houstonmethodist.org/for-patients/international-patients/.

GENERAL INDEX

Note: Page numbers in italics indicate photos; page numbers with "n" indicate endnotes. For names of persons, see the Names Index.

Note: Page numbers in italics indicate photos; page numbers with "n" indicate endnotes. For names of persons, see the Names Index.

Note: Page numbers in italics indicate photos; page numbers with "n" indicate endnotes. For names of persons, see the Names Index.

NAMES INDEX

Note: Page numbers in italics indicate photos; page numbers with "n" indicate endnotes. For subjects and names of institutions and places, see the General Index.

Note: Page numbers in italics indicate photos; page numbers with "n" indicate endnotes. For subjects and names of institutions and places, see the General Index.

Note: Page numbers in italics indicate photos; page numbers with "n" indicate endnotes. For subjects and names of institutions and places, see the General Index.

Note: Page numbers in italics indicate photos; page numbers with "n" indicate endnotes. For subjects and names of institutions and places, see the General Index.

Note: Page numbers in italics indicate photos; page numbers with "n" indicate endnotes. For subjects and names of institutions and places, see the General Index.

Note: Page numbers in italics indicate photos; page numbers with "n" indicate endnotes. For subjects and names of institutions and places, see the General Index.

Note: Page numbers in italics indicate photos; page numbers with "n" indicate endnotes. For subjects and names of institutions and places, see the General Index.